Guy Brown

is a Royal Society Research Fellow in the Department of
Biochemistry at the University of Cambridge. He is one of
the world's leading authorities on human bioenergetics. *The
Energy of Life* is his first book: it won Britain's biggest science
writing prize, the Wellcome Trust Prize for Popular Science

THE
ENERGY
OF LIFE

GUY BROWN

Flamingo
An Imprint of HarperCollins*Publishers*

Flamingo
An Imprint of HarperCollins*Publishers*
77–85 Fulham Palace Road,
Hammersmith, London W6 8JB

Flamingo is a registered trademark of
HarperCollins*Publishers* Ltd

www.**fire**and**water**.com

Published by Flamingo 2000
1 3 5 7 9 8 6 4 2

Published in hardback by HarperCollins*Publishers* 1999

A catalogue record for this book
is available from the British Library

Illustrations by Matthew Chilton

ISBN 0 00 653047 8

Set in PostScript Linotype Minion by
Rowland Phototypesetting Ltd, Bury St Edmunds, Suffolk

Printed and bound by Clays Ltd, St Ives plc

CONTENTS

ACKNOWLEDGEMENTS

My sincere thanks to Peter Nicholls, Chris Cooper, Sarah Radcliffe, Geoffrey Lloyd, Roy Porter, Jenny Radcliffe, Vilma Borutaite, Alan McBride, Philip Rubery, Tony Holbert, Philip Gwyn Jones, Georgina Laycock, Toby Mundy, Suzanne King and the Brown family for advice, encouragement and/or criticism. My deepest gratitude to Sarah and family for providing a fertile environment. The Wellcome Trust provided the inspiration and means to turn my dream into a real book, by awarding me the first Wellcome Trust Prize for popular science writing in 1997.

INTRODUCTION

Every morning of our lives we wake up and reach out from unconsciousness to consciousness, from nothingness to being, from dream to reality. And when the full force of reality hits us, we must choose between falling back into nothingness, or grabbing hold of reality. To wake up and get on with life we need energy: both body energy and mind energy. We need body energy to get out of bed, make the tea, run for the bus, beat our competitors, and drag ourselves home again. Whereas mind energy arouses and motivates us, to actually want to get out of bed and do something. This book is about what energy *is*, how we get it, and how we lose it again. But in discussing these practical things we will also be touching on more fundamental issues. What is life? How does it work? And why do we bother getting out of bed in the morning at all?

But what is this thing – energy – that divides the strong from the weak, the young from the old, the living from the dead? How does energy animate the body and mind? How does it enable a body to grow, a finger to move, a mind to think? Energy is the basic constituent of the Universe, even more fundamental than matter. Energy is the origin of all change. Every event in the Universe, from the collision of atoms to the explosion of stars, uses energy. And our own bodies, even when in dreamless sleep, require large amounts. To be alive is to be a continuous transformer of energy, a machine transmuting the food we eat and the air we breathe into a dancer's leap and a poet's dream.

There is abundant evidence that how energetic we feel is a major element of how happy, healthy, productive and creative we are. It may be more important for our overall well-being to track what boosts or drains our energy, than to follow our calorie intake or bank accounts. Energy is a central aspect of our lives. Without it, our personal world shrinks to a few essential tasks, people, and places: for we have no energy to face anything more than an essential minimum. But with an abundance of body and mind energy our world opens up, as we expand our interactions with people, projects and places to fill all the available time.

Vitality, passion, dynamism, confidence, the ability to concentrate and work without rest, to think fast and coherently, to resist fatigue and exhaustion – in short 'energy' – are the essential qualities, above all else, required to succeed in life. Top of the *Harvard Business Review*'s list of vital qualities for business success is 'a high level of drive and energy'. Everyone looks for that sparkle in friends and lovers to 'make things happen'. Most of all, everybody is looking for energy within themselves: the motivation and drive to get up and do something; the endurance, stamina and resolve to carry through what we are already doing and need to do; and the courage and will-power to change direction and break out of the old routines, when necessary. We may know *how* to do something, but without will and energy, it is not going to happen. Without mental energy there can be no joy, excitement or enthusiasm. But physical and mental fatigue seem to have infected almost everyone: the most common symptom reported by patients to their doctors today is lack of energy. Depression and exhaustion appear to be endemic to our society. Everybody wants more energy.

The Energy of Life follows the evolution of our ideas about biological energy, from their origins in the prehistoric concepts of life itself, to the latest research on the body electric and psychological motivation. The story of living energy twists through various manifestations as the vital heat or *pneuma* concocted in the furnace of the heart in ancient Greece; as *chi* energy coursing through meridian lines of the Chinese body; as *prana* convulsing the body of yogis in India; as the vital force sought by the alchemists in their dreams of gold and life everlasting and through, in more modern times, to the discharge of Freudian sexual energy.

The last fifty years have finally enabled us to answer the fundamental questions of what energy is, and how it drives body and mind. But the answers seem, at first, more fantastical than the questions. Our body and minds are powered by electricity. Our cells are energized by huge electric fields driving vast currents through tiny molecular machines: motors, gates, pumps, switches and chemical factories together creating cellular life. It would be possible to imagine a happy electrical hum within the cell were it not for the incredibly frantic pace of activity, the colossal forces, and sparks flying from the life-threatening leakage of electrons. The electric energy is produced by trillions of bugs that invaded the ancestors of our cells billions of years ago, and thousands of which now live in each cell of our body. But these invaders who appear to live peacefully in symbiosis with the cell, may also be the enemy within. Recent research shows they are the silent assassins and executioners of the cell and are implicated in a multitude of devastating diseases and disabilities, and in the processes of ageing itself, leading to an irreversible decline in body and mind energy.

The energy moving and motivating the mind has always been a mystery. But modern technology now enables us to image and visualize changes in energy inside our brains, from moment to moment, as we think and feel. The brain chemicals and pathways controlling arousal, anxiety and motivation have now been found, so that we are finally close to understanding what excitement and depression are, and how to control them with drugs. We now know that obesity and body weight are regulated by a signal released by fat and acting on the brain, to control appetite and energy expenditure. The origin of sexual libido has been traced back into the dark recesses of the brain. We are beginning to understand how the body and the mind communicate in health and disease, why stress and depression cause illness and why illness in turn causes fatigue.

No matter how fast knowledge accumulates, questions remain: Why do we use so much energy? Why is life so short? Is there a relationship between energy and time? Why does time seem to go faster and life get less exciting as we get older? Why do children have so much energy? Why do the body and mind tire, and why do we need sleep? What is chronic fatigue? What is the mind, and what motivates it? There are no solid answers to these questions yet, but there are fascinating possibilities.

Our feelings of energy and tiredness wax and wane during the day, and during the course of life, in predictable cycles. Perhaps you feel tired now. But what is tiredness and fatigue? Are you exhausted at the end of the day because you have run out of energy, or because your brain is trying to put you to sleep? What is this spectacular daily oscillation in energy level for? Do you get tired as you get older because you are running out of energy, or because your genes are trying to put you to sleep – permanently?

Current theories of body and mind energy are split between many different disciplines and conceptual frameworks. This book seeks to bring these ideas together, to show how central energy is to our lives. Literally everything we do uses energy. It ebbs and flows within us every minute of the day, with every burst of adrenaline and every thought swirling through our mind. During dreamless sleep, the body is still, and the mind empty. When awake the body and mind are in ceaseless motion. Whenever motion appears from non-motion, or activity from inactivity, we say that 'energy' is involved. This energy produces the motion or activity. The energy may be stored, or it may be supplied from outside. Thus, when a sleeper wakes, the energy to move and think comes from energy stored in the body and mind. But those stores need to be replenished from external sources. This is the everyday concept of energy: something invisible that produces motion or activity, but in producing activity is used up, so it needs to be replenished. When we complain we are short of energy, we mean that our capacity for physical or mental activity is low, and we need this capacity to be recharged.

There are many words expressing a high-energy state: vitality, vigour, vivacity, strength, arousal, ardour, drive, fervour, stamina, gumption, zeal and zest. Just as many words describe the opposite: lethargy, apathy, timidity, weakness, languor, weariness, tiredness, fatigue, and depression. These words cover many shades of meaning, but what they have in common is the idea of a capacity or desire to do things, beyond the technical skill to perform the particular task. The popular concept of energy has extended into many different capacities and fields; so now we have physical energy, mental energy, sexual energy, emotional energy, psychic energy, creative energy, etc. While the meaning of 'energy' in physical science is a much more restricted and concrete one, the flexibility of popular concepts of energy captures something crucial to all of our everyday lives.

The Energy of Life takes the popular and ancient concept of biological energy, and looks at it from the perspective of the latest science. In so doing we will cover a vast territory from history to physics, energetics to psychology, through the evolution of life to the origins of cell death. We will look at how and why energy was discovered. How the delicate machinery of our cells makes the miracles of motion and thought possible. And how that same machinery creates fatigue, obesity, disease, ageing and death. We will also examine how energy is related to the perception of time, why we sleep and dream, the connection between energy and sex, and the link between creativity and madness. Then finally we will return to the more practical question of why we, as individuals, sometimes lack energy, and what we can do to get more.

Chapter 1

ORIGINS

'In the beginning' the meaning of energy was inseparable from the meaning of life. 'What is life?' was an unavoidable question for people confronted with death and the dying on a daily basis. A newly dead body may appear identical to the live one existing only moments before, but it is missing an important ingredient: life. What is this invisible thing animating the living but disappearing with death?

Important clues are given by the subtle differences between the living and the dead: movement, breath, heartbeat, pulse, warmth, growth, and (less obviously) consciousness. These differences were central to the concept of life (and death) in most early cultures, and are still important to our own modern and scientific ideas of life. But a bare list of the differences cannot give us a general theory of life or death. What is the need for a general theory? Because daily confrontation with death prompted urgent, practical questions: can death be prevented? And if not, can it be reversed? Finally, if all else failed, the ultimate questions: was death the end? What happened to the body and mind after death?

Imagine a caveman bent over his recently deceased cavewoman: with knotted brow, Rodin pose and a thought bubble full of question marks, the dawning thought: 'What are life and death?' Of course, no such caveman ever existed – we are merely indulging in a narrative device. But if our prehistoric sleuth can mentally capture the essence of life perhaps he can feed it back into his mate and love once more. However, he must hurry, before her still warm and lovable body rots and turns to dust. To tackle this cosmic conundrum he must decipher the differences between his loved one before and after death. The only clues he has are those he can see, hear or feel; his only evidence the body. He must read the body. The meaning of life is not some grandiose theory, but instead the rather gruesome differences between a live body and a dead one.

The most obvious difference is movement. The dead can't dance, while the living gaily cavort. In early cultures, such as those of ancient Egypt and Greece, movement was often taken as a sign that the object in motion, even if it was the sun moving across the sky, *wanted* or *intended* to move, and thus that it had some kind of mind willing it. But there is some subtlety here: for a dead body can also move. If we lift up the arm and let go, it will fall. If we hold the body up on two feet, and wave its arm, it will stand and wave. If we push up the two ends of its mouth it may even give us a ghoulish smile (assuming *rigor mortis* has not set in). The essential difference between the living and the dead is not movement itself, but rather spontaneous or willed movement. Willed movement is a sign of mind, a kind of mind energy. It was this concept of self-generated motion that early cultures used to divide the world into the animate and the inanimate. If spontaneous movement was not due to living humans or animals, then it was attributed to souls, spirits, devils or gods. A stone is not living because it does not move of its own accord – even a rolling stone is not living if it has been pushed down a mountain – but an avalanche can suggest the work of an angry god or devil. The apparently spontaneous movement of wind, lightning, sun and planets was associated with spirits or gods, by the ancient Egyptians, Chinese, Greeks and American Indians. Indeed the distinction between living and non-living things was not as clear or important then as it is now, because the world was full of supernatural spirits, and even inanimate objects could be seen to have intentions and desires.

We should note that the type of movement regarded as 'self-generated' is dependent on the theory being used. Thales, known as the 'grandfather' of Greek philosophy and science who was active around 600 BC, thought that a magnet had a soul because it moved iron. It may be because all things move in apparently spontaneous ways in certain circumstances (e.g. when dropped) that he famously said, 'all things are full of gods'. Around 350 BC, Aristotle, perhaps the greatest ever philosopher and scientist, described God as the 'unmoved mover', the first source of free, unforced movement and change. Today we have gone to the other extreme, and many scientists believe that there are no spontaneous movements or change, even within humans (because each change is caused by a prior change via some mechanism), and thus there is no need for gods, souls, or spirits. However, the modern concept of energy has replaced gods and spirits as the source of all movement and change in the Universe.

When our caveman-penseur presents his beautiful new hypothesis (that the difference between life and death is self-generated movement) at neighbouring caves, it is not long before some overly smart cave-woman points out the flaw in his argument, that when he is asleep or knocked unconscious, he has no self-generated movements yet is, to all appearances, alive. She may continue that anyone with any sense knows that in such circumstances the way to tell the living from the dead is from subtle, internal movements: breathing, the pulse, and the heartbeat. These internal motions are still used today in the diagnosis of life or death, and it was the investigation of them, and their associated processes, that led to our modern concepts of life and body energy.

Breath was central to ideas of life and energy in most early historical cultures. In Egypt, breath was associated with *ka*, a soul which separated from the body after death. Breath-energy was known as *chi* in ancient China, *thymos* and later *pneuma* in Greece, and *prana* in India, although each of these terms meant different things to the different cultures involved. The first entry and final exit of breath from the body were synonymous with life and death. In Greek legend, the first man was fashioned by Prometheus from earth and water, but the soul and life were breathed into him by the goddess Athena. If breathing is stopped, it leads to loss of consciousness and finally death, and so it would have always been obvious that life depended directly on breathing. But breathing is associated with much more than just staying alive. Changes in breath and breathing occur during most emotional states, as is recognized in phrases such as: 'she took his breath away'; 'panting with eagerness'; 'gasping with astonishment'; 'sobbing with grief'; and 'yawning with weariness'. These emotions are associated with sounds and chest movements, which might lead us to believe that all emotions are located in the chest and expressed in sound (as in the phrase 'get it off your chest'). We may also consider talking itself to be a kind of breath, as words appear to be carried by the breath from the chest. In pre-literate and semi-literate cultures, thought was often considered to be a kind of talking, perhaps because much thinking was done out loud. And as talking and expressions of emotion were connected with breathing, then thought and emotions could be associated with the breath in the chest.

In the pre-Classical Greece depicted in the *Iliad* and *Odyssey*, thought and emotion were seen as a kind of breath-energy known as *thymos*, which was stored in the lungs or chest (*phrenes*), and breathed forth as speech, anger or grief. The Greeks appear to have conceived *thymos* to have been a hot vapour, coming from the body or blood, an idea perhaps inspired by the vapour in breath visible on a cold day, or by the vapour escaping from gushing blood. Thus, we have images of the spirit and soul as a partially visible vapour, as in the soul escaping from the body in a dying man's final breath. The root of the modern word 'inspiration' means both breathing in and the receipt of divine or supernatural thought and feeling. This usage may derive from Homer, where often exceptional thought, feeling, courage, strength, anger and dreams were derived from the gods, who 'breathed' them into humans, as *thymos* to be stored in the chest/lungs, before the humans exhaled them out as speech, feeling, willed action, or thought.

Breath may well have been important to conceptualizing life in another way. It is (usually) invisible, yet when we blow hard our breath can move things and we can feel it against our hands. In this respect it is like the wind, which was often conceived of as the breath and will of gods. Thus, breath was an invisible source of movement *outside* the body, and might therefore act as an invisible source of movement *within* the body, to move the limbs and vital functions.

In China breath-energy was known as *chi* (pronounced chee, as in cheese, and sometimes written as *qi*) and *chi* was a fundamental component of the Universe. According to the *Huangdi Neijing*: 'That which was from the beginning in heaven is *chi*; on earth it becomes visible as form; *chi* and form interact giving birth to the myriad things'. There are many different types of *chi*, sometimes earthly and material, at other times heavenly and immaterial, and its effect can be seen in the growth of a plant, the power of thought, or the energy that activates any process. Life originates from an accumulation of *chi*; and death from its dissipation. *Chi* also means 'air', but air was thought to be a non-material empty space; thus *chi* is not a material substance, but rather a process, force, or energy. Within the body *chi* is known as true *chi*, and was derived both from air by breathing, and from food and water by ingestion. The *Huangdi Neijing* states: 'True *chi* is a combination of what is received from the heavens and the *chi* of water and food. It permeates the whole body'.

True *chi* circulates around the body via twelve main pathways or meridians. These meridians are mapped onto the surface of the body, so that acupuncture can control the energy flows, although the meridians cannot be identified with any anatomical structures in the body. However, each meridian is also associated with a particular organ and function, and the flow of *chi* along the meridian actualized that function via the transforming action of *chi*. As the Chinese put it:

'The meridians are the paths of the transforming action of *chi* in the solid and hollow organs' (*Yijiang jingyi*).

There were several different types of *chi* associated with different organs and their functions:

'Thus one is able to smell only if Lung *chi* penetrates to the nose; one can distinguish the five colours only if Liver *chi* penetrates to the eyes; one can taste only if Heart *chi* penetrates to the tongue; one can know whether one likes or dislikes food only if Spleen *chi* penetrates to the mouth' (*Zhongyixue gailun*).

The Chinese thought of *chi* as flowing along the meridians, much as water flows along a riverbed. The meridians and their smaller branches irrigated the whole body, as a river and its canals irrigate the fields of a valley. If a disease arose in the body it affected these rivers of life, so that either no water flowed at all (lack of *chi*), or the river was blocked at a particular point, with excessive water and flooding above the block (swelling, and congestion of *chi*) and insufficient water below the block (atrophy, lack of *chi*). It was thought that the acupuncture needle removed the block, either directly or by increasing the force of the stream. In order to live a long and vital life people were encouraged to nurture their *chi*. And this was achieved by moderation in all things, avoiding either excess or lack in their diet, exercise, or sex. But also by avoiding external sources of 'bad' *chi*, such as cold, damp, fright, or even, sex with ghosts.

Indian concepts of breath-energy – *prana* – may have predated and inspired those of Europe and China. Hindus teach that in addition to the physical body, there is an astral body, occupying the same space and connected to the physical body by a thread, severed at death. The vital energy, *prana*, flows through this astral body within thousands of channels – *nadis* – connecting seven energy centres or wheels of light, known as the *chakras*. Health and consciousness can be controlled by regulating the flow of *prana*, using *pranayama* (breathing exercises), *asanas* (yoga postures), and meditation. Normally, most of our *prana* is carried by the Ida and Pingala *nadis*, which pass through the left and right nostrils respectively, and carry cooling moon energy or warming sun energy respectively. Yogis claim to control their level of consciousness by minutely regulating their breath and thus the flow of *prana*, by changing the depth, rhythm, and nostrils used for breathing. In one type of yoga, 'Kundalini Yoga', the yogi uses breathing techniques and meditation to mobilize the creative female energy (Kundalini) latent in all – men *and* women. This energy is symbolized by a sleeping snake coiled around the bottom *chakra* at the base of the spine. The yogi attempts to create an inner heat that rouses the serpent-power from its sleep, driving it up the central *nadi* along the spine, piercing each *chakra* in its path, and absorbing their energy, until finally uniting with the male energy of the crown *chakra* at the top of the head. Kundalini may be experienced as if a bolt of electric charge were passing up the spine, and, if successful, results in a higher level of consciousness where all illusions are dispelled.

The heart and heartbeat were associated with the soul or spirit in most early cultures, and it is not hard to see why. The heart beats rhythmically and continuously at the body's centre from birth to death. It speeds up during strong emotions and exertion. It slows down with age and rest. Its stopping is synonymous with death. It is the only internal organ with spontaneous motion, and can be extracted from the body still beating. It is associated with the pulse and the movement of the blood. In Egypt, the heart held the power of life and the source of good and evil. According to the *Book of the Dead*, the heart of each human was weighed on a scale against a feather after death to determine the balance of good and evil, and thus the fate of the spirit. In many Indian and Chinese languages, the words for heart and mind are more or less synonymous. The Toltecs and Aztecs of ancient Mexico ripped the still-beating heart out of their human sacrifices to offer to their sun god. Most early cultures located consciousness and emotions in the heart (or chest/lungs). Interestingly, the soul (*psyche*), which survived death and produced new life, was often located elsewhere, usually the brain. However, many early cultures did not have such a strongly dualistic concept of the separation of mind and body. Thus it is not always appropriate to talk separately of the mind and body, or of locating the mind in a particular organ of the body.

The Ilongot, a society of headhunters with relatively little contact with the modern world, living in the Philippines, have a word *liget* which means something like energy and anger. This force arises in the heart, because for them 'motions of the heart are emotions' – a belief not far removed from modern, psychological theories of emotion. However, the word *liget* is also used by the Ilongot in ways that we might regard as metaphorical. For example, chili gives *liget* to a stew, ginger revitalizes *liget* in a killer, and winds have more *liget* when obstructed. *Liget* is also revealed in people when they pant and sweat, flowing inwardly and generating redness in the self. It is dynamic, organic, chaotic violence, and also the stuff of life.

Early cultures often did not distinguish between the literal (or concrete) and metaphorical (or abstract) use of a concept – the concept of metaphor was only invented by Aristotle in the fourth century BC. So the ancient Greeks used a word such as *psyche* to refer to both a substance in the body and the behaviour of the soul. The temptation is to say that the ancient Greeks and other early cultures were more literal minded and their thought was less abstract. Yet, most modern discourse also fails to distinguish between literal and metaphorical uses of words. The word 'energy' is popularly used to describe everything from the charge supplied by electricity wires, to the intensity of an artistic performance. One manifestation of literal mindedness is the tendency to explain a property of something as due to a discrete substance within the thing (an unfortunate tendency known as 'reification'). For example, Dr Pangloss, in Molière's *Candide*, explained falling asleep as due to a 'dormative principle' within the body or mind. Similarly 'living', which is essentially a state or way of being, has been explained in terms of substance: life or *vis viva* (the life-force). Doing things intensely or passionately has been explained in terms of the possession of 'energy', the energizing substance swirling around the body or mind. In some cases, thinking of a property or behaviour as a 'thing' can be helpful, but more usually scientific or intellectual progress has been made by explaining 'things' in terms of processes. Thus most scientists no longer think of life or energy as things to be explained by separate substances, rather they are particular arrangements or processes of matter. However, in popular culture, life and energy still have mixed literal and metaphorical meanings, which partly reflect those of much earlier times.

In early cultures the heart's beating was associated with the movement of blood in the body, which was indicated by the pulse and by the rhythmic spurting of blood from severed arteries. The pulse was used in the diagnosis of health and illness, vigour and death in the medicine of ancient Greece, India and China. The violent colour of blood, its dramatic eruption from wounds, its ability to rapidly congeal once outside the body, and the fact that its loss was associated with death, all contributed to the idea that it was intimately connected with life. Indeed for some cultures, blood was seen as the substance of life itself. Many stone-age burials have been discovered where the bones have been covered with a red ochre probably representing blood, which would suggest that the connection between blood and life (or death) was very early indeed. The drinking of blood, either literally or symbolically (as in the Christian Eucharist), was a means of transferring the soul/energy of the human, animal or god to the drinker.

Our caveman has now got some theories, but it does not seem to be doing his cavewoman any good. She has gone cold. The caveman now needs to add one more item to his list of differences between living and dead: body heat. The body temperature of living mammals and birds is normally higher than their surroundings, cooling to that of their environment at death. If our body temperature is lowered by more than a few degrees, if for example we fall into freezing water, then we rapidly die. Clearly heat has an important connection to life. In pre-industrial times, the only significant producers of heat were animals, fire and the sun. Aristotle, for example, thought of the life-force partly as a kind of fire inside the body. And the association between heat (and movement) and the life-force, may well explain the widespread belief that the sun was a god, and the use of fire in religious rituals. In fact there are a number of other important similarities between life and fire: both are produced by the burning of organic matter (fuel/food) with air (supplied by a bellows or breathing), which generates heat, movement, and residual waste (ash/faeces). This analogy was important both in ancient Greece and in much more modern times. For it was the key concept in the development of the modern scientific idea of body energy, although the theory could not be used productively until chemical concepts of burning were developed by Lavoisier in the eighteenth century.

Back with our caveman, things are looking bleak. The cavewoman's body has started to decay. First the flesh rots away, leaving the skeleton, then the bones themselves disintegrate to dust. Although the process is slow, its effect is dramatic: we start with a highly organized human body and end with a pile of dust, which merges into the soil. There is obviously little hope of reversing this process, and nowhere for the soul to hide afterwards. This is clearly the great disaster of the human condition. Many cultures have expended immense efforts trying to either prevent or circumvent this problem. The ancient Egyptians were the most zealous, utilizing mummification, pyramids, tombs, sacred objects, temples, an extensive priesthood, literature and mythology to evoke a whole parallel world beyond death. In Egypt, bodies were at first buried in dry sand in which they could survive for up to a thousand years, but were shrivelled and dried out. Subsequent use of stone coffins resulted in the flesh disappearing – supposedly eaten by the stone. This is the origin of the Greek word *sarcophagus* (meaning 'flesh eating') perhaps reflecting a prehistoric notion that the body and soul of the dead could enter into and be preserved in stone. The bodies were, in fact, eaten by micro-organisms too small to be seen. The Egyptians developed mummification to prevent this process, although of course lacking any knowledge of the existence of bacteria.

Mummification was, however, never entirely successful, and the final resort of both the Egyptians and later cultures was to circumvent the problem by favouring the idea that the mind or soul could separate from the body at death, and either live independently (in heaven or another world), or in other objects (such as in statues), or another body (reincarnation).

The decay of the flesh leaves the bones. Some cultures believed that the bones represented the essential core of the human, the flesh its disposable clothing. The bones contained a vital fluid, which we would now identify as the marrow encased by major bones, the spinal cord encased by the spine, the brain encased by the skull, and the cerebro-spinal fluid permeating the cavities of the brain and spine. All these 'bones' surround, as if protecting, a greyish-white gelatinous material or fluid, which in ancient Greece was thought to be the origin of semen, another off-white gelatinous fluid. Thus, semen was thought to be derived from this vital gel, a kind of creative force, constituting the brain, spinal cord and bone marrow. The Romans consequently believed that men's tiredness after orgasm and ejaculation was due to the draining of creative force throughout the body. The myth that masturbation causes blindness may originate from this ancient concept that the sperm partly derives from the brain. In Greek legend, gods and goddesses were born directly from Zeus's head (Athena) or thighbone (Dionysus), because this is where the creative force was thought to be located. The belief that bones were the essential core of the human being, encasing an individual's procreative powers, may have motiv-ated the preservation of the bones of ancestors in many cultures.

The body's decay after death appears the counterpart of its growth in life. The growth of the body is dependent on food, and it is all too evident that when a human stops eating, they stop growing, shrink, then die. Clearly there was something in food or in eating that was related to life, and this link was all the stronger because food consisted of recently dead animals or plants. Food could thus be thought of as containing either a soul or soul-nourishment. In most early cultures, there were religious rites involving human or animal sacrifice and the eating of the flesh. Often the food was blessed or otherwise transformed so that a god or soul might enter and be absorbed into the body of the eater. The Christian mass is partly derived from earlier Greek

Orphic and Bacchic rituals, where food was magically transmuted into the body and soul of a god, which then entered into the body and soul of the person eating. A version of this is described in Euripides's *Bacchae*, where the normally well-behaved, upper-class ladies of Athens achieve an ecstatic state, hunting a wild animal representing the god Dionysus, tearing it limb from limb and devouring the raw flesh. This was a means of obtaining 'enthusiasm', which in Greek means the entry of a god into the person. Thus, enthusiasm is a kind of mind energy, and these rituals were a means of obtaining it.

The idea that food was incorporated into the body – that when eaten, the substance of the food became the substance of the body – predates Classical Greece, but just how this transformation might occur was not elaborated until the Greeks devised various schemes. One idea was that food was broken down and transformed into blood, then congealing (as in blood clotting) in various ways to produce the body's organs. While this might explain the growth of children, it did not really explain the fact that although adults do not grow, they require large amounts of food. Later the idea of 'dynamic permanence' was developed by Alcmaeon in the sixth century BC, according to which the structure of the body was continuously breaking down and being replaced by new structures and substances derived from food. This would account for the fact that the body slowly decayed after death, when no food could be eaten. The general concept that material things consist of smaller components, which can be rearranged to give all the different forms or structures of things (such as food or the body), was an extremely important and fruitful one. It was particularly developed by Greek philosophers, such as Plato and Democritus, leading to much speculation as to what the simple components might be, for example water, fire, air or earth or atoms of different shapes.

During illness and starvation, the fat of the body shrinks, while in times of health and plenty, it expands. Until comparatively recently, fat was often associated with health and riches. Some Andean Indians still associate the fat with the spirit, and thus when a man 'fades away' in chronic illness or starvation, his spirit fades away too, often thought to have been stolen by a sorcerer. Fat, blood and air are the basic body fluids in traditional Andean physiology, and fat is the energy principle distributed from the heart via a system of channels and rivers mirroring the hydraulics of the Andes. This imaginative physiology is indeed partly based on an analogy of the body with the mountains and rivers, so that the head is like the mountain peaks lost in the clouds, while the legs are the river valleys. Illnesses associated with particular parts of the body can be treated by offerings of coca, blood and fat at earth shrines located at appropriate parts of the mountains. In the modern West, where food is plentiful and wasting illness rare, being fat now has the connotation of being unhealthy and poor. But, of course, only a couple of hundred years ago a rotund outline was celebrated, and the skinny figure, favoured today, was feared and pitied.

Our caveman is now distraught. He has watched his mate die: first she stopped moving, then she stopped breathing, her heart and pulse stopped, then the heat left her body, which then started to decay leaving bones and then dust. Watching this process, he has formulated new ideas about life, but these are completely useless in actually dealing with death. Many thousands of years later, we are in the same position: although we know much more about death, we are completely incapable of reversing it. However, let us return to our caveman, who is now in a reflective mood. Many of the differences between the living and the dead are visible and obvious, but perhaps the most important difference is neither visible nor obvious: what happens to the mind? What happens to our perception, thoughts, feelings and will at death? Thoughts, feelings and perceptions are not visible in other people, even if we open up their bodies, and there is no obvious machinery for producing them inside the body. The caveman could not see his mate's thoughts and feelings when she was alive, so it is conceivable that when dead she is still capable of producing them, although they remain invisible to him. Perhaps the mind or soul enters the body at birth and leaves it at death. Accordingly, the mind of the caveman's mate may still be alive though her body is dead and gone. This thought may not provide the caveman with much immediate relief, but implies that when he himself dies his mind may survive in some form, and may even enable him to meet up with his mate again.

Different cultures had quite different ideas about whether and in what way the mind might separate from the body at death. But the ancient Egyptians, Indians and Greeks, believed that the mind could survive death. This belief has obvious repercussions on how we view the relations between mind, body and matter generally. If the mind can separate from the body at death and survive as an invisible but active entity, then we could conclude that life consists of two separate entities: an invisible active mind (or soul) which occupies a passive material body. Furthermore, all other entities in the world might also consist of a similar combination of mind and matter. This dualistic distinction between active mind (or spirit) and passive matter fore-shadows that between energy and matter, which replaced it: the modern concept of energy has its ancestors among the spirits.

Early explanations of the world attributed intentions or desires to objects, and interpreted events in terms of the desires of spirits and gods. This type of explanation (known as 'teleological' or 'intentional') mirrors that which we use to explain other people's behaviour. Thus, if someone hits me over the head with a baseball bat, I might explain this behaviour by attributing it to the attacker's anger or his intention to rob me. Similarly, if a stone fell on our caveman's head he may have seen this as the anger or intentions of a spirit, god or even the stone itself. Nowadays, we would look for a 'mechanistic' explanation of such an event (for example the stone fell from a building), rather than ascribing evil intentions to the stone or the event itself. In the ancient world, there could be relatively few genuine 'accidents' because most events were thought intended by someone, something or some god. Thus almost everything was seen as meaningful; in complete contrast, today most physical events (such as atoms colliding or the Universe exploding) are thought intrinsically meaningless and acciden-tal, except where human intentions are involved. And even where humans are involved, scientists often prefer mechanistic explanations. For example, the scientist may trace that blow to the head with a baseball bat to the effects of the attacker's upbringing on his brain biochemistry, rather than a premeditated intention to rob me.

Modern science is based on mechanistic rather than teleological explanations, making a strong distinction between passive matter and the invisible mind. And the advance of science has caused a gradual retreat of intention (and mind) from the world: first from non-living matter, then from the body to the brain, and, more recently, attempts have been made by both philosophers and neuroscientists to banish

it from the brain itself. Yet as individuals we prefer intentional or
anthropomorphic explanations of the world, rather than cold mechan-
istical explanations. We prefer to think that people and animals do
things because they want to, rather than because their brains make
them do these things. We like to see the world and Universe as having
meaning, rather than being meaningless accidents. Part of the reason
science alienates people is its rejection of intentional explanation; and
perhaps in turn much of the appeal of religion and literature could
be their generous use of anthropomorphism and intentional explanation. You may notice as you read this book that the parts that
describe the behaviour of molecules and cells in terms of their intentions, wants or needs, are more readable than the strictly scientific
parts cast in terms of cold mechanism. And, moreover, there may
well be a good mechanistic explanation of why we prefer intentional
explanation, which is that it is hard-wired into our brains. Recent
psychological research indicates we develop the ability to attribute
intentions to others at the age of three, and children who fail to
develop this ability (perhaps because of brain defects) are much more
likely to become autistic and unable to interact functionally. Thus,
our preference for intentional explanations of other people and the
world is because that's how our brains work, presumably because
such explanation has been successful in promoting survival during
evolution. However, during science's evolution, it has been found
that intentional explanation is relatively unsuccessful in predicting the
behaviour of the world in comparison to mechanistic explanation.

The relevance of intentionality to energy is that the concept of
energy has evolved partly to replace intentional explanation. Energy
has replaced gods, spirits and inanimate forces as the source of all
motion and change in the Universe. But fundamental theories and
concepts (such as mind or energy) are not labels that can be attached
to the world without distorting it, but are rather like a pair of coloured
spectacles through which we can see and interpret the world. If we
are short-sighted, it may be impossible to see the world at all without
some spectacles (or some theory). Or the spectacles may be locked on
(as happened to Dorothy and her companions in *The Wizard of Oz*),
or imprinted in our brains, so it is well-nigh impossible to see without
them. The concept of energy is one basic idea through which we now

perceive the world. And we have already seen how the origin of the concept of energy is rooted in even more basic ideas about life, movement and mind. In the following chapter we follow these ideas' evolution into our current conception of energy.

Chapter 2

THE STORY OF
LIVING ENERGY

The modern concept of energy originated in the nineteenth century, a child of the industrial revolution, but its origins extend back to ancient Greece, amongst the elements, humours and spirits of the classical world. We will follow the evolution of these ideas of energy and life up to the present, as it is extremely difficult to understand the current concept of 'living energy' without seeing where these ideas came from.

THE ELEMENTS, HUMOURS AND SPIRITS OF THE CLASSICAL WORLD

Science started in ancient and Classical Greece, and it is there that we can begin to pick up the trail leading to our current ideas of energy and life. The Greeks were astonishingly creative thinkers. Indeed it is almost impossible to characterize clearly what the Greeks thought about anything, because they thought so many different things about any one thing, most of them mutually contradictory. (Much like the White Queen in *Through the Looking-Glass*, who could believe six impossible things before breakfast, without spoiling her appetite.) Indeed the Greeks were spectacularly wrong about many things. And this in itself is important because for almost two thousand years after the fall of Athens, Greece's intellectual heirs in the Hellenic, Roman and Islamic worlds, and in Medieval and Renaissance Europe believed that whatever the Greeks thought was the unquestionable truth. The thoughts of the wise men of Greece on philosophy, science and medicine were held in the same awe and reverence as those of Moses, Jesus and Mohammed on religion and ethics. Now we know that many of the 'truths' discovered by the Greeks are 'false', but the forms of their ideas, the type of questions they asked, and the ways they went about answering them, have had a fundamental influence on the development of modern knowledge and ideas. Were it not for this relatively small number of thinkers in ancient and classical Greece, science, philosophy and western culture as we know them would not now exist.

Empedocles (c. 490–c. 435 BC) was one of the greatest all-rounders of all time, exemplifying the enormous diversity and creativity of ancient Greek thinkers. Born to an aristocratic family in the city-state of Acragas, Sicily, he assisted in a coup against the oligarchy ruling the city and was offered the crown. He refused, establishing instead a democracy, and becoming himself a politician. But, in his spare time, he also managed to be one of the greatest poets, scientists, philosophers, and doctors of his age. As if this were not enough, after banishment and exile from his home state, he became a prophet and god. Legend has it that he could work miracles, control the winds, restore the dead to life, and killed himself by jumping into the volcanic crater of Etna to prove his divinity. Whether this leap did in fact prove this or not, history does not say, though apparently all that remained of Empedocles physically were his sandals. However, his thoughts remained to haunt the intellectual landscape for over two thousand years.

Empedocles devised the theory of the four elements, described as the most successful scientific theory ever, in terms of popularity and longevity, although it was not, of course, correct. It held that everything in the world consisted of a combination of only four elements. This theory appears to be a diplomatic compromise between earlier contradictory ideas that the world consisted solely of water (Thales), an unknown and unknowable substance (Anaximander), air (Anaximenes), or fire (Heraclitus). Empedocles suggested that there was not a single fundamental substance at all, but rather four elements (or 'roots' as he called them): earth, fire, air and water. The advantage of having four elements rather than one, was that it was obvious to anyone that the world consisted of an incredible diversity of things, and it was hard to explain this diversity if everything consisted of the same single substance. It was also difficult to explain how anything could change, if everything was, in essence, the same. Empedocles suggested that each different type of thing in the world consisted of different proportions of the four elements, and further that change was due to exchange of some of its constituent elements. For example, he said that bone was composed of fire, water and earth in the proportions 2:1:1 and flesh was composed of all the elements in equal proportions.

However, change could not just be left to the elements. After all, why should objects alter if there was only inert substance in the world? Why should rocks fall? Why should volcanoes explode? Why should thunder and lightning wrench the skies? Change was a big problem for the Greeks. It is also intimately related to energy, as energy can be thought of as the hidden source and cause of change. How were the Greeks to explain it without invoking gods or souls or minds? How could matter alone cause change? How could something new appear from nothing? Empedocles proposed that, in addition to the four elements, there were also two forces, which he called 'love' and 'hate'. Hate (or 'strife') pushed things apart, while love pulled them together again; and when the two forces were balanced there was no change, a standoff. This sounds like a plot for a romantic novel, but Empedocles partly conceived of love and hate similarly to the modern conception of a force, as an inanimate pushing or pulling between matter. Thus, Empedocles' overall conception of the world as consisting of different immutable elements, pushed and pulled by forces, so that change is due to chance and necessity rather than purpose, is strikingly similar to that of nineteenth-century physics. This similarity is no accident, of course, since the modern concept is partly derived from Empedocles.

Empedocles' view of the world does, however, diverge radically from the modern in many ways: he also saw the two forces, love and hate, in a religious sense, as a struggle between good and evil (with the four elements each identified with a different god). His scheme of things also differs from ours in that his elements correspond more to the modern phases of matter (solid, liquid, gas, and plasma) rather than to modern elements (such as hydrogen, oxygen, nitrogen, and carbon). This difference partly arises from the fact that Empedocles appears to have rejected the idea of empty space – the void or vacuum – a space where there was nothing, no elements or anything else. Since he had shown that air was a substance, he saw no reason to believe in empty space between the elements. Thus he conceived of the elements as homogenous substances, which blended together when mixed, like different-coloured paints.

Earlier thinkers (such as Anaximenes) and later thinkers (such as Democritus) took the more modern view that a substance consists of a vast number of small particles separated by empty space, and conversion from liquid to gas is not due to a change of elements, but rather to the elements moving much further apart. Thus, ice consists of water molecules held rigidly together, while liquid water consists of the same water molecules flowing over each other, and steam, or completely evaporated water, consists of the same water molecules very far apart. The Atomists – Leucippus and Democritus (c. 460–370 BC) – pushed this view of the world to its most materialistic extreme, by taking Empedocles' world, ridding it of its religious components, but adding the void. Thus, their view was that there was nothing in the world except a vast number of tiny particles (atoms) moving through empty space. Each of the four elements had a different shaped particle, and this shape determined the properties of the element. This explanation of the world had great advantages over the no-void view, because it could explain easily how the elements could mix and then separate: particles simply passed between each other; whereas this was hard to explain if there was no empty space between elements. Similarly, Empedocles had considerable difficulty explaining why the millions of things in the world had such startlingly different properties, if only differing in the proportions of the four elements. Why should a difference in proportions cause new properties? Democritus (and modern science) could explain this by the arrangement of the atoms within the object. New properties arose from new spatial arrangements or configurations of the atoms. There were an infinite number of ways of arranging atoms of four elements, and consequently an infinite number of possible things or materials. This is the essential secret of the success of modern chemistry and biology: explaining the properties of things in terms of the microstructure of the elements of which they consist. Unfortunately for the Atomists, the technological means did not exist in Greece to probe the microstructure of things, and thus test their theories.

We have been pursuing these ideas about matter, because they lie at the root of modern notions of energy. But Empedocles was far more than a creative physicist (*physis* was Greek for nature), he was also an inventive biologist (*bios*, Greek for life). According to Empedocles, the body's flesh and blood consisted of equal proportions of all four elements, and these attracted similar elements from the environment. Thus, the same four elements constituted non-living and living matter, mind and the immortal gods. The blood circulated from the heart to the surface of the body, where air was taken in through the pores, and back again, alternately expelling and drawing in air. The motion of blood in and around the heart created thought, and so the heart was seen as the organ of consciousness. But Empedocles had a very concrete view of consciousness, seeing for example, thought as simply blood in motion. Perception occurred by elements in the blood meeting and mingling with the same elements in the environment. An external object was perceived by some elements from it entering the body and meeting the corresponding elements in the body, and their meeting or mingling was perception. Nutrition occurred through direct assimilation, that is, the elements of the body attracted similar elements in the environment to them, and these new elements fitted in place to form the growing body.

The theory of the four elements was astonishingly popular and long-lived, lasting from the fifth century BC until the chemical revolution of the seventeenth century. Yet it is hard to see quite why thinkers stopped at only four elements. Aristotle suggested a fifth – the ether – to compose all extraterrestrial things. The Chinese used five elements also (or phases): water, earth, fire, metal and wood. In modern science we have about 100 different chemical 'elements', which can combine to give an infinite number of possible molecules. But at the beginning of the twentieth century the Cambridge physicists J. J. Thomson, Ernest Rutherford, and James Chadwick discovered that these chemical elements were not in fact elements in the classical sense (fundamental and indestructible particles of matter), because they *were* destructible and composed of three simpler, indestructible particles – the proton, electron, and neutron. And these three particles were later found to interact via a fourth (short-lived) particle – the photon. Therefore, Empedocles' four elements and two forces theory is, in outline, not that dissimilar to much more modern theories of the Universe.

Hippocrates (c. 460–377 BC) is called the founding father of medicine, and his theories of disease, cure and physiology influenced medicine and biology up until the eighteenth century. However, his own life is so mythologized that it is impossible to distinguish the basic events of his life, or even whether he really ever existed. According to legend, Hippocrates was a physician from Cos, and he practised medicine in Thrace, Thessaly and Macedonia, before returning to Cos to found a school of medicine. This school flourished from the late fifth century to the early fourth century BC, producing a vast number of highly original medical texts. Copies of around seventy of these books survive. These were conventionally attributed to Hippocrates, although he probably wrote none of them himself. The defining characteristic of Hippocratic medicine was its rejection of religious and philosophical explanations of disease, and its search for an empirical and rational basis for treatment.

Since prehistoric times, disease had been thought caused largely by gods, evil spirits, or black magic. A cure could thus be effected by ejecting the sin, spirit, or magic from the sufferer via various processes of purification. In Greece, traditional medicine was practised by priest-physicians in temples dedicated to the god Asclepius. In these temples of health, disease was apparently diagnosed partly on the basis of dreams and divination, and partly on the symptoms. Cures were half rituals and spells, and half based on fasting, food, drugs and exercise. According to later legend, Hippocrates was descended from the god Asclepius and brought up on Cos as son of a renowned priest-physician. The relationship between secular medicine (represented by Hippocrates) and religious medicine (based on faith healing or magic) in ancient Greece is difficult to discern, although apparently not as antagonistic as today.

Hippocrates and his followers accepted the doctrine of the four elements as an explanation for the natural world, but their concern

as doctors was with disease's causes and treatment. The four elements
– earth, fire, air, and water – cannot be seen in anything approaching
a pure form in or on the body. Also they knew relatively little about
the inside of the body, because dissection was prohibited on both
religious and ethical grounds. So the Hippocratics concerned themselves with what they could see and use in the diagnosis of disease,
particularly the bodily fluids: blood, saliva, phlegm, sweat, pus, vomit,
sperm, faeces and urine. Gradually the doctrine evolved that there
were only four basic fluids (humours): blood, phlegm, yellow bile, and
black bile. Blood can appear in cuts, menstrual flow, vomit, urine or
stools. Phlegm is the viscous fluid in the mouth (saliva) and respiratory
passages and comes out through the mouth and nose in coughs and
colds. Yellow bile is the ordinary bile secreted by the liver into the gut
to aid digestion; it is a yellow-brown fluid that colours faeces. The
identity of black bile is not entirely clear, perhaps originally referring
to dark blood clots, resulting from internal bleeding, which may appear
in vomit, urine or faeces. However, the four humours did not only
refer to these particular fluids, but were thought to be the body's basic
constituents. Health was thought to be due to the balance of these
humours, and ill health an imbalance of the humours. Epilepsy was,
for example, thought to be caused by an excess of phlegm in the brain
blocking the flow of pneuma (vital spirits) to the brain. Thus treatment
sought to restore the balance between the humours by removing the
humour that was present in excess, for example by bloodletting, purg-
ing, laxatives, sweating, vomiting, diet or exercise.

The four humours (blood, phlegm, yellow bile, and black bile) were
associated with the four elements (air, water, fire and earth), the four
primary qualities (hot, cold, dry and wet), the four winds, and the
four seasons. A predominance of one humour or the other gave rise to
four psychological types. Thus, the 'sanguine' type, resulting from
a dominance of blood, was cheerful and confident. 'Phlegmatic' types
(with too much phlegm) were calm and unemotional. 'Choleric' or
'bilious' people (with too much yellow bile) were excitable and easily
angered. 'Melancholic' types (too much black bile) were, obviously,
melancholy, that is sad or depressed, with low levels of energy. This
was the earliest psychological classification of character or temperament, and was used to categorize different people right up until

modern times. No obviously superior way of classifying temperament has, in fact, yet been devised. The theory of the four humours dominated medical thinking until about three hundred years ago. Many patients were still being bled even in the nineteenth century.

The Hippocratics and Greeks generally believed in positive health – health could be improved much further than the absence of illness towards well-being. Modern medicine is mainly concerned with negative health (i.e. illness), and how to restore us to health, rather than with helping us feel 'on top of the world'. The Hippocratics were much concerned with regimen or lifestyle, both in health and disease, mainly involving the correct balance of food and exercise. The importance of exercise to both physical and mental health was recognized, and was institutionalized in *gymnasia* where exercise was practised on a social basis. If you had gone to Hippocrates in 400 BC (assuming you could find him) complaining of lack of energy he might have given you a detailed regimen involving an exercise programme, with a warning about too much or the wrong type of exercise; a diet, particularly including strained broths; a lot of hot and/or cold baths, and massages; some sex (if lucky); and some obscure advice about the relations between your energy and the wind direction, season of the year, etc. This would have been, in general, a reasonably effective regimen, and you would be lucky to get better advice today from your doctor.

Aristotle (384–322 BC) was a colossus of thought, straddling the end of classical Greece and Renaissance Europe. He dominated the world of the intellect, sometimes as a benign sage and other times as malevolent dictator. His thoughts were worshipped to such an extent that they circumscribed any attempts at original thought, until their eventual rejection by Renaissance Europe, when he was blamed for stifling two thousand years of thought. Much of Aristotle's influence derives from his having been a pupil of Plato (possibly the greatest thinker ever), and then tutor to Alexander the Great (possibly the most successful conqueror of all time).

Aristotle's views of the physiology and energies of life were derived mostly from Empedocles, Hippocrates and Plato. Nutrition, vital heat and *pneuma* (vital spirit) were pivotal to this view. The heart was central to the body, the origin of consciousness and the instrument of the soul, and the source of heat, *pneuma*, blood, and movement for the rest of the body. *Pneuma* was an air-like substance or spirit, containing vital heat, which was always in rapid motion, and as such was a source of both heat and motion inside the body. *Pneuma* was derived from air, and brought through the mouth, nose and skin to the heart, where it supplied the vital heat. A steady flow of nutrient fluid from the gut supplied the heart, and the heating of the fluid within the heart produced blood. The blood and *pneuma* were then distributed through vessels to the rest of the body, where the blood coagulated to form the tissues of the body under the influence of the 'nutritive soul'. There was no circulation of blood, rather the blood was produced in the heart (and liver and spleen) and then distributed to the tissues, with no return flow. Many vessels (the arteries) were thought to be hollow (as indeed many are if the blood escapes from them after death), and were, thus, thought to carry air or *pneuma* through the body. The brain cooled the blood, and functioned to prevent the blood from overheating. The muscles were simply a protective layer, keeping the rest of the body warm, and had no function in movement. Nerves, as such, were unknown, as most are difficult to see; but large nerves and tendons were collectively called *neura* and were thought to function in movement of the limbs, by acting as cords pulling the bones. The *pneuma* supplied the 'go', energy or movement throughout the body.

Aristotle's *pneuma* was also the motivating force outside the body – in the physical world. According to his mechanics, the natural state of things was rest rather than movement; so that the continuous movement of an object such as an arrow in flight required *pneuma* to be continuously pushing the arrow from behind. Thus we can see that *pneuma* was energy for Aristotle, although of course it had a rather different role in classical thinking. Aristotle was also partly responsible for the theory of the four qualities: hot, cold, wet, and dry, which were components of the four elements. Thus earth was cold and dry, water cold and wet, air hot and wet, and fire hot and dry. This became a very important doctrine in later medicine and alchemy, because it gave a key as to how to alter the ratio of the elements; thus, for example, water could be converted to air by heating, or air could be converted to fire by drying.

Aristotle was the first authority to use the term *energeia*, from which we derive the word 'energy'. But he used it to mean the 'actual', as opposed to the 'potential', as he had an obscure theory that 'change' involved turning from a potential thing into an actual thing. So when something happens, a potential happening changes into an actual happening. Thus for Aristotle *energeia* was tied up with change and activity, but in what seems now a rather obscure and abstract way.

Although Aristotle's view of physiology and energetics was most influential, it was far less original and interesting than that of Plato. Plato was not really interested in physiology, as he had his mind set on higher things, but he wanted to find a physical location for the various parts of the soul that he had identified. For, according to Plato, the body is peopled by a bickering community of souls, ruled over by a somewhat prissy head. The immortal soul is in the head, and the mortal soul located from the neck down. The courageous part of the mortal soul is found above the diaphragm, where it can both listen to reason (from the head) and subdue the lower regions. This soul's main home is the heart; when the head thinks that the passions are out of control it informs the other organs, and the heart starts leaping with excitement and overheating. The lungs can then save the day by cooling and providing a cushion for the overtaxed heart. Below the diaphragm dwells the 'appetitive' soul, which while necessary for life needs to be kept chained, far from the seat of reason. This part of the soul is controlled by the liver, capable of listening to reason. The liver regulates the nether regions either by contracting to block passages causing pain and nausea, or by spreading cheerfulness and serenity to the surrounding parts of the soul. The length of the gut is intended to prevent food passing through too quickly, which would cause an insatiable appetite, and make mankind impervious to culture and philosophy. The spinal marrow is called the universal 'seed-stuff' (also the source of semen) fastening the soul to the body. The different kinds of soul are found in various parts of the marrow, while reason and intellect occupy the brain. This community-of-souls theory of the body shows how appealing, but empty, intentional explanations of physiology can be. In order to progress, the supernatural had to be replaced by mechanical causes and energy as the source of change.

The deaths of Aristotle and Alexander in 322 and 323 BC respect-

ively marked the end of classical Greece. But Alexander had spread
Greek culture across the known world, ushering in the age of Hellenism, which was a fusion of Greek and Persian culture. Hellenism's
most successful centre was in Alexandria, briefly flourishing under
Ptolemy I. A former pupil of Aristotle, Ptolemy attracted some of the
greatest Greek scientists and thinkers to Alexandria's Museum and
Library. Two brilliant physicians, Herophilus and Erasistratus, were
able for the first time to practise dissection of the human body there
and used this to great effect. This had been impossible previously
due to the commonly held assumption that the body retained some
sensitivity or residual life after death. Changing beliefs about the soul's
relation to the body enabled Herophilus and Erasistratus to dissect
dead humans, and even, it has been claimed, live criminals. The result
caused a revolution in anatomy: the exploration of a whole new realm
below the human skin. The nerves, and their relation to the brain and
muscles, were discovered. The brain was explored and the fluid-filled
cavities within (ventricles) were thought to be filled with a new form
of *pneuma*: psychical *pneuma* (animal spirits). This psychical or mind
pneuma radiated out from the brain, through the nerves, to energize
the muscles. However, Alexandrian scientific creativity gradually
declined and the influence of eastern mysticism increased.

In the second and first centuries BC, Rome swept the political stage
while largely adopting Greek culture and thinking. Into this new world
was born Galen (AD c. 129–216), antiquity's last great physician and
biologist. An architect's son from Pergamon, he studied philosophy
then went to Alexandria to learn dissection. Returning to Pergamon,
he became surgeon to a school of gladiators, where he gained invaluable
experience in treating wounds. In AD 169 Galen was summoned to
Rome to become personal physician to Marcus Aurelius, the Philosopher Emperor. These duties do not seem to have been too onerous
as Galen continued his writing and scientific work, in the end producing over 130 books. Many are commentaries on and syntheses of
previous medical knowledge, including textbooks and treatises on
almost all diseases, treatments and methods of diagnosis. These books
became the central texts of medicine for fifteen hundred years. Galen
was seen as a kind of medical theologian, for whom anatomy was both
praise and veneration of the one true God. And this, twinned with

his interpretation of the body in Aristotelian terms, guaranteed the acceptance of his writings by later Christian and Islamic authorities.

Galen's doctrine of *pneuma* synthesizes earlier ideas of the Hippocratics, Aristotle, the Alexandrians and Stoicism (a philosophy founded by Zeno). *Pneuma* can be translated as 'airs', and was thought to be an invisible force within the air. *Pneuma* was translated into Latin as *spiritus*, but is most naturally translated today as 'energy'. To the Stoics, *pneuma* was a non-material quality or form imposed on matter. *Pneuma* pervaded the universe and was the vehicle of cosmic 'sympatheia', by which each part of the universe was sensitive to events in all others. *Pneuma* acted as a force field in the air, immediately propagating movement to the edge of the universe and then back again. This is reminiscent of modern concepts of sound waves or of electromagnetic waves moving through the air. Inside the body, *pneuma* pervaded the blood vessels and nerves and enabled the transmission of sensitivity, movement and energy.

Galen distinguished three different kinds of *pneuma* inside the body: natural spirit, vital spirit and animal spirit. These were produced by the three main organs and their associated faculties or souls (the idea was derived from Plato). The liver, hub of the appetitive soul and supposed source of the veins, produced natural spirits. The heart, centre of the spirited soul and source of the arteries, produced vital spirits. And the brain, home of the rational soul and source of the nerves, produced animal spirits. The liver took digested food from the stomach and guts, concocting it into dark, venous blood containing natural spirits, which when distributed to the rest of the body was assimilated forming the substance of the organs. This was the basis of the appetitive (or nutritive) faculty of the liver. Taking venous blood, the heart concocted it with *pneuma*, derived through the lungs from the air, producing red arterial blood, full of vital spirits. These vital spirits, distributed throughout the body by the arteries, were then responsible for all other living processes, apart from those of movement and thought. The brain transformed vital spirits into psychical spirits, which then became responsible for consciousness, and when distributed by the nerves, for muscle movement and sensation.

Pneuma is the closest we get in antiquity to the modern concept of energy. It is a non-material, potential form of motion, action and heat, and its transformations correspond to the transformations of energy. The ghost of *pneuma* still haunts the modern idea of energy, but has been transmuted into an altogether more pragmatic concept by today's more materialistic scientists.

After Galen, there was little innovation in Greek and Roman science and an increasing emphasis on mysticism and theology. In the fourth century, the official religion of Rome became Christianity, at that time diametrically opposed to the scientific spirit. In the fifth century, the western half of the Empire was invaded by German tribes, ushering in the Dark Ages, which lasted almost a millennium. The eastern, Greek-speaking side of the Empire lasted much longer, gradually diminishing in power. In the seventh and eighth centuries, the Islamic Arabs conquered Syria, Egypt, North Africa and Spain, absorbing Greek knowledge. Although it was not until the eleventh century and later that Christian Europe was finally able to reabsorb Greek learning from the Arabs, and, at last, to spark the Renaissance.

Alchemy forms a bridge between the ancient Greek and Roman learning and the birth of modern science in seventeenth-century Europe. While the alchemists' quest started two thousand years ago in Alexandria, China and India, as late as 1680 Isaac Newton still devoted most of his time to the mysterious art. Because it existed through the dark ages of knowledge and science, alchemy reflected the time's religious, symbolic and mystical forms. But it also kept many of its practitioners in contact with classical knowledge and experimental science. The alchemists appear to modern eyes as a bunch of wacky mystics. It seems incredible that sober citizens came up with this bizarre combination of chemistry and religion. Why not engineering and sex, or poetry and gardening? However, many alchemists were intent on the very practical goals of limitless money and life everlasting. What could be more modern than that? Unfortunately for them, the theories of alchemy were completely wrong.

The importance of alchemy to our story is that it attempted at least to understand what things are made of, and much more importantly how they change. If we look at a stone or egg naïvely, it is hard to see what they consist of and where their potential for change comes from. What is it about an egg that enables it to turn into a chicken? What is it about a piece of wood allowing it to burn? What is it about a lump of gold that makes it last forever? The alchemists put all these questions into the fire. Fire was the great transformer and transmuter: separating metals, distilling essences and cooking food. In many ways the alchemist was a cook, his technology was derived from the kitchen, and he sought to transform his raw materials, through recipes, herbs, and inspiration into perfection. The alchemist also sought to isolate (by distillation and other methods) the essence or spirit of things, as a metal is isolated from ores or alcohol distilled from wines or a drug 'purified' from a plant. They thought adding the essence of gold (known later as the 'philosopher's stone') to other metals would turn the base metals into gold. Unfortunately for the alchemists, they did not yet realize that gold was an unchangeable element, more fundamental than earth, fire, air or water and that there was no essence of gold to be given to other metals. The alchemists' real achievement was that by their slaving over a hot stove and forging mental concepts, they slowly transformed the categories and concepts by which matter was seen, eventually enabling the evolution of chemistry and biochemistry.

What have we learnt from our journey through the scientific progress of the classical world? From Empedocles, Aristotle and the Atomists, we discovered that the world and its changes do not have to be understood in terms of the wishes and desires of gods, spirits or even matter itself. It can rather be explained in terms of the structure and interactions of a small number of basic particles or elements, each too small to see, but that when mixed together make up visible matter. The changes we see are due to forces of attraction or repulsion between these particles, leading to changes in the composition of matter. From Hippocrates and Galen, we learnt that death and disease are not due to the will of gods, devils or sorcerers, but can be explained in terms of the workings and malfunctions of the body machine. And this can be understood in terms of the body's various solid organs with different functions, the various vital liquids that flow within and between them, and the various invisible spirits or gases that animate the body. However, this knowledge does not explain how someone moves a hand by willing it, how thought is possible, or how life differs from death. Our journey must continue into the modern world in pursuit of the energy of life.

THE ENLIGHTENMENT

Our modern world was sparked into existence by the scientists and thinkers of seventeenth and eighteenth-century Europe. Without their intervention, we could now be living very differently, perhaps in some sort of impoverished, fundamentalist state. But it required revolutions and counter-revolutions, heroes and anti-heroes, blood and tears to achieve the transformation of thought that came to be known as 'The Enlightenment'.

It was the work of four scientists in particular that prepared the ground for this new scientific approach. Their discoveries exploded the medieval conventions of cosmology. The first scientific bombshell unleashed on an unsuspecting medieval world was the discovery that the earth was not at the centre of the Universe. Copernicus (1473–1543) wisely did not ever openly state this while alive, but the shock-waves from his heliocentric theory rocked the medieval church none-theless. Then, Kepler (1571–1630) showed that the planets do not move in circles, but ellipses. Furthermore, Galileo (1564–1642) used a telescope to show that all was not perfect among the 'heavenly bodies'; the moon was pitted with craters and volcanoes, Jupiter had moons, and the blanket of the Milky Way in fact consisted of millions upon millions of stars. Isaac Newton (1642–1727) then went on to show that the planets were not a law unto themselves, but rather followed the same rules as everything on earth.

Even more fundamentally important, Kepler, Galileo, and Newton stated that everything, ranging from teapots to planets, 'obeys' mathematically precise, mechanical 'laws', conjuring up a clockwork universe, policed by cold, mechanical 'forces'. There was no more room for spirits, gods or God. No room even for Empedocles' forces of love and strife. Things did not move (or even stop moving) because they wanted to do so, but because they were 'forced'. According to Newton's (and Galileo's) first law of motion, movement itself was no longer a sign of life or spirit. Only a change in speed or direction was an active process, and this was due to an external 'force'. Thus, amazingly, all movement in the world, apart from that of living animals, could be explained as passive and mechanical. The non-living world suddenly became frighteningly cold, empty and dead. In place of spirits, forms and purposes, there were forces. In fact, the 'forces' that inhabited Newton's universe were not so radically different from the preceding 'spirits'. The new 'forces' were unexplained and inexplicable, but had an inanimate mechanical basis, as opposed to the living freedom of 'spirits'. These forces rigorously obeyed precise, mathematical laws, whereas the spirits had followed their desires. The technological wonder of the age was the mechanical clock; this in turn became a metaphor for the Universe itself. With the invention of the clock, Time itself began to tick, and the whole Universe was forced to beat in time.

But it was not only the non-living things that were forced to bow to the new mechanical spirit of the age. René Descartes (1596–1650) proposed that animals were also purely mechanical devices, automata with no feelings or consciousness. The processes of the body could be explained just using mechanical laws. Thus, for example, the nerves acted as pneumatic pipes, transmitting pressure changes of animal spirits (psychical *pneuma*) at the nerve endings to the brain, and from there through other nerves to the muscles, where the pressure inflated the muscles.

'Now according as these spirits enter thus into the concavities of the brain, they pass thence into the pores of the substance, and from these pores into the nerves; where according as they enter or even as they tend to enter more or less into the one or the others, they have the power to change the shape of the muscles in which these nerves are inserted, and by this means to make all the limbs move.'

He went on to compare the nervous functions of the body and mind to the automatic puppets, then fashionable, which, driven by hydraulic pipes, could move and even seemingly speak.

Descartes did leave a small bolthole for the soul in the pineal gland, a small almond-shaped organ at the centre of the brain. He suggested the soul was radically different to matter and not subject to the laws of physics, but interacted with the body, through the animal spirits inside the pineal gland. The soul consisted of an unextended, indivisible, thinking substance, constituting the mind, all thoughts, volitions and desires. But all else on earth, including the human body and brain, was a vast clockwork mechanism.

Descartes has been much demonized as the inventor of 'Dualism', which purported that the world consists of two radically different substances: mind and matter. Dualism is, however, an ancient concept present in all early cultures; in Classical Greece, it is Plato's concept of two separate worlds of appearances and perfect ideas, and in Aristotle's substance and form; it is consistently found throughout Hindu, Jewish, Christian and Islamic thought as the separation of body and soul. Descartes did not invent Dualism. He was, on the contrary, a radical materialist, considering almost everything to consist solely of one substance, matter, but perhaps his nerve failed when it came to a denial of the soul. It is conceivable Descartes might have done this were it not for the Inquisition, which had, in 1616 and 1633, condemned Galileo for his heretical scientific beliefs.

Whether Descartes intended it or not, his and other mechanical philosophies separated body and mind even further, so that they were commonly regarded as radically different. The body and brain was seen as a cold machine and analysed in relation to the latest technical toy, which ranged across clocks, levers, hydraulic puppets, steam engines, electric robots and electronic computers. Whereas the mind became some wishy-washy, non-material thing, too slippery to analyse, and best left to theologians and philosophers to chew over. Consequently the trail to body energy and mind energy splits in two here, only rejoining relatively recently.

One of the world's greatest philosophers, mathematicians and scientists, Descartes appears to have been intrinsically lazy. Rarely getting up before midday, he worked short hours, and read little. Where did he find the energy for his great works? One answer may lie in his lack of routine. He had no need of a job, as after selling his father's estates he lived off his investments. So he immersed himself in his studies and whenever boredom threatened he joined an army – trying out those of France, Holland and Bavaria. He was sociable, but when friends distracted him from his conceptual tasks, he moved away. Descartes never married, and his only natural child died at five, so there was never any need to adapt to a domestic routine. He was capable of short bursts of extreme concentration. On a cold morning of the winter of 1619–20 when he was with the Bavarian army, Descartes climbed into a large oven to keep warm. He stayed in there all day thinking, and when he eventually emerged had half completed his critical philosophy, which then became the foundation of modern philosophy. This anecdote stresses the importance of removing all external distractions to intense thought. But Descartes would never have managed this feat without also removing the further internal distractions of routine thoughts, feelings and desires. And, most importantly, he would never have got anywhere without supreme self-confidence. Only powered by optimistic egotism could he reject all previous thinking, rebuilding the conceptual map of the world. Confidence is the *sine qua non* of creativity. Descartes' power finally gave out when lured to Sweden by Queen Christina, he was impelled to give her daily lessons at five in the morning. This proved too much for his weak constitution and he was dead within six months.

Although Descartes tried, he didn't succeed in his application of the new mechanical approach to biology. But, in the hands and mind of William Harvey (1578–1657), this approach yielded a remarkable success with his discovery of the circulation of the blood. Blood had been thought made in the liver and heart, passing directly from the left to right sides of the heart, and then out to the rest of the body, never returning to the heart; although it might ebb and flow in the same vessels. The heart's beat was thought due partly to breathing and partly to the formation of heat and spirits inside the heart. Thus the heart was not thought to pump the blood. Harvey showed by experiment and quantitative argument that it received as much blood as it pumped out. It was not making blood but circulating it. The heart was not an alchemist, but a mechanical pump. Furthermore, Harvey proved it was a double pump: veins brought blood from the rest of the body to the right side of the heart, which pumped the blood to the lungs; it returned from there to the left side of the heart, then was pumped to the rest of the body, through the arteries. It is telling that the function of the heart and vessels was elucidated by the use of a mechanical analogy, inspired by a pump and pipes for circulating water.

There was one glaring hole in Harvey's scheme. He could not see how the blood got from the arteries, through the organs and back to the veins. This was because the vessels involved, the capillaries, were too small for Harvey to see. So it was left to Marcello Malpighi (1628–94) to complete our image of the circulation by finding the capillaries using the newly discovered microscope. The microscope opened up a new miniature world to discovery, just as the telescope had laid bare the heavens, and the dissecting knife had opened the body beneath the skin. The first users of the microscope must have experienced the thrill of entering unknown territory. Malpighi described for the first time the structure of the lungs, spleen, kidneys, liver and skin. Many features of the human body still bear his name (such as the Malpighian tubes of the kidney), just as the explorers of sea and land left their names on the Americas. Antoni van Leeuwenhoek (1632–1723), a Dutch draper and pioneer microscopist, discovered striped muscle, sperm, and bacteria. And then it was the English scientist Robert Hooke (1635–1703) who first saw and named 'cells', but failed to recognize their significance.

Comprehension of the microscopic structure of living things is essential to any understanding of how they work. In this respect they differ from mechanical machines, which are constructed on a macroscopic level from components that at a microscopic level are both homogenous and uninteresting. By contrast, living things appearing to the naked eye as fairly simple, reveal mindboggling complexity at a microscopic scale. This vertiginous intricacy continues down to the atomic scale. Both the mechanical biologists, and all previous generations of biologists were, of course, completely unaware of this vital piece of knowledge. Some biological functions (such as how the blood circulates) are understandable at the macroscopic level but the most important secrets (such as why the blood circulates) are located on a molecular scale, beyond the reach of even the microscopists. So, mechanical biologists made relatively little progress, despite their occasional breakthroughs with the circulation of the blood and the optics of the eye.

In reaction to the mechanical (and chemical) explanations of life proposed in the seventeenth century, many scientists and thinkers defended life as radically different from the non-living, due to the possession of a 'vital force'. One such vitalist was Georg Ernst Stahl (1660–1734), who explained life and disease as the actions of a sensitive soul or 'anima', inhabiting every part of the organism preventing its decay. This 'animism' was an example of 'vitalism', the belief that life was not explicable in purely mechanical and chemical terms, harking back to Aristotle and earlier. Stahl was also a chemist, and proposed the infamous phlogiston theory. This theory interpreted combustion, i.e. burning with its accompanying flame and heat, as due to the release of a special substance called phlogiston, a stored heat energy. Stahl believed that plants took phlogiston from the air, and incorporated it into their matter, so if the plant was then burnt (as wood or straw) the phlogiston could escape into the atmosphere again. Or if, alternatively, the plants were eaten by animals, phlogiston could be released by the animal's respiration, a kind of combustion inside the body. The phantom of phlogiston beguiled chemists for about 100 years until finally extinguished by Lavoisier, who also disproved Stahl's vitalism. However, Stahl had already died in a state of severe depression long before the demise of his theories.

This historical journey has led us to a cold and abstract world of science, stripped bare of gods and spirits, ruled instead by laws and forces. We have ventured below the skin of appearances, and must travel inwards to ever smaller scales if we are to penetrate the meaning of life. The human body has become a machine, to be taken apart piece by piece. But the next veil of mystery which hides the secret of life is not a physical or mechanical one. The old dream of the alchemists is suddenly to bear fruit in the form of the chemistry of life.

THE REVOLUTION

Human attempts to find the secret to the energy of life had stalled for a thousand years but now were finally beginning to make some progress. This was due to the startling achievements of one man: Antoine Laurent Lavoisier (1743–1794), creator of the Chemical Revolution and victim of the French Revolution. Aristotle, Galen, Paracelsus, Stahl and others had all recognized that there was some relation between breathing, heat and life but the nature of this relation was no longer clear. Harvey had shown that blood circulated from the lungs to the rest of the body and back again, via the heart, but why did it circulate in this way? Was it bringing something to or removing from the tissues? The analogy between life and combustion had been noted, but combustion was seen as a kind of decomposition, so its relevance to life was still unclear.

Several British scientists had shed light on these mysteries. Robert Boyle (1627–1691) discovered an animal could not survive long in a jar after the air was removed by a vacuum pump, suggesting animal life is dependent on air or on some component of air. Boyle's assistant, Robert Hooke (1635–1703) showed that the mechanical movement of the chest in breathing was inessential to life, since he was able to stop the chest moving in animals while maintaining life by blowing air in and out with bellows. Richard Lower (1631–1691), a pioneer of blood transfusions, showed that the colour change in blood from blue-black in the veins to red in the arteries occurred as it passed through the lungs.

Incredibly, some seventeenth-century scientists believed that life was powered by something akin to gunpowder. The invention of gunpowder in the late middle ages had led to the belief that its components (sulphur and nitre) were also responsible for thunderstorms, volcanoes and earthquakes. This supposition was apparently confirmed by the sulphurous smell of volcanoes and thunderstorms. Lightning was thought to result from a nitre-like component of air, the nitrous spirit. It was proposed that this nitrous spirit was extracted from the air by the breathing body, then combining with sulphurous compounds already contained in the body to produce a combustion – the explosion of life. The gunpowder theory of life is another fascinating example of how technological change provided new analogies and innovative ways of thinking about biology.

Between 1750 and 1775, the main gases were discovered by British chemists: carbon dioxide by Joseph Black in 1757; hydrogen by Henry Cavendish in 1766; nitrogen by Daniel Rutherford in 1772; and oxygen independently by Joseph Priestley in 1774 and the Swedish chemist Karl Scheele in 1772. However, these gases were not considered distinct chemical substances, but rather, types of air, as Empedocles' four elements theory still held sway – 2,200 years after his death. So, for example, carbon dioxide was known as fixed air, and oxygen as dephlogistonated or fire air. But the scientific stage was set for a revolution: the overthrow of the four elements, the extinction of phlogiston, the rejection of vitalism, and for the creation of chemistry and physiological chemistry.

Lavoisier was an unlikely revolutionary: his father was a lawyer and his family was part of the prosperous French bourgeoisie. He received the best possible education and studied law, gaining an interest in chemistry from a family friend. The French Academy of Sciences had been in existence since 1666, and at only 21, Lavoisier decided he wanted to be a member. He successfully investigated various methods of public street lighting, and was awarded a gold medal by the king and at just 25 was elected to the Academy. He then embarked on the series of chemical experiments that was to reshape the world of science. But, like most other contemporary scientists, he had to finance his own experiments, so he used his maternal inheritance to purchase membership of a tax-collecting firm. While this provided him with financial security, it was to eventually prove fatal, as tax collectors were not popular at all after the French Revolution. His career did, however, also provide him with an introduction to his thirteen-year-old future wife, Marie, the daughter of another tax collector. This turned out to be a wise move, as Marie rapidly became a proficient scientist herself, serving as an able assistant to all Lavoisier's works.

In 1775 Lavoisier was appointed scientific director of the Royal Gunpowder Administration, and started working on methods of improving the production of gunpowder and on the general nature of combustion, oxygen and respiration. When he finally disproved the phlogiston theory, the Lavoisiers staged a celebration in which Marie dressed as a priestess, burning the writings of Stahl on an altar. But 1789, the year of publication of Lavoisier's great work *Traité élémentaire de chimie*, also marked the start of the French Revolution. Although he served in the revolutionary administration, his bourgeois and tax-collecting credentials finally told against him, and he was imprisoned during the Reign of Terror. Marie was given the chance to plead for his life, but chose to energetically denounce the regime instead. Lavoisier was tried and guillotined in 1794.

Lavoisier's first target was the theory of the four elements. Alchemists had found that boiling water for a long time resulted in the disappearance of water and appearance of a solid residue. They thought this resulted from the transmutation of one element – water – into another – earth – by the action of heat or drying. We now know the solid residue is derived partly from salts dissolved in impure water and partly from the container in which the water is boiled. Lavoisier showed this by boiling purified water in a sealed glass container for one hundred and one days. He found that a small amount of solid matter appeared in the water but by weighing the matter, water and container demonstrated that all this matter was derived only from the container, thus proving water could not be transmuted into earth.

Lavoisier next turned his attention to the burning of metals. Heating metals results in a rusting of the surface, which had been compared to combustion. But according to phlogiston theory (equating phlogiston with the element of fire) combustion results from the release of phlogiston from the material into the air, and should thus result in a decrease in weight of the remaining material. Lavoisier tested this by measuring the weight of the metal before and after heating. He found that the metal always gained weight after heating; and furthermore, part of the air around the metal disappeared after the heating. Thus, the phlogiston theory of metal combustion could not be correct: Lavoisier interpreted his findings to mean that during the heating of the metal, some of the air combined with the metal to form rust, thus increasing the weight of the metal. But *what* was it in air that combined with the metal?

At this point (October 1774) Joseph Priestley visited Paris, dining with Lavoisier and other French scientists. This crucial meeting was to provide the essential key to Lavoisier's research, but also resulted in the two scientists' long-running, bitter dispute over scientific priority and plagiarism. Priestley (1733–1804) was a Presbyterian minister from Yorkshire who developed a surprising bent for science. While investigating the properties of carbon dioxide, derived from the brewery next door, Priestley discovered that when the gas was dissolved in water, it produced a pleasant drink (soda water, present in most soft drinks today). He received a prestigious medal from the Royal Society for this invention and was subsequently recruited by the Earl of Shelburne to be his secretary and resident intellectual. Priestley set up a laboratory at Shelburne's country estate and proceeded to isolate a number of gases. In August 1774, Priestley first isolated oxygen by collecting the gas resulting from heating mercuric oxide. He found a candle burned more brightly and a mouse survived longer in a jar of this gas than in ordinary air. Priestley considered the new gas to be a variety of air ('pure air') and adhering to the phlogiston theory, later named it 'dephlogisticated air'. At this crucial point Shelburne took Priestley to Paris and at a fateful dinner with Lavoisier, Priestley told of his recent experiments. Whether or not this meeting was the inspiration for Lavoisier's subsequent experiments was later hotly disputed. But Lavoisier immediately repeated Priestley's experiment of producing oxygen by heating mercuric oxide, realizing that this new gas must be the substance in air combining with the heated metal to produce rust (metal oxides). But Lavoisier interpreted the new gas as a separate substance (or element), not a variety of air, and later named it 'Oxygen' – which is Greek for 'acid former', because he believed (wrongly) that all acids contained some oxygen. In April 1775, Lavoisier presented his findings at the French Academy without reference to Priestley, claiming he had independently discovered oxygen. Priestley subsequently disputed his priority in the discovery of oxygen. There now seems little doubt that Priestley and Scheele discovered oxygen, but because they used the phlogiston theory and only had a crude conception of chemical elements, they failed to interpret their findings as a new substance.

Another bitter dispute followed over the composition of water. Water was still regarded as an element, but Priestley, Cavendish and James Watt (famous for his discovery of the steam engine) had found that if a mixture of hydrogen and oxygen (or air containing oxygen) was ignited with a spark, then water was produced. They were, however, slow to publish their findings. An assistant of Cavendish visited Paris in 1783, innocently telling Lavoisier of their findings on the production of water from hydrogen and oxygen. Lavoisier immediately returned to the laboratory repeating the experiment, and went even further by reversing it; he heated steam to produce oxygen and hydrogen. He swiftly published the result, claiming priority for the discovery. This understandably caused a furore. But the important knowledge was that water was not, as previously thought, an element, but a combination of oxygen and 'hydrogen' (another name coined by Lavoisier, meaning 'generator of water'). At last the four elements theory was falling apart and something had to take its place. Lavoisier provided that new system, essentially modern chemistry, according to which there are many elements, including oxygen, hydrogen, nitrogen, carbon and phosphorus, which can combine in various ways to produce compounds, which depending on their nature and conditions may be either solids, liquids, or gases.

Lavoisier's key contribution here was to accurately measure the change in weight and to use the principle of conservation of mass – the idea that regardless of what you do to an object it will not change in weight (as long as no mass escapes). Before Lavoisier's breakthroughs it was not clear whether matter could appear or disappear during reaction or transformations. Lavoisier showed by weighing that the mass stayed the same during a reaction, and explicitly stated the principle of Conservation of Matter: matter could not be created or destroyed. He used this principle to track where the matter was going in a whole series of reactions. Because of Lavoisier's principle, contemporary improvements in weighing techniques contributed to the development of chemistry, as much as the microscope contributed to biology. He also provided a nomenclature for chemicals, still in use today. All these changes amounted to a Scientific Revolution, which transformed alchemy into chemistry. The new system was rapidly adopted throughout Europe, only rejected by a few die-hard phlogiston theorists, including perhaps unsurprisingly, Priestley. There was no love lost between these two great scientists. Priestley, the experimentalist, regarded Lavoisier's theories as flights of fancy; while Lavoisier, the theoretician, characterized Priestley's investigations as 'a fabric woven of experiments hardly interrupted by any reasoning'.

Priestley moved to Birmingham in 1780 and joined the Lunar Society, an influential association of inventors and scientists including James Watt, Matthew Boulton, Josiah Wedgwood (engineer and pottery manufacturer), and Erasmus Darwin (poet, naturalist and grandfather of Charles). In 1791 Priestley's chapel and house were sacked by a mob angered at his support for the French Revolution. He fled to London, and then, in 1794 at sixty-one, emigrated to America, settling in Pennsylvania, and becoming one of the New World's first significant scientists.

Lavoisier then teamed up with Pierre-Simon de Laplace, one of the greatest mathematicians in France. They wanted to investigate the relation between combustion and respiration. Combustion is the process of burning, usually accompanied by flame, such as the burning of a candle. Respiration had originally described breathing, but it had been discovered that this process was associated with the consumption of oxygen and production of carbon dioxide; 'respiration' thus came to stand for this process of gas exchange by organisms. Both combustion and respiration consumed oxygen from the air, replacing it with carbon dioxide and both produced heat. But could the conversion of oxygen to carbon dioxide by a living animal quantitatively account for all its heat production? In other words, was respiration really combustion, accounting for the heat produced by animals? They decided to compare the heat and carbon dioxide production of a respiring guinea pig and of burning charcoal (pure carbon). Lavoisier and Laplace invented a sensitive device to measure heat production, although it only worked well on days when the temperature was close to freezing. When, at last, everything was working, they found the burning of charcoal and the guinea pig's respiration produced the same amount of heat for a given amount of carbon dioxide. They concluded therefore that the heat production of animal respiration was due to combustion of carbon (from food) within the animal, and that respiration was in fact slow combustion. From this result they had the audacity to claim that a vital living process was in fact a simple chemical reaction. And they were right – well, partly.

Priestley had again been working on similar lines. He had shown that candles and mice lasted approximately five times longer in a jar of oxygen than in a jar of ordinary air. This is because ordinary air consists of one fifth oxygen and four fifths nitrogen, a gas which does not support life. Priestley said of oxgyen (or rather, as he called it, dephlogisticated air):

'It is the ingredient in the atmospheric air that enables it to support combustion and animal life. By means of it most intense heat may be produced; and in the purest of it animals may live nearly five times as long as in an equal quantity of atmospheric air. In respiration part of this air, passing the membranes of the lungs, unites with the blood and imparts to it its florid colour, while the remainder, uniting with phlogiston exhaled from venous blood, forms mixed air.'

But if all the animals of the world are continually consuming large
amounts of oxygen, why doesn't the oxygen in the atmosphere run
out, as it does in the jar? Priestley discovered that plants produced
large amounts of oxygen when a light was shone on them, and went
on to suggest that all the oxygen used by the animals of the world is
produced by plants. This suggestion is more or less correct, although
the photosynthetic bacteria and algae of the sea (also now classified
as plants) contribute as well to the production of oxygen, and it would
take over two thousand years for the atmospheric oxygen to run out
if all plants stopped producing oxygen. So both the food we eat and
the oxygen we breathe come ultimately from plants; this means all
energy is derived from plants, who in turn get their energy from the
sun.

But if animal respiration was a type of combustion, where within
the animal did it occur? Lavoisier and Laplace believed it happened
in the lungs. They thought that carbon (and hydrogen) derived from
food was brought to the lungs by the blood, and was burnt there
with the breathed-in oxygen to produce the waste products of carbon
dioxide (and water) then breathed out; and heat, which was absorbed
by the blood and distributed to the rest of the body. Their belief that
respiration was the combustion of food using oxygen was correct, but
they were wrong in thinking that this combustion occurred in the
lungs. Their view prevailed for fifty years, although Lagrange, the
famous French mathematician, argued that the combustion could not
occur solely in the lungs because if all the heat were released there
they would be burnt to a cinder. He postulated that oxygen was taken
up by the blood and the combustion of food occurred within the
blood. This theory was very influential and competed with that of
Lavoisier and Laplace. But in 1850, it was found that a frog muscle,
separated from the body, still takes up oxygen liberating carbon dioxide; subsequently it was shown that the liver, kidneys, brain and all
the body's other tissues do the same. In the 1870s, the role of blood
was demonstrated to be solely the transport of oxygen from the lungs
to the tissues, where respiration occurred within the cells, the blood
then carrying back the carbon dioxide generated to the lungs. The
colour change of blood, from blue-back to red on passing through
the lungs, was due to a single component of blood, haemoglobin,

which picked up oxygen. Haemoglobin carried oxygen in the blood: it picked up oxygen in the lungs (changing from blue to red), then carried it to the tissues, where it released the oxygen (changing back from red to blue). Thus respiration (or combustion) was occurring not in the lungs but all over the body.

But it was still not clear what relations, if any, respiration and its associated heat production had to life and its processes such as movement, work and thinking. Lavoisier and Séguin, a co-worker, had shown (using Séguin as the experimental subject) that respiration increased during work, after a meal, in the cold, and in deep thought. Thus, there appeared to be a relation between respiration and physiological work, but it was hard to imagine how oxygen consumption or heat production could cause the movement of an arm, let alone the thinking of great thoughts. To bridge that conceptual gap required the imagining of something entirely new, and that something was 'energy'.

THE VITAL FORCE

The collapse of the four elements theory opened up a cornucopia of matter. If 'air' was a mixture of different gases, 'water' was a combination of hydrogen and oxygen and 'fire' was not an element at all, then what on earth was 'earth'? The science of chemistry, newly constituted and emboldened at the start of the nineteenth century, was salivating at the prospect of dividing 'earth' into thousands of different 'species'. The concept of species and family had been successfully used by Linnaeus in the eighteenth century to bring order to biological taxonomy, but what were the building blocks of matter and how were they to be classified?

The theory of the elements was recast by Lavoisier, so that there were at least thirty different elements (now known to be about a hundred), existing as elementary, indivisible 'atoms' (proposed by Dalton in 1808) and combined in fixed ratios to form more or less stable 'molecules'. Chemists divided their task between the analysis of inorganic and organic (or 'organized') matter, the latter being the constituents or products of living organisms. The alchemists had treated organic matter as if it were a single substance or a small number of elements, for example they had treated distillates of egg or urine as single substances. The chemists set about analysing the many components of egg and urine, using new methods of organic analysis. Lavoisier had pioneered such analysis by burning organic compounds in jars of oxygen and collecting the carbon as carbon dioxide and hydrogen as water. By quantifying the amount of carbon (C), hydrogen (H), and oxygen (O), a formula of the compound could now be written down; starch was, for example, thought to be $C_{12}H_{10}O_{10}$. This formula was mistaken, and arose from the misconception that water was HO rather than H_2O. But these methods were rapidly improved and applied with great enthusiasm by several German chemists, in particular Liebig and Wöhler. In 1835, Wöhler wrote: 'Organic chemistry appears to me like a primeval forest of the tropics, full of the most remarkable things'. These first optimistic biological chemists did not, however, comprehend the full complexity and extent of their new field. It is now thought that there may be roughly five million different organic compounds in the human body and these compounds may be organized in an almost infinite number of different ways.

Nineteenth-century Germany, although not yet united, had become the major centre for scientific and technological innovation. Perhaps partly in reaction to the rise of science and industrialism, the Romantic movement developed in late-eighteenth-century Germany producing a scientific philosophy known as *Naturphilosophie*. This bizarre hybrid of Romantic philosophy and science contributed to a resurgence of interest in the vital force and the relationships between all forces.

Justus von Liebig (1803–1873) dominated German chemistry and biochemistry in the nineteenth century, sometimes to the detriment of biology. The son of a dealer in drugs, dyes, oils, and chemicals, von Liebig gained an interest in chemistry assisting his father. But he did badly at school and was derided when he suggested a career as a chemist. He learned to make explosives from a travelling entertainer, terminating an apprenticeship in pharmacy when he accidentally blew up the shop. His father packed him off to university to study chemistry but he was soon arrested and sent home after becoming too involved in student politics. Somehow he eventually earned his doctorate and went to work in Paris with one of the best French chemists of the time, Joseph Gay-Lussac. In the 1820s he took a position at a small

German university at Giessen, and over the next twenty-five years produced a veritable mountain of chemical data.

However, von Liebig did not produce this data himself, rather he invented the research group as a quasi-industrial means of producing scientific results. Taking over an unused barracks as a chemical laboratory, he staffed it with junior scientists as lieutenants, students as foot soldiers and with himself as the distant but all-powerful general. This model of the research group was so successful in producing the large volumes of research required in the industrial world that it was widely adopted and remains the main means of producing scientific research today. This is in strong contrast to the pre-industrial system of the individual scientist thinking up experiments and carrying them out himself, with or without assistance. Von Liebig was both arrogant and argumentative and had a number of angry disputes with other scientists. His success gave him considerable power, through his control over scientific journals, appointments, and societies. The parallels with science today are unavoidable. It is dominated by a relatively small number of politicians of science who control the boards of scientific societies, journals, conferences, grant-giving bodies, and appointment boards. Success in a scientific career still depends to a certain degree on gaining the patronage of these politician-scientists.

Von Liebig started the prodigious task of analysing the millions of different combinations of elements – molecules – that make up a human being. Some kind of order was brought to this chaos by distinguishing three main types of molecule: carbohydrates, fats, and proteins. At first it was thought that these 'organic' molecules could only be produced by living organisms, using some kind of vital force. But in 1828 Friedrich Wöhler, a friend and colleague of von Liebig, found that he could chemically synthesize urea (an important component of urine) without any living processes being involved. Ultimately, this would lead to the melting of the boundary between the living and the non-living, but not yet.

Although von Liebig showed that living organisms were constructed from a large number of organic chemicals, he believed that a 'vital force' was required to prevent these complex chemicals from spontaneously breaking down. He came to this conclusion because, in the absence of life, they did tend to break down, either by oxidation (combination with oxygen as in burning), putrefaction (as in flesh after death), or fermentation (conversion of sugar to alcohol). Von Liebig's concept of vital force was similar to that of a physical force such as gravity or the electric force, but was only present in living organisms. Within the living body, this vital force opposed the action of the chemical forces (causing oxidation, putrefaction and fermentation), thus preventing the decay of the body so evident after death. Von Liebig also claimed that the vital force caused muscle contraction because he thought there could be no other way to account for the control of muscle by mind. When a muscle contracted, some of the vital force was used up to power the contraction. Consequently, immediately after the contraction, there was less vital force to oppose the decay (oxidation) of chemicals in the muscle, which therefore speeded up with an associated increase in respiration. The vital force acted as a brake on the chemical forces and when it was consumed by muscle contraction, the chemical forces speeded up. This is akin to the famous story of Peter, the little Dutch boy, sticking his finger in the leaking dam, trying to prevent the sea washing away the fields and town (just as the vital force prevented the chemical forces from eroding the body). This erroneous interpretation was used to explain Lavoisier and Séguin's important discovery that respiration (the process of consuming oxygen to produce carbon dioxide and heat) greatly increased when a human or animal was working or exercising. Although von Liebig's conception of the vital force was a form of vitalism, in the tradition of Aristotle, Paracelsus, and Stahl, the concept was more mechanistic in its appeal to Newtonian forces and foreshadows the concept of energy, formulated in the mid-nineteenth century.

Von Liebig's belief that everything could be explained by chemistry and the vital force was opposed by Theodor Schwann (1810–1882). This clash proved catastrophic for the sensitive and as yet unestablished Schwann. Schwann's productive work lasted just four years (1834–1838), while he was still only in his twenties, but it was enough to spark a reorganization of biology almost as fundamental as that of Lavoisier's of chemistry. Schwann's first venture was to isolate a muscle from a frog and measure the force produced by the contracting muscle when it was held at different lengths or pulled against different weights.

He found the muscle contracted with the greatest force when it was at the length that it was naturally found in the body. These experiments were seen as sensational in Germany, because for the very first time a vital process supposedly mediated by a vital force was treated and quantified in the same way as an ordinary physical force. It was now possible to give a physical account of vital processes, or reduce them to physical forces. This approach, however, did not please von Liebig and other champions of the vital force. Indeed Mayer later used Schwann's experiment specifically to disprove von Liebig's account of muscle contraction.

Schwann's next achievement was the isolation of an enzyme which he called pepsin from the digestive juices. An enzyme is a biological substance present in small quantities which promotes a chemical reaction without being itself converted by the reaction. But 'enzyme' is a twentieth-century notion, in the nineteenth century they were known as 'ferments'. For the alchemists, a ferment was a small quantity of active substance which when added to a passive substance could transform it into an active one similar to the ferment. For example, fire was the ferment converting flammable substances into flame and the philosopher's stone was the ferment transmuting base metals into gold. Fermentation is the process responsible for the leavening of dough producing bread and for converting grapes into alcohol, making wine. This apparently magical transformation had been recognized since antiquity, but how exactly this happened was unclear, although it was known to require a ferment – yeast. Having discovered a ferment in digestive juice, Schwann concluded that digestion was a kind of fermentation. Von Liebig and the other chemists considered digestion, on the other hand, as a purely chemical process due to the action of acids on food. So when Schwann published his findings in von Liebig's journal, von Liebig added a rather sceptical note to his paper.

Schwann then turned his attention to the nature of fermentation itself: one of the central scientific and technological problems of the nineteenth century. Von Liebig and the chemists believed fermentation was purely chemical and did not involve any biological organisms or processes. Schwann and two other researchers independently discovered that fermentation was a biological process caused by a fungus – yeast – the cells of which could be viewed through a microscope and could be destroyed by boiling. Schwann also showed that the putrefaction of meat was biologically mediated too, it could be slowed by heating and sealing the meat. These biological breakthroughs incensed the chemists who soon got their revenge. In the meantime, Schwann embarked on a microscopic study of the role of cells in animal development and in biology generally. The resulting 'cell theory' published in 1839 revolutionized how the body was viewed.

Since the theory of the four humours, the important components of the body had been thought to be the fluids and airs: the blood, phlegm, bile, urine, semen, cerebral-spinal fluid and *pneuma*. The important locations inside the body were the cavities (of heart, lungs, brain, guts, and blood vessels) where life was manifested in the turbulent motions of fluids and airs. The solid parts of the body (the 'flesh') were regarded as largely structural, perhaps because their very solidity and lack of motion argued against any involvement in change; therefore it was hard to conceive how they might be involved in the vital processes. Schwann changed all that, showing that the tissues were composed of cells and it was within the cells that most vital processes were generated. The cells were not static structures: they had a life of their own. They grew, reproduced, changed into different forms and died. Most importantly the power to cause change was located within the cells themselves, not their surroundings. Schwann called this power 'metabolism', from the Greek word for change. This 'intracellular metabolism' was responsible for fermentation by yeast and for respiration and heat production by all cells. If the secrets of life and energy were to be found, science would now have to follow the trail into the cell rather than pursuing phantom airs and vital forces. And this would require entirely new concepts and methods.

Cells were first seen by Robert Hooke in the early days of microscopes. But Hooke had only seen the large woody cells of plants. It was much harder to see animal cells, because they were smaller and their walls (membranes) were almost invisible. So the structure of animal tissue was unclear, and it had mostly been described in terms of fibres and 'globules' of unknown function. Schwann benefited from a great improvement in microscope optics, using this to show that not only were cells everywhere in the body, but that they were the body's organizing principle. All cells in the body were derived from embryonic cells which divided and differentiated to form the hundreds of different types of cell making up the organism. If there was a vital principle in the body, Schwann believed that it had to be located in the cells, because all the essential processes, such as reproduction, growth, and respiration, were located in individual cells. Doubting the possibility of a vital force, Schwann thought all the properties of cells could be explained in terms of physical and chemical forces. He also believed that living processes within cells could be explained in terms of the physical structures and movements of the molecules. This was an important and influential insight which foreshadowed the spectacular explosion of cellular and molecular biology in the twentieth century. Though intensely religious, Schwann argued persuasively that the concept of a vital force was completely unnecessary, denying God's achievement in originally producing the Universe and its physical forces: these were all that was necessary to create life.

Schwann did not have the whole answer to how cells created life, but he had found important clues in his notion of 'metabolism' and his discovery that digestion was partly due to pepsin. Pepsin was thought to be a 'ferment', but at the end of the nineteenth century it was found that ferments consisted of single biological molecules, now called 'enzymes'. Enzymes are the magic molecules inside cells that actually cause the 'change' of metabolism. Enzymes are made from protein. They act on the chemicals and structures inside and outside the cell changing them from one form to another. For example, pepsin cuts other proteins into pieces without itself being cut up. Each type of enzyme can cause only one type of change but there are roughly 10,000 different types of enzyme in a cell. These enzymes are the alchemists of the cell. But each enzyme molecule can be regarded as a minute, exquisitely designed, molecular machine. Machines, because they are designed structures, performing specific tasks and transforming things by physically interacting with them; and molecular, because they consist of single molecules. Enzymes and the other molecular machines of the cell are the engines of life.

Enzymes were first discovered within yeast, as the word itself reflects – 'enzyme' means 'in yeast'. Although Schwann and others had shown that fermentation was caused by yeast cells, this discovery was ridiculed by von Liebig and the chemists and replaced by von Liebig's own nebulous chemical theory. So, the biological theory of fermentation (that it is caused by living cells rather than dead chemicals) had to be re-established later in the century by Louis Pasteur. Pasteur was unable, however, to isolate from yeast cells a 'ferment' which could cause the fermentation of grape juice into alcohol, in the absence of live cells. Thus it was unclear whether fermentation was a truly vital process, only occurring within living cells. This was crucial because if the sub-processes of life such as the transformation of chemicals, could not occur in isolation from a living cell, then this implied that there was indeed some vital force involved. In more practical terms, it also meant that science would never penetrate far into the cell, because the individual processes could not be studied in isolation. It was left to Buchner at the very end of the century to at last successfully grind up yeast cells, and isolate something (a bunch of enzymes) that could cause fermentation in the absence of living yeast cells. It is this event that marks the true beginning of Biochemistry, in part because it destroyed the concept of the vital force, but mainly because science had finally broken into the cell and was able to study the processes of life at the molecular level.

Schwann had opposed von Liebig and the other chemists' views on virtually everything: the role of biology rather than chemistry in digestion, fermentation, putrefaction, metabolism, tissue structure, muscle function and the vital force. The chemists, clearly rattled by this upstart, went onto the attack, writing a satirical article on the views of the 'biologists' on fermentation. This article, drafted by Wöhler and made more vitriolic by von Liebig, ridiculed the cell theory of Schwann and others, scathingly describing it in terms of anthropomorphized cells shaped like distilling flasks with big mouths and stomachs, gulping down grape juice and belching out gases and alcohol. Schwann's credibility was destroyed, he lost his job and was prevented from obtaining another academic post in Germany. He escaped into exile in Belgium, with a post in the Catholic University of Louvain, where his time was filled teaching anatomy. He never did any significant biological research again, keeping his head well below the parapet, and the chemists held the field once again in Germany. However, the experiments and book Schwann had produced in his four years of active research proved immensely influential, eventually leading to the demise of von

Liebig's ascendancy and the transformation of biology. Von Liebig publicly battled on against Pasteur, but after thirty years of denial eventually had to admit that he had been mistaken about the biological basis of fermentation. The stresses of the struggle and eventual defeat may well have contributed to his death soon afterwards. The idea of the vital force died with him, later to be reborn in the transmuted form of 'Energy'.

We have now learnt our 'chemistry'. We know life is not created by spirits sucked in from the air to push and pull the body's levers; but rather an element of air, oxygen, is combined with molecules of food within the cells of the body, producing something then able to animate our bodies and minds. The stage is now set for the discovery of energy itself.

THE BIRTH OF ENERGY

The modern scientific concept of energy was an invention of the mid-nineteenth century. 'Energy' is a child of the industrial revolution: its father a thrusting steam engine; its mother, the human body itself, in all its gory physicality; and its ancestors the ethereal spirits of breath and air. The evolution of this concept was aided by an eclectic group of engineers, physicians, mathematicians, physiologists and physicists, with a strong supporting cast of soldiers, sailors and, inevitably, accountants. Today, the scientific concept of energy has a harsh façade of cold forces and austere maths, but its core is much softer and more appealing, reflecting its biological origins in vital forces and wild spirits.

The physical heritage of energy begins with Watt's invention of the steam engine in the eighteenth century. A steam engine produces work (movement against a force) from heat, something never before possible. The question is how? Is heat somehow converted into work or does the flow of heat from hot to cold drive work as the flow of water in a stream drives a water-mill? Sadi Carnot (1796–1832) thought the latter was true but was only half right. Carnot's father was a Minister of War in Napoleon's government and Sadi fought in the defence of Paris in 1814. The total defeat of Napoleon's armies and France's ignoble subjugation turned Carnot's thoughts towards one source of

England's growing power: James Watt's steam engine. The engine seemed to promise limitless power derived from hot air and steam alone but the elaborate contraptions of the early nineteenth century did not always deliver what was promised. Carnot wanted to improve the efficiency of steam engines but there was still no good theory of how they actually worked. So Carnot produced one, based on Lavoisier's conception of heat. Lavoisier had disposed of the phlogiston theory of combustion but had replaced it with something rather similar: the caloric theory of heat. According to Lavoisier, heat was a substance, a massless fluid called 'caloric', which he considered one of the elements, like oxygen or phosphorus. This caloric theory was mistaken but its legacy still remains in our unit of heat energy: the 'calorie'. Carnot thought if heat was an indestructible fluid, then steam engines must be driven by the flow of heat from a hot source (the boiler) to a cold sink (the condenser), just as a mill-wheel is impelled by the flow of water. His important insight was that there had to be a large temperature difference to cause the heat to flow and that there was a quantitative relation between this heat flow and the power output of the engine, which could then be used to predict the efficiency of conversion of coal into work.

Carnot's theory was, however, based on Lavoisier's mistake, that heat was an indestructible substance or element. This mistake was revealed by James Joule (1818–1889), a rich brewer from Manchester. In the brewery workshops, Joule measured the heat produced by passing electricity through water. His results showed electricity was being converted into heat, which was impossible if heat and electricity were two indestructible fluids. The fellows of the Royal Society were unimpressed by his findings, so Joule went back to the workshop and started meticulously measuring the small amount of heat generated by turning paddles in water. From these experiments it appeared that work could be quantitatively converted into heat. The cautious Royal Society again rejected Joule's findings as impossible. Joule became so obsessed with proving his case that when on honeymoon in Switzerland, ignoring the romantic situation and scenery, he spent much of the time dragging his wife up and down a waterfall, trying to measure the temperature difference of the water between the top and bottom – an impossible task. Slowly, other scientists started paying attention to Joule; if work could be converted into heat, then heat could not be conserved, and perhaps heat could be converted back into work.

Joule's revolutionary finding disturbed one particular scientist, the precocious William Thomson, later Lord Kelvin (1824–1907). Kelvin had joined Glasgow University at ten, was a professor by 22 and went on to a meteoric career in theoretical physics. He also had a strong practical streak, and made a fortune from his invention of telegraphy. Kelvin heard Joule describe his discoveries at a scientific meeting in Oxford in 1847 and afterwards he struggled with his inability to reconcile Joule's finding that heat and work were incontrovertible with Carnot's assumption that heat was indestructible but that the flow of heat drove work. The resolution of this conundrum produced two new laws for the Universe to 'obey': the First and Second Laws of Thermodynamics, joint products of the minds of Joule, Mayer, Kelvin, Helmholtz and Clausius. The First Law stated that heat and work (and other forms of energy) were incontrovertible but energy itself was indestructible. The infamous Second Law of Thermodynamics implied that although energy could not be destroyed in any conversion between its forms, it was inevitably 'dissipated' into other forms (mainly heat) less able to do work. Thus although work could be fully converted into heat, heat could not be completely converted into work, because, as Carnot had indicated, part of the heat had to be released to the cold sink in order that the flow of heat could continue and this heat could not then be converted to work. The implication of the Second Law was that all energy was continually running down or 'dissipating' into heat. Therefore the clockwork Universe must eventually run down unless there was something – or someone – outside the Universe to wind it back up again.

The First Law showed that heat could not be indestructible and this led to the resurrection of an old theory that heat (and perhaps all forms of energy) were hidden forms of motion. In hot water, water molecules move around very rapidly, while in cold water the molecules move slowly: when hot and cold water are mixed, the rapidly moving molecules of the hot collide with the slow-moving molecules of the cold, slowing the rapid molecules and speeding up the slow molecules which results in lukewarm water. Thus, the transfer of heat is really a transfer of motion. The exchange between all types of physical force in a common currency of energy gave a great unity to late-nineteenth-century science; a unity missing in the eighteenth century when electricity, magnetism, heat, light and work were all different and discussed in different terms. In the nineteenth century, because these apparently different physical forms could be interconverted they came to be regarded as different forms or manifestations of one thing: energy. But energy was not a type of matter but rather the motion or arrangement of matter. This concept of energy gave a new boost to the hopes of mechanists, who thought they might finally be able to describe everything in the Universe in terms of matter in motion. It has been argued that the origin of this energy concept was partly due to new concepts in accountancy accompanying the rise of industrialization: it is certainly true that energy acted as a new currency within physics keeping track of mechanical transactions. Prior to the 1850s 'energy' did not exist as a useful concept in science, afterwards it became the central concept. However, the word 'energy' entered the English language in the sixteenth century, meaning roughly 'vigour of expression', and later 'vigour of activity'. Originally the word was derived from Aristotle's term *energeia*, meaning actuality/activity; this in turn is derived from the Greek *en* for in or at and *ergon* for work. Today the word 'energy' has a rather schizoid existence, meaning something technical and quantifiable to scientists, but having a variety of metaphorical meanings in the wider community.

The scientific concept of energy did not arise purely from physics, but also at the same time from biology. Indeed the principle of energy conservation was simultaneously discovered by about twelve different scientists but was first formulated by the physicians Mayer and Helmholtz with reference to the forces of life. Robert Mayer (1814–1878) was a German physician with an unlucky life. A mediocre student, he was arrested and expelled for joining a secret society. He eventually graduated and joined a ship bound for the East Indies as the ship's doctor. At that time doctors still followed Hippocrates and Galen's advice to bleed patients for a variety of maladies. While bleeding sailors in the East Indies, Mayer was alarmed to find that blood from the veins was much redder than usual, almost like arterial blood. At first, he worried he was puncturing arteries by mistake but local doctors assured him it was normal for venous blood to be redder in the tropics than in the cold north. This set Mayer thinking. He knew that Lavoisier had proposed respiration functioned to produce heat for the body and he also knew that the change from red to blue blood from arteries to veins was due to the removal of oxygen from the blood for respiration. Thus redder blood in the veins of a sailor in the tropics might be due to less respiration and heat production, which would make sense since the body needed to produce less heat in the tropics than the cold north. He also knew Lavoisier had shown men doing hard work respired more but had not given a convincing explanation of this important finding. Mayer proposed that fuel, heat and work were interconvertible: that it was possible to convert one into the others. Thus work done by men could be produced from heat (as in a steam engine) and this heat could in turn be produced by respiration (the burning of food). More work required more heat and more respiration as Lavoisier and Séguin had found experimentally. This reasoning, although partly wrong, was definitely getting closer to the secret of the energy of life.

When Mayer got back to Germany he wrote up his ideas in a scientific paper, but his thinking was muddled and the paper was rejected. On a second attempt he sent the paper to von Liebig, who published it in 1842. However, when von Liebig published soon after a related theory, Mayer accused him of plagiarism. As Schwann would have agreed, it was not wise to oppose the powerful von Liebig. Mayer then got into even deeper water when he started a priority dispute with Joule as to who had first thought of the conservation of energy. But Mayer lost both arguments due to his unestablished position. The 'Joule' is now the standard scientific unit of energy and the 'Kelvin' the standard unit of temperature, while Mayer's name is nowhere to be seen in the virtual world of scientific units. Understandably, he became depressed, suffering a mental breakdown and attempting suicide.

Mayer's ideas on the conservation of forces were not sufficiently general and quantitative to convince most scientists that something important had been discovered. This situation was dramatically changed by the great German physiologist Hermann von Helmholtz (1821–94), who in 1847 at twenty-six published his famous paper *On the conservation of force*. Helmholtz gave an exact quantitative definition of energy, explaining how the conservation of energy followed naturally from the known laws of physics. Using these principles, he suggested that heat and work generated by animals must derive entirely from the burning of food in respiration. Although Helmholtz was strongly sympathetic to von Liebig's work, he pointed out that the vital force was incompatible with the conservation of energy (because the vital force could be converted into physical forces but not vice versa), and must thus be discarded by the new science of energy. Helmholtz was a founding member of a school of German physiologists (known variously as the Helmholtz, Berlin or 1847 School of Physiologists) who sought to explain all biological processes in terms of known physical, rather than vital, forces.

According to Helmholtz's version of the conservation of energy, there was a single, indestructible and infinitely transformable energy basic to all nature. This 'Energy' was more fundamental to the Universe than matter and force, as the overarching theory of the conservation of energy constrained the manifest forms of matter and motion. Energy was well on its way to replacing God. The good news of the First Law was that the Universe was now a vast reservoir of protean energy awaiting conversion into work. The bad news of the Second Law was that this conversion was taxed by the dissipation of some energy into heat. Although all forms of energy were equal, some forms were more equal than others.

The discovery of the conservation of energy was partly due to the recognition that any quest to build a perpetual-motion machine was doomed. In the eighteenth century the French Academy of Sciences had set up a commission to examine proposals for building such a mythical machine: although many tried (including the young Mayer) all had failed. Such a machine would produce motion and work out of nothing. It would be an 'unmoved mover', something that Aristotle had associated with God alone. The recognition that perpetual motion was impossible led to the idea that all motion must arise from some prior, actual or potential motion: no change without a prior change. Therefore the whole history of the Universe was locked into one single causal web. Helmholtz criticized von Liebig's concept of the vital force powering muscle contraction because the concept allowed the possibility of a perpetual motion machine which he considered impossible.

But if energy conservation prevented the vital force from acting, some thought it would also prevent God interfering with the material world. Lord Kelvin magnanimously gave God a special dispensation to create or destroy energy. But others were less generous, relegating Him to the role of creating a fixed amount of energy at the start of the Universe and then sitting impotently on the sidelines as the consequences of His creation unfolded. Surprisingly some physicists now believe that the net amount of energy at the beginning of the Universe was zero, so perhaps it was God who was lacking in generosity.

The ancient Greeks said Prometheus had stolen fire from the gods, given it to mankind and with it part of their divine knowledge and power. Now, through Helmholtz and the others, mankind had acquired the concept of energy itself, and with it a greatly increased power for good or evil. If this concept of energy could be used to understand the secret of life and death, then perhaps death itself could be conquered and humans might at last become immortal gods.

The relation between respiratory heat production and muscle work and in general the coupling between respiration and energy use in the body still remained obscure throughout the nineteenth century. It was gradually established that respiration – oxygen consumption, carbon dioxide and heat production – occurred within the tissue cells, rather than in the lungs or blood. It was thus suggested that muscles might work as biological steam engines using the heat generated by respiration to drive contraction. But by the end of the century, it was realized that this would not work, as the Second Law of Thermodynamics indicates that heat is a very inefficient source of work unless the temperature difference between machine and environment is very high. At normal physiological temperatures a heat engine would therefore be extremely inefficient, generating very little work for the amount of food burnt. The only realistic way of using respiration to drive muscle contraction was to bypass heat production and pass the energy released by respiration through some intermediate energy store to muscle contraction, without releasing the energy as heat. But it took another century to work out how this feat was achieved.

The historical trail we have followed in pursuit of the secrets of life and energy has branched many times as the questions have multiplied, and the answers have led us off into territory ever more obscure and abstruse. To summarize, before pressing on in the next chapters to the summit of present understanding of body energy: we started by looking at the general modes of biological explanation in early cultures where energy and life were not distinguished from each other and where all movement and change were attributed to anthropomorphic souls, gods or spirits. Energy, enthusiasm and life were given by the gods and equally spirit and health could be taken away by the gods or devils. Mechanisms were not considered, because 'mechanism' was not involved. In ancient Greece and Rome the role of gods and souls gradually diminished. Energy came in the form of *pneuma*, a spirit of the air, circulating in the body and providing the 'go' of life. In Renaissance and Enlightenment Europe, spurred on by advances in technology, gods and souls were ejected from science and replaced by cold mechanics. Crucially, hypotheses were now tested by experiment rather than rational plausibility and this was aided by the injection of mathematics into scientific theories and experiments. *Pneuma* and spirits were replaced by 'forces' and 'laws'. A component of the air, oxygen, was found to be essential to life and consumed inside the living body in the process of burning digested food, resulting in the production of body heat. This process of respiration was eventually found to be located in the cells of the body and carried out by enzymes, the molecular machines of the cell. The various forces of nature were found convertible between each other and into movement and heat and, thus, were united in the common concept of energy, the universal source of all movement and change. The body then became an energy converter (or engine), channelling the energy released by burning food into movement and thought, but how exactly this was effected was unknown.

The appealing idea of the history of science as a continuous ascent towards the pinnacle of modern truth, is, of course, anathema to most historians. They point out this view of history arises from taking the contemporary truth and weaving a narrative towards it – carefully selecting from the past. My brief historical overview gives little idea of how scientists really thought and operated in the past. It does, however, give us a sense of where our present-day concept of energy came from and how it evolved; and now we must follow it right up to the constantly moving present, where a number of shocks await.

Chapter 3

ENERGY ITSELF

WHAT IS ENERGY?

I taught bioenergetics (the science of body energy) in Cambridge for many years before I realized that I did not, myself, understand what energy was. Tutorials are meant to be cosy but fiercely intellectual chats between a teacher and one or two students. However, teachers can often rattle on without knowing what they are talking about. One fine day I discovered that was true of me and energy. Part of the problem with energy is that it is an abstract idea, so that one answer to the question 'What is energy?' is 'A concept existing in a scientist's head'. But another, more subtle problem is how the concept of energy has evolved historically, so that many layers of meaning, not always consistent, have been superimposed on the words and symbols. So take heart, if at first you do not understand the meaning of energy, it will not necessarily disqualify you from either doing scientific research or teaching bioenergetics at Cambridge! In science, as in life, you do not necessarily have to understand a concept in order to be able to use it.

According to current scientific ideas, energy is *not* an invisible force field coursing through the body, moving arms and legs and cooking up thoughts in the brain like some benign ghost dashing around pulling the levers of body and mind. The modern idea of energy is more like that of money. Money gives the capacity to buy things, coming in many forms, such as coins, notes, cheques, credit cards, bank accounts, bonds, gold etc. It can be used to buy many sorts of things, such as hats, houses and horses. Money allows the exchange of these things at a fixed rate, so that I can, for example, exchange a fixed quantity of coins for one horse. 'Energy' is a capacity for movement or change in a physical or biological system. It comes in many forms, such as chemical energy, electrical energy, or mechanical energy and can be used to 'purchase' many forms of change, such as movement, chemical change, or heating. Energy quantifies the exchange between these things at a fixed rate, so that, for example, a certain amount of heating requires the expenditure of a certain amount of chemical energy. One important difference between money and energy is, however, that money and monetary value are not exactly conserved. You may pay £100,000 for a house one year, selling it for £110,000 or £90,000 the next year without having altered or improved the house and this £10,000 does not suddenly appear or disappear from elsewhere in the economy. You can burn a £10 note and money simply disappears in smoke. Neither money nor monetary value is absolutely conserved: there is no Economic equivalent to the First Law in Thermodynamics. If there was, Economics would be easier but we might also be poorer. Energy is strictly conserved, as expressed by the First Law of Thermodynamics, which states that during any change of any sort the total amount of energy in the Universe stays the same. If you use one hundred units of energy to raise a rock one hundred feet in the air, on your return a year later lowering the rock to the ground one hundred units of energy will be released. It may not be released in wholly desirable ways – the energy may be released as heat, sound or work depending on how the rock is lowered, but when the energy released is added up the total will be one hundred units.

Money or monetary value is an abstract concept since it can reside in very different objects, such as coins or a bank account. Energy is similarly abstract since it is contained in many different types of thing, while not actually being them; energy rather is their capacity to produce movement or change. Energy is not in addition to the things themselves: it is rather as if an accountant were examining the situation, assessing the capacity for movement or change. For example if a rock is balanced at the edge of a chasm, it is possible to work out that if it were tipped into the chasm so much energy would be released as movement, noise, heat etc. Before the rock is moved, this energy does not reside in the rock or chasm any more than monetary value resides in coins or horses: this is because energy or monetary value are not tenuous forms of matter, but rather ways of quantifying the potential for change. Energy quantifies the capacity for movement or physical change within any particular situation.

Energy is like money in another way. Money does not determine how or when it is to be spent; that is determined by the people spending it. Similarly, a rock balanced over a chasm may have a lot of energy but this does not determine if or when the rock may fall. Rather it determines whether the rock can fall or not. The presence of a million dollars does not determine how or when it will be spent but does mean that x number of houses, y amount of strawberries or z number of horses *could* be bought. Similarly the presence of one million units of energy does not determine how or when the energy will be used, but it does mean that x amount of heat, y amount of movement or z amount of electricity *could* be produced.

The great American physicist Richard Feynman warned us of the abstract nature of energy in his famous *Lectures on Physics*:

'It is important to realize that in physics today, we have no knowledge of what energy *is*. We do not have a picture that energy comes in little blobs of a definite amount. It is not that way. However, there are formulas for calculating some numerical quantity... It is an abstract thing in that it does not tell us mechanisms or *reasons* for the various formulas.'

So energy is not a thing or a substance. We can calculate it, using the figures for predictions, but have no idea what it is in itself. Energy seems just an abstract accounting concept like money quantifying the amount of movement that could be produced by a particular system. How boring! Yet, according to physics, energy is perhaps *the most* fundamental property of the Universe. Energy is the one constant conserved through all change. Everything can be created from or dissolved into energy, including even matter itself: which is demonstrated by atomic explosions and Einstein's famous equation $E = mc^2$. In this rather abstract scheme of things, energy is the ultimate substance and fabric of the world, from which all else evolves and into which all else ultimately dissolves.

But energy itself does not produce movement or change. So what does? Newton said all movement or change is brought about by forces.

In our lives we experience only two types: gravitation and contact forces. Gravitational force pulls everything towards the earth's centre and causes all heavenly (and not so heavenly) bodies to attract each other. Contact forces occur when we push or pull something; when I lift a chair; when a car hits a lamppost; or when a volcano explodes. Gravitational force exists because every bit of matter is attracted to every other bit, causing them to accelerate towards each other. All the contact forces are different manifestations of one immensely powerful force: the electric force. Electric force is the force of attraction or repulsion between all charged matter. Gravitational force and electric force account for virtually all movement and change in our universe. There are two other forces known: strong nuclear force and weak nuclear force but their range of action is so small, they can only be observed by breaking open the nucleus of an atom. Thus nuclear forces have no apparent effect either on biology or our everyday lives.

Although gravitational force is important for large objects like us, it has no significance for small objects like cells. The electric force is – roughly – one thousand million million million million million million times stronger than the gravitational force and is the only force that matters at the level of molecules and cells. Gravitational force causes attraction – that is, two objects will accelerate towards each other. But the electric force causes either repulsion or attraction depending on whether the matter carries the same or different charges: opposites attract, likes repel. The electron carries a negative charge: the proton a positive charge. Everything, including our bodies, can be considered made up of different arrangements of protons and electrons. (There are also neutrons, but they have no charge, and behave like an electron and a proton stuck tightly together.) Everyday objects are made up of approximately equal numbers of electrons and protons. If this were not so, an excess of positive or negative charge would create a huge force pushing out (or exploding) the extra charge, leaving a roughly neutral group of electrons and protons. The power of the electric force is truly immense. If two people, standing at arm's length, each had one per cent more electrons than protons in their bodies, they would be blown apart by an electric force sufficient to move the weight of the entire earth.

The power of the electric force is not always evident at an everyday level since most things contain a balance of protons and electrons and thus there is no net force between objects. We do notice this force when things get up close and the electrons actually get to feel each other. When we push a cup with a finger, it is electrons on the surface of our finger repelling those in the cup. Similarly all contact forces (whenever something touches, pushes or crushes something else) are due to electron repulsion. If you want to experience directly what electrons feel like, just touch somebody with your hand – all you can feel is electrons.

You might imagine that the forces get weaker and weaker at smaller and smaller scales within the body. In fact the opposite is the case. At the level of molecules the electric force is vastly, unimaginably stronger, because the strength of the force quadruples each time the distance between charges halves. And because the mass of molecules is so small, they experience colossal accelerations and decelerations, bouncing around the cell like billions of ping-pong balls on speed.

Essentially everything happening in the body is due to electrons and protons bumping into each other and rearranging themselves. Some arrangements of protons and electrons are more stable than others, i.e. last longer. We call these stable arrangements, molecules. As molecules collide, they may break up and rearrange forming new molecules. Various molecular arrangements have different energies associated with them – due to the particular arrangement of protons and electrons within each molecule. For example, a molecule may contain a number of electrons packed close together – producing such an arrangement requires lots of energy, because the electrons have to be pushed together against the strong repulsion of their negative charges. But if that part of the molecule is broken apart and rearranged, much of this energy will be released as the different electrons and associated molecules fly apart. This happens with ATP, a very important molecule for the transfer of energy in cells. So, some arrangements of protons and electrons have more energy than other, different arrangements. Thus, turning one arrangement or molecule into another either requires or releases energy, depending on whether the new arrangement has more or less energy than the old.

The essential trick of animal life is to take molecules from the environment, and rearrange them so they have a lower energy. The excess energy must be released. But the random release of energy is undesirable, that would just produce heat. We need to ensure the energy is passed on to other molecules and then used to work muscles, transport atoms or to build molecules. The art is to take molecules (food and oxygen) from the environment, and rearrange the protons and electrons so that there is less repulsion between the electrons in the molecules produced (carbon dioxide and water). This process releases energy, just as burning the food would. However, the body cannot afford to release the energy as heat because living organisms are unable to use heat as an energy source, for reasons that were first guessed at by Carnot in the early nineteenth century. Energy alone is not enough to power life. Something even more fundamental drives all living processes. Erwin Schrödinger (the great Austrian physicist and creator of quantum mechanics) called it negative entropy (or negentropy). To understand it we need to traverse the infamous Second Law of Thermodynamics.

THE SECOND LAW AND THE SECRET OF LIFE

The temptation is to discreetly pass over the Second Law, to ignore it hoping no one notices, because it is a notoriously slippery idea – like a banana skin on the pavement, why don't we cross the road discreetly averting our gaze? Yet up close the Second Law is both awe-inspiring and beautiful. Some creative scientific minds have described the Second Law as one of humanity's greatest achievements. C. P. Snow in *The Two Cultures* compared its cultural value to that of Shakespeare, suggesting that for those aspiring to be 'cultured' an ignorance of the Second Law was equivalent to that of Shakespeare's plays. Snow's targets were those intellectuals who condemned scientists' apparent ignorance in classical cultural matters, without realizing there was an alternative scientific culture as valid as theirs. Whether we aspire to be 'cultured' in this sense or not, the Second Law is central to any real understanding of change, as Darwin's theory of natural selection is to any understanding of evolution. But the Second Law is slippery: there are almost as many interpretations as there are interpreters. So if you are worried by banana skins you may want to avert your gaze and skip this section.

The Second Law arises from the general principle that if something is randomly disturbed (jiggled around) its components will become more randomly distributed. Thus if we put children's bricks in a tin box and shake the box, the bricks will become more randomly distributed. Whether the bricks were initially stacked up neatly, piled in one corner of the box or separated into different colours, after shaking they will be arranged much more randomly. The bricks will become unstacked, spread around the box and the colours will be mixed up. The opposite does not happen. If the bricks, indiscriminately distributed in the box, are shaken up, they won't arrange themselves into a more ordered pattern. This is due to the general principle: a system undergoing random perturbations will become more randomly distributed with time, not more ordered. Why? Because a random distribution is much simpler to obtain than an ordered one. A random distribution isn't a *particular* distribution, it is lots and lots of different distributions which only have in common the fact that they are not ordered. Whereas an ordered distribution (such as the different coloured bricks separated into piles) is a very particular distribution which can only be brought about in a small number of ways. Thus if the components (bricks) are subjected to a random perturbation (e.g. the bricks randomly jumping between piles), then it is much more likely that each perturbation will result in a more random distribution (such as one of the many blue bricks from the blue pile jumping into the red pile), rather than a more ordered distribution (the only red brick in the blue pile jumping into the red pile). This is the essence of the Second Law.

The same principle can be illustrated more clearly with a pack of cards. If we start with the cards in order, arranged in suits from ace to deuce and then shuffle them extensively (that's the random jiggling) we then end up with a disordered layout of cards. But the opposite does not happen; it would be extremely rare to see a disordered pack being shuffled into an ordered one. This is because there are only a few different arrangements that are considered ordered, whereas there are millions of different arrangements that are thought of as disordered. When we shuffle the cards, the pack jumps from one to another randomly selected arrangement. If there is one ordered arrangement and a million disordered, then a randomly selected one (as produced by shuffling) has a one in a million chance of turning up the ordered one, but a near certainty of producing a disordered arrangement.

The type of system the Second Law deals with is generally a group of molecules bumping into each other, such as a lump of wood, an animal, the sun, a cell or the Universe. The random perturbation is provided by the heat in the system: anything hotter than absolute zero consists of molecules which are jiggling randomly. The heat is simply the molecular jiggling which is random in the sense that different molecules bang into each other in random directions at a range of different speeds and at various times. This jiggling causes the system's matter and energy to redistribute and as the jiggling is random the new distribution of matter and energy will also be more random than before. Imagine a group of molecules are in one corner of a box: thermal jiggling will eventually redistribute them all over it. If some molecules in the box are moving at first much faster than others, then random collisions will redistribute the energy more evenly. If there are various types of molecules in different parts of the box, then random jiggling will mix them together. Thus if two liquids, say, orange and blackcurrant juice, are layered on top of each other (as my four-year-old son insists) they will eventually mix together, as this is a more random distribution of the molecules. If the temperature is high enough that the atoms start redistributing between molecules (that is get torn off some and stuck onto others), then we end up with a more random arrangement of atoms between molecules. Therefore, if two molecules *can* chemically react, then they *will* eventually react, until there is a significant amount of the product molecules.

The extent to which the matter and energy of systems (such as the box full of children's bricks) are randomly distributed can be measured and is called 'entropy'. A random system has high entropy, an ordered system has low entropy. The Second Law can therefore be stated as: 'During any natural change entropy always increases'. The concept of entropy was invented by Clausius, but its real meaning in terms of atoms and molecules was only discovered by Austrian physicist Ludwig Boltzmann in the late nineteenth century. Unfortunately for Boltzmann, atoms were not then yet in vogue and his explanation of change in terms of the purposeless movement of atoms was thought to undermine purpose in the Universe, akin to Darwin's earlier undermining of purpose in Biology. Boltzmann, though recognized as one of the great physicists of his day, was scorned by his contemporaries, and in a fit of depression, killed himself. But his grave in Vienna bears testament to his legacy with his simple equation which relates disorder to entropy (S = k.logW, where S is the amount of entropy, k a constant number – now known as Boltzmann's constant – W the number of possible ways of arranging the matter and energy of a system to achieve the same state, and 'log' effectively means that a manifold increase in W only increases S by a relatively small number).

The movement of an object, say, a bullet, involves all the atoms moving in the same direction, at the same speed, at the same time. The heat of an object, on the other hand, involves all the molecules moving in different directions, at different speeds, at different times. Thus when energy is transferred from the motion of an object to heat (for example when a bullet hits a wall) the energy of the system becomes much more randomly distributed. According to the Second Law, this is a natural, irreversible process: motion energy can be converted into heat because the matter and energy become more randomly distributed. The reverse cannot happen: heat cannot be (fully) converted to motion as this would require the system to become more ordered. All the atoms moving in different directions at different times would somehow have to arrange for themselves to shift in the same direction at the same time and this is impossible according to the Second Law.

The use of the world 'natural' in the statement that entropy always increases is important. Interference with the system could make it less random and more orderly. We could arrange the movement of individual atoms to co-ordinate producing orderly motion. We could supply some fuel or motor to maintain or increase the order of the system. But these interventions require the continuous importing of order into the system or the exporting of disorder. Taking into account both the changes outside and inside the system, the Second Law still holds: the total change in entropy arising from any change must always increase.

Heat is the most disorganized form of energy, therefore in any natural process the conversion of stored or motion energy into heat will greatly increase the entropy. In almost every process around you, heat is being released from some stored form of energy. The reverse is impossible due to the Second Law. This explains why we need stored energy to do anything because during the process some stored energy will be converted to heat and we cannot reconvert this into stored energy. In a sense it is the conversion of other forms of energy into heat that is driving all processes in the world. To continue doing things, we need continuously to renew our stored energy from elsewhere. Though surrounded by a vast ocean of heat energy, we cannot convert it into other forms because of the Second Law. Heat energy is only useful if it is supplied at a high temperature and can be disposed of at a low temperature because diffusion of heat from high to low temperature is a spontaneous process, which increases entropy and therefore can be used to do some work. This was the crucial insight that Carnot dimly perceived in the nineteenth century.

But if everything tends towards disorder, randomness and chaos, how can we explain the existence of living organisms, which are stupendously non-random structures? How can we explain the growth of a seed into a complex tree? How can we explain the creation of a bird's wing, an octopus' eye or a spider's web? Surely the result of these creative processes is more complex, ordered and non-random than the ingredients? So then has entropy decreased? Does Life itself violate the Second Law? It is possible to say Life violates the spirit but not the letter of the Second Law. We need to look at all the starting ingredients and end results. The creation of the bird's wing, octopus' eye and spider's web were not the only changes; a lot of food was burnt and heat released. The release of heat to the surroundings caused an increase in their entropy (disorder). Adding up the increase in entropy in the surroundings and decrease in entropy of the animal, there is a net increase. This trick gets organisms around the Second Law: decreasing their own entropy (disorder) by at the same time importing stored (ordered) energy and exporting heat (disordered) energy. Thus Life exports disorder to increase its order. This is also why Schrödinger said Life feeds on negentropy. Negentropy is negative entropy (order), and life feeds on ordered food or light (negentropy) excreting disordered heat (entropy).

Life is confronted by the problem that most processes essential to its continuance are not spontaneous (or not 'natural'), because they result in more ordered matter or energy. For example, a cell needs to collect together randomly distributed molecules and to put together complex ordered molecules (such as DNA) and cellular structures. How can Life construct this order without violating the Second Law? The solution is 'coupling': Life couples the forbidden process that *decreases* entropy to another spontaneous process that *increases* it so that there is a net increase in entropy. The cell, for example, manages to concentrate molecules from outside inside itself, thus *decreasing* entropy, by coupling this process to the transport of sodium inside, which *increases* entropy because there is much more sodium outside the cell than inside. This coupling is simply done by a molecular machine located in the cell membrane (the thin wall surrounding the cell), only allowing sodium into the cell when accompanied by another molecule the cell wants. The molecular machine acts as a gatekeeper coupling the transport of sodium to that of other desired molecules and the entry (or exit) of one cannot occur without the other. So sodium entry into the cell drags in other molecules. Similarly, the cell makes DNA by coupling this ordering-inducing process to a disordering one – the breakdown of ATP. ATP is a general purpose energy source (or currency) within the cell and its breakdown or disordering can be coupled to essential ordering processes, such as the synthesis of DNA by cellular machines. This cannot, however, go on forever, eventually (actually in a few seconds) all the ATP in the cell will be broken down and the cell will be full of sodium. The ATP must then be remade and sodium be pumped out of the cell again. But these processes decrease entropy so have to be coupled to some others that will increase it. Thus the cell requires a chain of coupling processes, which is eventually tied to the burning of food, continuously maintained by the import of food and oxygen from outside and the export of carbon dioxide and heat. This is the key trick of life, the coupling of processes that you want but are impossible, to processes that are possible and can be continuously replenished.

The chain of energy linking every molecular event in the body does not end in the environment immediately outside. The food and oxygen on which we feed to power ourselves must be replenished from some-where, otherwise they would rapidly become depleted. Animals must feed on other animals or plants, using them as a source of energy, thus linking them in a food chain or web of energy. It is ultimately the plants of the world that produce and replenish the food energy and oxygen powering us and the world's other animals. But where do the plants get their energy? From the earth? No, almost all energy on earth comes from the sun. Perhaps the ancients were right to see the sun as a god, source of all earthly things. A star, our sun spews out stupendous quantities of energy as light into empty space. A tiny fraction of that light is caught by plants on earth and used to power the conversion of water and carbon dioxide into their complex molecules (becoming in turn food for animals) and into oxygen (released into the air). In terms of the Second Law, the conversion of earth and air into all the improbable forms of Life is made possible by coupling this to the conversion of pure starlight into random heat energy.

Now you know the Secret of Life *and* the Second Law you are entitled to call yourself a 'cultured' person, at least according to C. P. Snow. However, before you rush off to that dinner party, you had better brush up on Shakespeare too.

Chapter 4

THE MACHINERY
OF LIFE

'Our body is a machine for living. It is organized for that, that is its nature.'

Napoleon in Tolstoy's *War and Peace*

Is man a machine? This is an old question, slowly changing its meaning as our concepts of man and machine have evolved. We now need to ask the question again in this new era of genetic engineering, cloning, smart computers and the internet. Our concept of a machine now extends beyond a mechanical device made of metal, to include such entities as virtual machines made of software and perhaps even living organisms redesigned to perform specific functions. To consider this question seriously, it is necessary also to examine the composition of man in more detail, to see whether his components are in fact machine-like. This will help us understand what we now know about the energy of life, which will be pursued in the following chapters. We are entering the realm of modern cell and molecular biology, currently the most successful of all the sciences and perhaps the most successful cultural activity in contemporary society. Modern biology describes the body as made up of a vast quantity and variety of tiny molecular machines, coded by our genes and designed by evolution, perhaps with the goal of ensuring the survival of those genes.

Since the Second World War, excitement has steadily mounted among biologists as the phantasmagoric happenings inside the cell have slowly come into focus. Some things get less and less interesting as you look at them in more detail. The opposite has happened with biology. Like a set of Russian dolls, more and more intricate as you open each one, or a pharaoh's tomb revealing increasingly astounding treasures as you get closer to the sarcophagus. A human looks quite a simple kind of thing on the surface: a few limbs for manipulating the world, and orifices for getting things in and out of the body. But go down to a million-fold smaller scale, to a single cell and its machinery and we enter a different world of almost unimaginable complexity. Hundreds of thousands of entities are doing tens of thousands of different things at an invisibly frantic pace, within a stupendously complex and dynamic structure. And this complexity is not a result of chaos or random forces, everything is designed, manufactured and controlled inside the cell – or so it seems.

The cell is a vast, teeming metropolis; its life cannot be captured by a single image, scheme or science. This metropolis was not discovered all at once, but gradually came into focus as the tools of molecular and cell biology evolved over the last few decades. Luckily the increase in complexity on smaller scales is not infinite otherwise the task of the biologists would have been a hopeless one. As we move down to a scale one-billion-fold smaller than the human body, suddenly we find a layer of relative simplicity and familiarity once again. We are in the realm of atoms, protons and electrons: already thoroughly explored by chemists and physicists, a sphere of reassuringly rigid and simple laws. But this reassuring simplicity and familiarity should not distract us from the fact that these particles are ruled by the laws of quantum mechanics, the very edge of the knowable, whose delicate frontier can only be touched by mathematics. This, then, is a world literally unimaginable: no image or metaphor can truly depict the behaviour of electrons, protons and photons. Electrons and photons have no structure or image, rather they are the theoretical entities by which structure and image are explained. Biochemistry sits uneasily between the familiar sphere of everyday objects and the unimaginable one of quantum mechanics. Biochemists tend to be somewhat schizophrenic in their treatment of molecules, using familiar images and metaphors to describe entities that have one foot in an entirely different world.

A cell is a bag full of water with many different molecules floating in the water. The surrounding wall of the bag is called the cell membrane, controlling which molecules come in and out. Inside the cell are lots of other membranes, enclosing separate compartments. So here is a bag full of water (and other molecules), containing lots of smaller bags of different sizes and shapes, also containing water (and other molecules). It doesn't sound much like an efficient machine so far – more like a soggy paper bag – but if we swap our light microscope for an electron microscope, we can penetrate to a smaller scale and see the cell's machine-like nature.

A cell is very small and of variable size and shape – an average human cell might be twenty microns (0.02 millimetres) across – but it is vast compared to the molecules it contains. If we increased the scale by one hundred million times, we could then see an atom – it would be a centimetre across – roughly the size of a pea; and small molecules like sugars, amino acids and ATP would be five to ten centimetres – the size of apples, cups and light bulbs. While proteins would be twenty centimetres to a metre – the size of machines, children or small robots. On this scale, an average cell (although very variable in size) would be two kilometres across – the size of a city. But a three-dimensional city – a vast, spherical metropolis. As there is effectively no gravity inside a cell, let's locate this city out in space, its inhabitants floating around inside. Bounded by the cell membrane, the cell is divided up into many compartments by internal membranes, each of which is half a metre thick – like, say, the wall of a house on our expanded scale. These compartments include a maze of tunnels – the width of a small road – connecting different parts of the cell. Attached to these tunnels and floating throughout the cell are many 'ribosomes', the factories that make proteins, which would be the size of a car. And the cell is criss-crossed by a vast number of filaments – that on this enlarged scale, are the size of steel girders or pylons – which act as the cell skeleton, and to which the proteins may attach themselves. Mitochondria, the power stations of the cell, would be the size of a power station – and there would be around a thousand in each cell. There is only one nucleus – a vast spherical structure, about a kilometre across – brooding over the cell, repository of aeons of evolutionary wisdom. Imagine then, this vastly expanded cell, as a metropolis floating in space, peopled by billions of small specialized robot-machines, doing thousands of different tasks, making, breaking and moving trillions of other molecules to feed, power, inform and maintain the cell. All the cell's molecules are packed in tightly, but their movement is lubricated by water molecules, which act like ball bearings. So the cell is huge in comparison to its molecules, but on this outsize scale the human body would be ten times the size of the earth itself, so there are many, many cells in the body.

This, however, gives a rather static picture of the cell which is in fact frenetically busy. All the molecules vibrate, rotate and collide with their neighbours about a billion times a second. This incessant, shaking movement is powered by the body's heat energy, the random motion of the molecules. It is this random shaking causing all of the smaller molecules to move endlessly around the cell, held back only by the membranes, and their tendency to stick to other molecules. It is like an out-of-control pinball game, with trillions of balls, speeded up a billion times. But as there is effectively no friction nor gravity, it is a three-dimensional game. This random walk of all molecules, called diffusion, causes a molecule such as ATP to visit most parts of the cell every second, colliding with literally billions of other molecules. Larger molecules like proteins, machinery of the cell, move at a more stately pace, but unless attached to membranes or filaments, they still vibrate and rotate roughly a million times a second. An enzyme or other molecular machine performs its function, assembling, disassembling or transporting other molecules roughly a thousand times a second.

Within this teeming metropolis, there are two major types of machine doing most of the interesting things in the cell: the enzymes and transporters. Enzymes convert one kind of molecule to another (by removing part, adding something or taking a piece from one molecule and adding it to another). The transporters carry a molecule across the membranes from one compartment to another. They, naturally enough, sit in and across the various membranes of the cell and function by binding particular molecules, and the transporter then changes shape and the molecule is released on the other side of the membrane. Enzymes generally float in the different compartments of the cell (particular enzymes in particular compartments) or bind to the various cell structures.

Enzymes and transporters are regarded today as tiny but exquisite molecular machines and there may be as many as ten thousand different types in each cell. The number of copies of each type present in a single cell varies between ten and more than one hundred million, depending on how quickly the cell needs to do the particular task that each enzyme or transporter performs. Each performs only one job but does it over and over again, one thousand times a second. For example, a particular enzyme may take one type of molecule (the substrate), out of thousands of different molecules in a cell, turning it into a slightly different molecule (the product). The enzyme collides with the substrate molecule, binds it, converts it to the product molecule and then releases it. The enzyme is then free to bind the next molecule of substrate, and converts many molecules of substrate to product every second.

But enzymes and transporters are only two of a large variety of molecular machines existing within the cell. The cell structure is maintained by a complex scaffolding, which consists of many different types of criss-crossing fibres, known as the cytoskeleton. This structure is not fixed, it rather is continuously forming and dissolving, because it is constructed not from dead bricks but living proteins, using ATP to power their union and disjunction. Other machines then use this scaffolding to transport all kinds of things around the cell. A dozen different types of 'motor' proteins are known, which drive along the different fibres carrying various loads, such as other proteins or mitochondria. Different motors travel along different fibre types, some in one direction and some in another and the various adapter proteins enable them each to carry different loads. Their motoring is again powered by the ubiquitous ATP. (A similar machinery is used to power muscle contraction itself.) The ATP providing energy for these machines is itself made by a huge, electrically-driven, rotating motor. This energy input allows protein machines to have dynamic functions – such as clocks, motors, switches, assembly factors, and information processors. Even more complex machines are used to make DNA, copy genes, make proteins, destroy proteins and transfer information across the cell membrane. Each of these processes requires the coordinated activities of ten or more proteins acting together as an integrated machine, so each activity can be performed in turn before moving on to the next activity. In principle all these processes could go backwards, but this would prove disastrous for the cell; imagine if, for example, the machinery making proteins were to run backwards and start disassembling proteins. So the machines use ATP to drive the tasks they perform in one direction only.

The manufacture of proteins is the most energy expensive process inside the body. When you are resting, about one-fifth of your energy is expended on protein synthesis, even though this protein is continuously broken down again. During growth, protein synthesis consumes even more energy – about half the rapid energy production of babies is used for this. It is a very expensive business, but proteins are the most important elements of the cell. Proteins are the machines that do everything: they transport, regulate, synthesize and break down all molecules (including other proteins). They make the energy, contract the muscles, and process the information. They are also hormones, antibodies, receptors, and structural components of the cell. All the active processes of the cell are performed by proteins, while DNA acts simply as a passive store of information (about protein structure) used by proteins. Fats are used either as an energy fuel or to make the membranes of the cell. Most of a cell's volume is taken up by water (roughly seventy per cent), but of the remaining space forty to eighty per cent is protein: so a cell really is packed with protein. But this is not homogenous; each cell has ten thousand to twenty thousand types of protein, each doing a different job.

There is so much focus on DNA and genes today that most people assume DNA is the cell's most important part. However, in terms of the everyday business of the cell, DNA is relatively unimportant. In fact some cells, such as red blood cells, discard their DNA altogether, surviving quite happily – until they need more proteins. It is proteins that do almost everything in the cell, including manufacturing and regulating the DNA. DNA is a static form of information, like a library, providing a blueprint for the proteins – the actual machinery of the cell. Each gene (unit of DNA) codes for a single, particular type of protein in the cell. So the hundred thousand genes in the human genome (all the DNA in a cell) provide the necessary information to produce the hundred thousand different types of protein that go to make up a human.

Sequencing the DNA in the human genome (the total set of genes) is extremely expensive and time-consuming. But it is as nothing, compared to working out what the hundred thousand proteins coded for by the hundred thousand genes actually do. We only know what two per cent of these proteins do in sufficient detail and that has taken about one hundred years. First described by Justus von Liebig in 1824, proteins were identified with enzymes at the end of the century. Their structure was slowly elucidated during the twentieth century. First it was worked out that proteins consist of a long string of amino acids, that is a sequence of small molecules of which there are about twenty different types. Then the British biochemist Fred Sanger devised an ingenious method for working out the sequence in which these amino acids were strung together, and he used this method to sequence insulin, the protein hormone deficient in diabetics. But the string of amino acids that makes up a protein folds up into a distinctive three-dimensional shape, different for different proteins. It was this three-dimensional structure that was so difficult to work out, yet so essential to understanding how proteins actually worked as machines.

Max Perutz solved this crucial problem of determining the 3-D structure of proteins using X-rays. Perutz was born in Vienna in 1914, moving to Britain after the rise of Nazism, but yet ended up interned in Canada as an enemy alien during the Second World War. He then returned to the Cavendish laboratory in Cambridge to study how X-rays might be used to determine the structure of biological molecules. Francis Crick and James Watson joined the same laboratory in 1949 and 1951 respectively and had worked out DNA's structure by 1953. Perutz's job was a more difficult one, taking him until 1960 to determine finally the structure of a single protein – haemoglobin. He then went on to demonstrate how haemoglobin acted as a machine for the uptake, transport, regulation and release of oxygen in the blood; showing how the structure of haemoglobin moved or 'breathed' during its function of transporting the molecule of life. He also set up the MRC (Medical Research Council) unit for Molecular Biology in Cambridge which has claimed so many Nobel Prizes since, including Perutz's own in 1962; two for Fred Sanger for devising the methods to sequence protein and DNA; Aaron Klug's for determining how proteins assemble together; César Milstein's for working out how to make immune system proteins (monoclonal antibodies), and John Walker's for finding the genes and determining the structure of the motor protein that makes ATP. Also at this unit were Sidney Brenner, who discovered messenger RNA, and helped determine the genetic codes and Hugh Huxley who determined the mechanism and structure of muscle. This MRC unit has thus helped to create the science of molecular biology dominating the twentieth century. The twenty-first century looks set to be dominated by the application of that knowledge in fields as diverse as genetic engineering, agriculture, medicine, electronics and pharmaceuticals. Much of biology is now concerned with proteins in one way or another, and the sequencing of the human genome provides an even greater stimulus to working out what these protein machines do, how they do it and how that can be changed.

A series of enzymes converting a molecule from one form to another through intermediates is known as a metabolic pathway. A molecule may follow this pathway inside the cell, being converted from one form (the substrate of the pathway) to another (the product of the pathway) through a number of intermediate forms. There are many different metabolic pathways in a cell which link many different molecules, and most of these pathways are connected so the product of one pathway may be the substrate or an intermediate of another. Thus these form a huge web within the cell. Molecules enter the cell from the blood, through the transporters and then follow one or more of these pathways, until converted into end products (such as carbon dioxide and water) which then leave the cell, taken away by the blood. Transporters are an integral part of these pathways, as substrates must be transported into the cell; intermediates need to be carried across different membranes within the cell and the end products may need to be taken out of the cell.

There are actually three different types of pathway in the cell, that each transfer a different type of thing:

1. Mass transfer (or metabolic) pathways, transferring parts of molecules;
2. Energy transfer pathways, transferring energy;
3. Signal transfer pathways, transferring information.

The history of biochemistry in the twentieth century has been concerned mostly with attempts to trace these pathways through the huge web of interactions occurring within cells. Metabolic pathways were mapped mostly in the first half of this century; energy transfer pathways from the 1940s to 60s; and signal transfer pathways from the 60s and on into the future. Signal transfer pathways lead from hormones or other signalling molecules outside cells, through receptors spanning the cell membranes to 'second messenger' pathways inside the cell and through specialized enzymes which convert other enzymes in a cascade, ending at last on particular protein-machines turned off or on. Or the signal pathways may lead to the cell DNA, controlling whether particular genes are turned off or on and thus whether particular proteins are made or not. These pathways transfer and process information from the cell's environment (and from other cells in the body) in order to help determine which enzymes, transporters and genes the cell should be using and at what rate they should be working. Most routes of signal transfer are probably still unmapped.

Maps of metabolic, energy and signalling pathways adorned the walls of biochemical laboratories all over the world until recently, although they are considered somewhat naff now as molecular biology has pushed metabolism out of fashion. These maps served a similar function to geographical maps of little-known territory, helping to orientate and acting as a psychological prop for the cell-explorer wading through an almost impenetrable jungle of cellular interactions. If a realistic map of all these pathways with all the information now available was attempted, it would be a vast mess – thousands of molecules connected by thousands of different pathways. It would be easy to end up lost in our own map. However, mapping the cell and its machinery will provide work for biologists for the foreseeable future.

So to sum up, on a molecular scale, the cell can be seen as a vast metropolis, inhabited by billions of throbbing machines, interacting with trillions of other molecules in an apparently chaotic fashion. There is no overall director of this activity. Only with a map or plan can we discern that this – apparently chaotic – activity is producing coherent, meaningful behaviour on a much larger scale: the import and distribution of food, energy and information, necessary for the maintenance, function, and reproduction of the cell – or metropolis.

Now that we understand more about cell life, can we say whether a cell is in fact a machine? Part of the reason for calling something a machine is that we think we understand all its parts, how they interact and what function they perform. If we don't know what constitutes something, how it works and what it is for, then it is unlikely we would think of it as a machine. On these criteria, cells are slowly becoming machines. However, our concept of a machine is also dependent on current fashion and technology. Returning to our original question: is man a machine? For man to be a machine, he would need to have been designed for some purpose. In the past, religion could have supplied both the designer and purpose. Today evolutionary biologists would say that evolution by natural selection provides the designer and survival and reproduction of the genes provides the purpose. So if man is a machine, perhaps his true role is to service women. There remains the question of free-will and subjectivity. The reluctance to describe man as a machine stems from a belief that he has a mind directing his body's activity. But the mind or soul has been dismissed by some biologists (e.g. Francis Crick) and philosophers (e.g. Gilbert Ryle) as merely a 'ghost in the machine'. In the future it may not matter so much whether we are classified as machines or not, as machines are likely to become more human, and we are likely to become integrated with our machines.

Chapter 5

THE BODY ELECTRIC

The body and mind work on electricity. Our cells are energized by huge electric fields driving currents of charged particles through a myriad of tiny wires. Four different types of cellular electricity drive minute machines: motors, gates, pumps, latches, and chemical factories. The pace is unimaginably frantic, the electric forces are colossal and the flying sparks are life-threatening. This is the real secret of living energy and electricity is the true vital force.

It seems hard at first to believe that humans run on electricity. If we touch the body we do not get a shock, there are no visible sparks and our hair does not stand on end. This is because of the minute scale on which these biological electric circuits run. They are miniaturized beyond the dreams of any microchip designer. The electric charges are separated by the thickness of a membrane – about five nanometres or less than a millionth of the width of a fingernail. And the voltages are equally tiny, about 0.1 volts, so there is not much chance of getting an electric shock (for comparison our domestic electric supply, from which you *can* get a shock, runs at 120 or 240 volts). However, 0.1 volts across a five nanometre membrane gives an electric field of twenty million volts per metre and this is much larger than the field in a thunderstorm causing lightning – about a million volts per metre. This field produces a huge electrical force which tries to push an electrically charged molecule across the membrane. Thus the cellular membranes become electrically energized, and distribute electricity around the cell. The inside of the body is wet, soft and gooey and seventy per cent water. This seems unpromising territory for electricity, as the electricity we know is carried in hard, metal wires, surrounded by plastic insulation, and causes trouble if mixed with water. However, why water and electricity should not be mixed is that water is a reasonably good conductor of electricity; although the electricity in the cell is not carried by electrons (as in wires) but rather by protons and salt (sodium chloride) within the water. Thus if we stick live electric wires into the bath we can electrocute the cat (and ourselves) and this current can be increased by adding salt to the bath-water. Similarly, inside cells, electric currents are carried by protons and salt moving in the water of the cell.

Electricity seems mysterious. It creeps under our floors and through our walls to silently energize our homes and cities. It streaks across the sky as lightning, the weapon of gods. Now it seems our own bodies and souls are powered by it. What is electricity? It is a flow of charge – just as a stream is a flow of water. Water flows wherever it can from high ground to low ground under the force of gravity. Electrical charge flows by whatever route it can from areas of high charge to areas of low charge, driven by the electrical force. Charge is just matter which can be pushed and pulled by the electrical force. All matter is made up of a mixture of electrons (negatively charged), protons (positively charged) and neutrons (neutral – that have no net charge). Most matter has exactly equal numbers of electrons and protons and has no net charge. But if there is an excess of electrons then matter is negatively charged; or if an excess of protons then positively charged. Inside a wire, the flow of charge is due to the flow of electrons, which can pass through the metal because of their infinitesimal size and loose binding to the metal. But electricity does not have to be carried by electrons, any mobile charge will do. Inside the cells of our body, electricity is carried by electrons, protons, phosphate, or sodium ions. Sodium makes up half of common salt (sodium chloride). When salt dissolves in water sodium floats free of the chloride, but loses an electron to the chlorine, so the sodium has one excess positive charge. An 'ion' is an atom or molecule with a charge, so a sodium ion is just the sodium atom with its positive charge. Phosphate is a small molecule that gardeners fertilize their plants with and has a negative charge when dissolved in water. As water flowing down a stream can do work by pushing a mill-wheel, so electrical charge flowing in a wire can do work by pushing the charges within an electric motor. The electrical force is much greater than the gravitational force and thus can do correspondingly more work.

The ancient Greeks were aware of some of electricity's strange properties. Thales knew rubbing amber caused it to attract other objects. Hippocrates knew that the electric torpedo fish gave a shock, later used to treat headaches. But the first scientific studies were performed by William Gilbert, Elizabeth I's physician, who distinguished between electric and magnetic forces, coining the term electric (from the Greek *elektron* meaning amber). Many other scientists, including Benjamin Franklin and Joseph Priestley, contributed to the progress in comprehension of the properties of electricity in the seventeenth and eighteenth centuries; and electricity was identified by some with the vital force or spirit. This was apparently confirmed by Luigi Galvani's dramatic discovery in the 1770s of 'animal electricity'. Galvani (1737–1798) was an Italian physician who found by chance that, when dismembering a frog, an electric spark passed from scalpel to leg nerve causing a contraction of the frog's leg. This led to a number of ghoulish experiments, including one stormy night cutting a frog in half and connecting its leg nerves to a wire pointing into the sky. Remarkably, the legs contracted in time with the thunder and lightning and the myth of Frankenstein's monster and the electric life-force was born. Count Alessandro Volta (1745–1827), an Italian physicist, used these insights to show that electricity really was the force behind nerve transmission and muscle contraction. Thus, for a while electricity was regarded as intimately connected with the vital force; and as much as anything deserves to be called the vital force, electricity is it.

So where does the electricity driving us come from? It comes from the food we eat and the air we breathe. Inside our cells electrons are torn from the food and fed to the oxygen. In crossing from food to oxygen, the electrons pass down an 'electron transport chain', consisting of a little wire of copper and iron atoms located within the proteins in a membrane. Electrons are fed into the wire from food molecules at high energy and electrons are pulled out of the other end of the wire to oxygen at low energy. Thus, an electric current flows along this wire and can be used to do work as the wire passes through various protein machines in the membrane. This is akin to water flowing in a pipe or river: it can be pushed in at one end and pulled out at the other, and wheels can be pushed by the flow of water to do work. A mill-wheel is thus pushed around by water passing from a high energy level (above the wheel) to a low energy level (in the stream below). Similarly, a stream of electrons passing down the electron transport chain, from a level of high energy to one of low energy, drives various machines (the 'proton pumps'). But the streaming of electrons down the electron transport chain is not continuous, as they have to stop and be carried between various molecules in the chain. In water imagery it would be like a canal with various locks, mills and millponds.

The concept of the electron stream passing down a transport chain was developed as a synthesis of the opposing views of Heinrich Wieland (1877–1957) and Otto Warburg (1883–1970). These two great German biochemists spent much of their illustrious careers in dispute with each other, although calling a truce in the First World War, when Warburg served with the cavalry on the Eastern Front, and Wieland directed research on chemical warfare. Wieland could be seen as the archetype of the coldly analytical scientist, dissecting the very heart of nature. He made and determined the structure of many deadly poisons and worked on the chemical composition of the pigments giving colour to butterflies' wings. He was awarded the Nobel Prize in 1927 for determining the chemical structure of steroids, although this later turned out to be mistaken. Warburg had to wait until 1931 to get his Nobel Prize, which irritated him intensely, but his arrogance and pettiness were outweighed by his brilliance as a scientist. He was Director of the Max Planck Institute of Cell Physiology in Berlin until 1941, when he was removed from this position by the Nazis because he was part-Jewish. But such was his international prestige and usefulness that he was soon reinstated, and was in 1944 nominated for a second Nobel Prize – although Nazi rules prevented him from accepting.

Eighteenth- and nineteenth-century scientists showed that food digested by the gut was burnt using oxygen from the air we breathe inside each cell of the body: the processes of cellular respiration. The problem that Bioenergeticists faced in the early twentieth century was how did the electrons get from the food to the oxygen. This is not a trivial question because electrons cannot easily travel by themselves (unless transported by a metal, such as iron or copper) – that's why most things cannot conduct electricity. But electrons can be transferred from molecule to molecule if packaged together with protons as hydrogen atoms (one electron and one proton makes a hydrogen atom). Wieland proposed that molecular machines (enzymes) within the cells tore hydrogen from the food and this 'activated hydrogen' (H) somehow reacted with oxygen (O_2) to produce water (H_2O). Wieland's proposal was based on the findings by many other biochemists in the first two decades of the twentieth century that there were indeed molecular machines in our cells that could take hydrogen from food and other organic molecules. These machines were named 'dehydrogenases', their name meaning a molecular machine that removes hydrogen, and the theory was called the dehydrogenase theory of respiration.

Otto Warburg strongly disagreed – his theory was that respiration occurs because there is a machine containing iron inside cells which binds oxygen, oxygen takes electrons from the iron, and iron then takes electrons from food. Warburg believed that there was a single machine, the 'respiratory enzyme' which was an oxidase, a machine using oxygen and taking electrons from other molecules and this consumed all oxygen the body breathed in and used. Warburg came to this conclusion after his 1913 discovery that tiny amounts of cyanide completely inhibited the oxygen consumption of cells and tissues. Cyanide and oxygen were both known to bind to iron and Warburg believed (correctly) that cyanide bonded with iron within the respiratory enzyme, preventing the binding of oxygen, resulting in the inhibition of respiration (and consequently death).

Neither Wieland nor Warburg emerged victorious, as both were right and wrong, each looking at opposite ends of the same chain of machines: the electron transport chain. At the top of the chain were the dehydrogenases which ripped electrons off the food and at the bottom was an oxidase (now called cytochrome oxidase) which contained iron, feeding electrons to oxygen. Wieland and Warburg had been examining opposite ends of a great elephant (respiration); Wieland had the head (where the electrons went in) and stated firmly that this was all there was to the elephant, while Warburg had the backside (where they came out) and thought that this was the essence of the elephant. Their apparent blindness is unsurprising considering the methods available to them. They ground up body tissue and looked for various activities of the tiny machines within, without knowing that there were in fact about fifty thousand different machines each with particular activities in the tissue. But had they known, they might never have tried.

Their opposing views were eventually reconciled when the link between them was discovered by David Keilin, a Polish-born Jew working in England as a Parasitologist. In between the front and back of this imaginary elephant was a chain of cytochromes, molecular machines that took electrons from the dehydrogenases, passing them on to the oxidase. The word 'cytochromes' means cell colours, and they are indeed the constituents of cells giving them colour. They change colour when gaining or losing electrons, and this was how Keilin discovered them and their role in respiration. He was working on the pigments and colours of insects and used a hand-held prism which split the light from tissue into its rainbow spectrum so he could see directly which colours were changing in the tissue. He found some moths with no haemoglobin, which made it much easier to see the non-haemoglobin pigments of the body (the cytochromes). He glued a moth by its back to a slide, noticing that when it frantically beat its wings attempting escape, its flight muscles changed colour and changed back again when they stopped beating. Similar colour changes occurred when Keilin deprived the moths of oxygen. Keilin had tortured Nature into revealing one of the secrets of living energy. He then isolated the cytochromes and showed how they form a chain receiving electrons from food (through dehydrogenases) and passing the electrons on to oxygen (through cytochrome oxidase), thus forming the electron transport chain, linking the ideas of Wieland and Warburg.

The electron transport chain allows electrons to flow from food to oxygen, generating a continuous supply of electricity inside the cell. But what does this electricity do? How does it drive our muscles and minds? The next link in the chain of discovery was not forged until the 1960s, when it was discovered that electron electricity is used to generate proton electricity. Electrons flowing down the transport chain are used to drive machines that are part of the chain itself. These machines are 'proton pumps' and their function is to pump protons out of the mitochondria. First isolated by Warburg, mitochondria are particles within cells that function as the power stations of the cell. The pumps sit in the membrane of the mitochondria with the electron transport chain and take protons from inside the mitochondria, pumping them outside. These protons have a positive charge and as they are pumped out, positive charges accumulate on the outside while negative charges are left inside the mitochondria. This generates a voltage difference across the membrane of about 0.2 volts and an electric field of about forty million volts per metre. Because this electricity is based on protons rather than electrons, it is sometimes called proticity or proton electricity. Thus electron electricity generated by the burning of food in the mitochondria is used by proton pumps to generate proton electricity. This proton electricity is then used to generate the next form of energy used by the cell – ATP or phosphate electricity.

An English scientist, Peter Mitchell (1920–1992) received the 1978 Nobel Prize for his discovery that proton electricity was a major energy form in cells. Both idea and man proved intensely controversial. Mitchell worked in research at both Cambridge and Edinburgh for years, but left, finding the academic atmosphere claustrophobic. He set up his own laboratory on the edge of Cornwall's Bodmin Moor surrounded by sheep and desolate moorland. His work there showed mitochondria could pump protons and generate an electric field used in the production of ATP. Meanwhile many scientists tried to prove Mitchell wrong, often wrecking their careers in the process. Bitter disputes arose about priority of ideas and the interpretation of obscure experiments. Before Mitchell proposed that ATP was linked to the burning of food via an electrical intermediate (proton electricity), the field had been dominated by chemists believing the intermediate was a chemical. Because this chemical intermediate was both unknown and hypothetical it was (somewhat disparagingly) known as 'squiggle' and described with a semi-mystical symbol ~ which symbolized an energized chemical bond. Many fruitless years were spent searching for this squiggle intermediate. But few 'squiggle' chemists were converted to the idea of proton electricity. The field itself was slowly converted as younger scientists entered, taking up the cause of proton electricity, while some older scientists retired or abandoned this area for more fruitful fields of research. This confirms Max Planck's proposition that many scientific ideas do not succeed by the conversion of scientists, but by their opponents dying off.

Virtually all energy used to produce proton electricity is then used to make ATP. So what is ATP? It is the general, immediate energy currency of the cell. Any machine that needs an immediate burst of energy gets it from ATP. How is this possible? Well, ATP is like a toy air-gun – where the bullet is forced against a strong spring into the barrel and held in place by the trigger; when the trigger is pressed the spring is released, ejecting the bullet at high speed. ATP is a chemical gun; its title stands for adenosine triphosphate; adenosine and two of the phosphates are the gun, and the terminal phosphate the bullet. Phosphates are negatively charged, so repel each other but, in ATP, three phosphates are directly linked to each other. These phosphates strongly repel each other. When the link between the terminal phosphate and the others is cut, it shoots off like a bullet from a gun. The remaining molecule, now minus one phosphate, is known as ADP – adenosine diphosphate. To stick a phosphate back onto ADP, and reload the gun takes a lot of energy; this is done by ATP motor machines in the mitochondria, powered by proton electricity.

ATP is a small molecule that wanders randomly around the cell, bumping into many different machines. ATP is a loaded gun that cannot pull its own trigger; it needs a hand to do that. The hands are located on many of the molecular machines around the cell. Essentially, these hands reach out and grab a passing ATP, which they then use to supply a burst of energy. But it is no use just pulling the trigger, without harnessing the energy to perform some task. ATP is held tightly by the machine and positioned so that when the link is cut to the terminal phosphate, the repulsion between phosphates is used to do work, such as causing the machine to change shape. ADP and phosphate can then be released and when the machine needs more energy, it grabs another ATP.

Sometimes instead of releasing the phosphate from ATP, the terminal phosphate is attached to the protein machine. This can cause the molecular machine to change shape permanently, or at least until the phosphate is removed again by yet another machine. The change in shape induced by the phosphate can switch the machine on or off. This is the most common way protein machines are controlled. Some protein machines are specialized so that they receive information from the many signalling pathways of the cell and add phosphate from ATP onto a range of other protein machines, turning them off or on; while different protein machines have specialized in removing attached phosphate from proteins when signalled to do so. ATP is thus also used to control the transfer information inside the cell.

Produced by the mitochondria, ATP is used by machines throughout the cell. The residue of this reaction, ADP and phosphate then return to the mitochondria to be reconverted to ATP. The cycle of ATP and ADP inside the cell functions to distribute energy to thousands of different users. The ATP cycle was discovered in the nineteen thirties, by a number of biochemists who included Warburg and Meyerhof and for a time ATP was even sold in a bottle as the ultimate energy booster. Unfortunately, eating ATP has no effect on your energy level, because it cannot get through the cell membrane. ATP is the main carrier of phosphate electricity in the cell and can pass phosphate to other molecules. Another important carrier of phosphate is creatine, particularly in skeletal muscle, and recently body-builders and athletes have enthusiastically taken large doses of creatine as a supplement. There is substantial evidence that dietary creatine does enter muscle cells, improving performance in exercises such as weight-lifting and sprinting. These increases in level and performance are marginal, however, requiring very high levels of dietary intake, which in themselves may be a health hazard.

The concept of the ATP cycle was crystallized by Fritz Lipmann (1899–1986) from a mass of fragmentary data and ideas into a general theory for energy transfer in living cells. Lipmann was involved in the dramatic migration of scientists from central Europe to Britain and America caused by the rise of Nazism in the thirties. This migration marked the end of Germany's one hundred years of supremacy as pre-eminent scientific nation and the rise of the United States to replace it. Lipmann was born in Königsberg, then capital of East Prussia (now Kaliningrad), studying medicine there, until called up as a medic by the German army in the final year of the First World War. After the war Lipmann turned from medicine to biochemistry and studied in Berlin with the great biochemist Otto Meyerhof (1884–1951). Meyerhof was searching for the energy of life in extracts of frog muscle and had shown these could ferment glucose. This process was similar to fermentation in yeast, although the end-product was not alcohol but lactic acid (the acid causing a burning pain if you use your muscles when unfit). This pathway from glucose to lactic acid was at first called the Edman–Meyerhof pathway after its discoverers, but now is more commonly known as glycolysis. Glycolysis is important for muscles because it can rapidly produce energy even in the absence of oxygen. Meyerhof showed contraction of the frog muscle (in the absence of oxygen) always produced a fixed amount of heat and fermentation of glucose to lactic acid, so it appeared the fermentation somehow powered the muscle contraction. But was there an unknown intermediate, capturing the energy released by fermentation and supplying it to muscle contraction?

Meyerhof and others had found that once glucose got into cells it was combined with phosphate – and so perhaps energized phosphate was the missing intermediate. At Meyerhof's suggestion, Lipmann started working on the newly discovered phospho-creatine in the muscles. Lipmann found that if glycolysis was poisoned in the muscles of live rats then contraction could continue, but this resulted in the break down of all the muscle's phospho-creatine (loosing its phosphate), and subsequently both the muscle and the rat became rigid (a condition known as 'rigor', as in 'rigor mortis'). Phospho-creatine thus appeared to be an intermediate between glycolysis and muscle contraction, and perhaps carried energized phosphate from glycolysis to the muscle contraction machinery. Later experiments showed rather that ATP served this role of carrying the energized phosphate, while phospho-creatine served as a buffer or battery of phosphate energy in the cell. Fleeing the rise of Nazism, Lipmann left Germany for Denmark in the early nineteen-thirties, subsequently migrating to the United States when the Nazis gained influence in Denmark. Meyerhof also fled Germany at the same time, initially to Paris, and on the invasion of France in 1940, to America. As a refugee, Lipmann formulated the concept of energized phosphate, which he called 'squiggle phosphate' or ~P, as the central intermediate or energy currency of the cell. He introduced the squiggle ($\sim$) symbol to represent an energized bond between two atoms, and thus was the original 'squiggle' scientist. In his ground-breaking 1941 paper, he concluded:

> The metabolic dynamo generates $\sim$P-current. This is brushed off by adenylic acid [ADP], which likewise functions as the wiring system distributing the current. Creatine$\sim$P, when present, serves as a $\sim$P-accumulator.

The energy delivered by ATP is partly electrical in nature (the electrical repulsion between the phosphates), and partly chemical. The flow of phosphate charge from the mitochondria to the rest of the cell is not, however, driven by electrical fields within the cell, but rather by the relative strength of the chemical bonds binding the phosphate to its various carrier molecules (ADP, creatine and proteins). Thus phosphate electricity is largely powered by chemical, rather than electrical, forces. This new concept of the ATP cycle brought Lipmann scientific fame in his adopted country, and he went on to elucidate other means by which energy is transported within the cell, for which he received the Nobel Prize in 1953.

ATP is used by hundreds of different types of machine in the cell but the main users are muscle contraction, protein synthesis and the sodium pump. The sodium pump is located on the cell membrane and pumps sodium across this membrane from inside to outside the cell. Because sodium is positively charged, this pumping of charge out of the cell produces a huge electric field across the membrane. This field acts as a convenient source of energy for many different activities throughout the body, including the transport of molecules, the control of cell volume and the generation of electrical impulses in muscle, heart and nerves. Simply plugging a protein machine into this energized membrane is enough to power the machine, as the electric field and sodium act like a battery pushing any charge through the protein and across the membrane. Thus the cell uses another form of electricity, this time sodium electricity, to energize the cell membrane. And it is sodium electricity that powers our brains and mind.

Thus, there are four forms of electricity in the cell: electron, proton, phosphate and sodium electricity. Electron electricity is generated within the mitochondrial membranes by the burning of food. This electricity is used to pump protons out of the mitochondria and generate proton electricity. This proton electricity flowing back into the mitochondria is used by the ATP motor machine to load the ATP gun, by forcing a negatively charged phosphate onto ADP. This, in turn, produces phosphate electricity, which is partly a chemical form of energy, being carried by ATP and other phosphate-carrying chemicals. Some ATP diffuses to the cell membrane, where it is used by the sodium pump to force sodium across the cell membrane, thus generating sodium electricity. The sodium electricity can then be used to drive the transport of many other molecules across the cell membrane. Thus these four forms of electricity are continually converted from one form into another in a chain of energy.

The structures of several molecular machines powered by cellular electricity have recently been solved to atomic resolution. In other words, we now know the location of each atom (to within one tenth of a nanometre) within a molecule which may contain about a hundred thousand atoms. Although this is a stupendous achievement, the structure of the molecular machines does not necessarily tell us how they work. This is true of 'cytochrome oxidase', one proton pump of the electron transport chain, the structure of which was recently worked out by the research group of Shinya Yoshikawa in Japan. The structure of such a 'huge', complex molecule can only be appreciated by exploring a three-dimensional model of it on a computer. After a scientific conference in Moscow at which Professor Yoshikawa first described the structure, he and I were marooned in the airport for twenty-four hours. He told me then how he had spent many happy hours and weeks exploring his new model, stunned at its beauty and at the privilege of being one of the first people to 'see' this molecule, one of the oldest and most important in life. For him, these molecular structures are the modern equivalent to the great cathedrals of the Middle Ages.

Although the structure of cytochrome oxidase gives many clues to its mechanism, we are still far from being able to give a detailed account of how this proton pump actually pumps protons. Another great structure only recently solved was that of the ATP motor (the molecular machine making ATP from ADP and phosphate) by the

English scientist John Walker and his colleagues (for which he and Paul Boyer received the Nobel Prize in 1997). Here, the structure suggests that this 'huge' molecule is a tiny motor, the smallest motor in existence. It actually spins, like a mill-wheel, driven by the flow of proton electricity, but makes ATP not flour. The motor has a shaft plugged through the mitochondrial membrane, and this is turned by proton electricity passing through a channel in the membrane. The shaft then rotates within the 'engine' of the machine, and this rotation forces phosphate onto ADP bound within the engine, to make ATP. This engine can also work in reverse, using ATP to pump protons back out of the mitochondria, generating proton electricity. The spinning of the ATP motor was actually videotaped by Kazuhiko Kinosita and colleagues in Japan. They stuck one end of the motor onto a glass slide and attached a minute, fluorescent rod to the other end. When ATP was added the Japanese team could see through a microscope the rotation of the rod like the beams of a lighthouse sweeping the darkness. Although this motor consists of a single molecule and is the smallest rotational motor known to exist, many other types of motor have been found to power: the movement of molecules along the cytoskeleton, the contraction of muscle, the manufacture of DNA and RNA and the propulsion of bacteria.

It does seem, in some ways, incredible we are powered by electricity. In the early nineteenth century there was Frankenstein's monster, a creature constructed from several bodies, brought to life with electricity. Then, in the first half of the twentieth century there were robots: electrical machines made to look and act like humans. Then more recently there were cyborgs, who were half human, half machine. Now it turns out that we were electrical machines all along.

Chapter 6

MITOCHONDRIA: THE MONSTERS WITHIN

Our bodies contain roughly ten million billion bugs, known as mitochondria (pronounced my-toe-con-dria), which invaded the ancestors of our cells about one billion years ago. They are so used to living inside us and we have got so used to having them around, that now we cannot live without each other. They are part of us and we are part of them. They produce almost all our energy and we feed and shelter them. Our mitochondria still have their own DNA, inherited from our mothers only, and indeed it may be derived from a single woman at the origin of modern humans: a mitochondrial Eve. But these cellular guests who appear to be living peacefully in symbiosis with the rest of the cell, may also be the enemy, quietly killing from within. Whenever a cell dies, a trail of clues leads back to the mitochondria, implicating them in many devastating diseases and disabilities, as well as the process of ageing itself. The indispensable houseguest turns out to be a serial killer of monstrous proportions.

Almost every cell in our body contains mitochondria – about one thousand per cell. The single 'mitochondrion' is a restless beast taking many shapes and forms. Caught in a single, unflattering snapshot, it looks a little like a worm, but one that writhes, splits in two and fuses with other worms. So sometimes we may catch a mitochondrion looking like a zeppelin, and at other times like a multi-headed and multi-tailed beast, or like a network of criss-crossing tubes and plates. The mitochondrion is an ancient, maternal monster – a dragon. A dragon with a monstrous appetite, which eats again everything we eat and breathes it forth as fire. Virtually all the food and oxygen taken into the body is consumed by mitochondria and most of the heat generated by the body is produced by them. But this monster is minute – one micron in size, one thousandth of a millimetre: one billion mitochondria would fit easily inside a grain of sand.

Mitochondria have their own DNA and identity, but that does not mean it is a case of them against us. We are partly mitochondria; they constitute about one tenth of our cell volume, one tenth of us. As they are virtually the only coloured part of the cell, mitochondria constitute the colour of our cells and tissues. Were it not for the melanin in our skin, myoglobin in our muscles, and haemoglobin in our blood, we would be the colour of mitochondria, a browny red. And if this were so, we would change colour when we exercised or ran out of breath, so that you could tell how energized someone was from his or her colour.

Mitochondria are the power stations of our cells producing almost all our energy. They are, however, rather leaky power stations, which has dire consequences. I was brought up to believe that the products of biological (evolutionary) design – life and all life forms – were vastly more efficient and effective than products of human creativity such as machines and culture. We were taught that billions of years of evolution had perfected cell design to such an extent that no human planner could improve on the design; no miser could economize on the energy usage; no management consultant could improve on the allocation of resources; no engineer could engineer fewer faults. The belief that human culture should not interfere with nature because nature is better designed than culture is widespread, and the belief motivates fears of scientists' meddling with nature, as in medicine, genetic engineering, cloning or pesticides. Scientists do, however, often grow arrogant and over-confident in their ability to improve on nature, as illustrated in spectacular failures such as DDT or thalidomide. Whatever the merits of these beliefs, our cells are certainly not as efficient or effective as we once thought them. This is illustrated by what appear spectacular design faults in our mitochondria – they leak. Electron electricity leaks out of the mitochondria to produce toxic free radicals and proton electricity leaks out producing heat: these are not small, insignificant leaks, they are large and life-threatening.

Electrons leak out of the mitochondrial electron transport chain to produce 'free radicals'. Their name suggests a benign group of political intellectuals, but they are in fact a subversive group of toxic chemicals. The first of this group is 'superoxide', which is produced when electrons leak from the transport chain or other molecular machines landing on oxygen. Superoxide is not a superhero or a brand of washing powder but oxygen with an extra electron. But it is this extra electron which causes trouble. Most stable molecules have their electrons in pairs because this arrangement requires less energy. Molecules that have an unpaired electron are called free radicals and are very reactive because the unpaired electron wants to pair with electrons in other molecules. This sounds fair enough for the poor lonely electron, but if it snatches an electron from some other nearby molecule then that molecule is in turn left with an unpaired electron. So a new free radical is produced with an aggrieved single unpaired electron. This sets off what is known as a 'chain reaction', which only terminates when two free radicals meet and react, satisfying their lone electrons. This may provide a happy ending for lone electrons, but their wandering through hundreds of other molecules has left a trail of havoc. Some molecules have been ripped apart, some membranes torn to shreds and some molecular machines wrecked beyond repair. Free radicals are major causes of cell death and destruction in the body.

Superoxide is the first member of that subversive group but goes on to produce a second; hydrogen peroxide. It is only an honorary member of the free radical society, not actually having a free radical, a lone electron. But it is associated with the others because it is equally good at snatching electrons from other molecules. Outside the body, we use hydrogen peroxide to bleach hair, and to kill germs. Inside the body it can react with superoxide to produce an even nastier piece of work: the hydroxyl radical. The hydroxyl radical can rip an electron off almost anything and this free radical is probably responsible for considerable cellular destruction, including the mutation or ripping apart of DNA.

Free radicals are increasingly suspected as being either the villains or accomplices in a wide range of diseases: heart disease, cancers, inflammatory and neurodegenerative diseases. This is an impressive record of death and destruction but the definitive evidence of their involvement is still lacking. One line of evidence linking free radicals to disease is the protective effect of anti-oxidants and free radical scavengers. Free radicals are oxidants, which can snatch electrons off other molecules. Anti-oxidants are molecules that prevent the toxic effects of free radicals by giving them electrons without turning into toxic radicals themselves, thus quenching the radical chain reaction inside the cells. Vitamins C, E and β-carotene are important anti-oxidants, normally present in the body to stop free radical damage. Large-scale trials where people are given high doses of these anti-oxidants on a regular basis have shown they reduce the incidence of heart disease and cancer, the two main killers in the western world. This is strong evidence suggesting that free radicals are up to mischief in the human body. Yet, other trials have indicated that taking high doses of anti-oxidants has little effect on, or even worsens, these diseases. And nutritionists have suggested that these purified anti-oxidants are not as effective as those found in nature, such as in, for example, vegetables, red wine and tea. There is evidence that the process of ageing itself may be due to the build-up of free-radical damage to the body. Certainly the wrinkling of the skin and the eyesight's decline with age appear to be due to this damage. And most free radicals are derived from electrons leaking out of the electron transport chain of the mitochondria.

The second leak is of proton electricity through the mitochondrial membrane, somewhat imaginatively called the 'proton leak'. Protons are pumped out of the mitochondria by proton pumps, generating a huge electrical field and proton gradient. This drives the protons back into the mitochondria, through the ATP motor in the mitochondrial membrane. If proton electricity is to drive the motor of ATP production, it cannot be allowed to leak back through the membrane without passing through the ATP motor. But it does. Martin Brand and I have shown this leak occurs in mitochondria and cells and that up to one quarter of the energy that we generate may be apparently wasted in this way. How or why this leak comes about is not clear. It may be the inevitable consequence of having a huge electrical field across a very thin membrane; or perhaps or that the energy wastage has some function itself, either to produce heat or burn off excess food.

This is indeed what happens in the so-called 'brown fat'. Fat under our skin comes in two varieties: white and brown. White fat stores fat as an energy reserve but does not burn it. Brown fat both stores and burns fat producing heat. Brown fat is brown because it contains a lot of brownish-coloured mitochondria. And these mitochondria burn the fat, ripping electrons off and passing them down the electron transport chain to oxygen. This electron electricity then powers the proton pumps to pump protons out of the mitochondria, which generates a huge electrical field and proton gradient across the membrane. In mitochondria from other tissues, the protons would then go back through the ATP motor, and generate ATP. But brown fat mitochondria contain very few ATP motors. The protons return instead into the mitochondria through a 'gated channel': a channel through the membrane with a gate on it. When this gate is open, the protons speed through the channel dissipating the electric field and generating heat. When the gate is closed protons can only return through the scarce ATP motors and the burning of fat is inhibited. The opening of the gate is controlled by hormones that activate heat production. Brown fat thus acts as a controlled source of heat for the body, and burns off excess fat.

Many of the secrets of brown fat mitochondria were uncovered by David Nicholls in Dundee, in the 1970s – perhaps the cold winds of Scotland were an extra motivation. It certainly seems an excellent idea for cold or obese humans to have brown fat to keep them warm or burn off their excess fat. Unfortunately, adult humans have very little brown fat. New-born babies have brown fat, which functions to keep them warm through this very sensitive period. Rats and other small mammals activate their brown fat when they are cold or overeat. However, humans and other large mammals must rely on other sources of heat. One of those sources of heat may well be the proton leak of mitochondria throughout the body. But in contrast to the gated proton channel of brown fat, the proton leak of other mitochondria is not gated or controlled, and may simply be an unavoidable design fault of energy production. There is a great deal of interest currently in the nature of this leak, because if we could stimulate it we might be able to treat obesity or produce an effective slimming drug, while if we could inhibit it we might produce super-efficient animals.

So contrary to what most textbooks say, the cell appears a rather inefficient user of energy, in fact it has leaks everywhere. A partial explanation may lie over one hundred million years ago, at the end of the reign of the dinosaurs. At that time, some animals (future mammals and birds) evolved endothermy or warm-bloodedness, producing up to ten times the heat of their cold-blooded ancestors, to maintain a constant high body temperature. This was risky, as in order to produce ten times as much heat the animals had to eat and process ten times the food. The reward was that, at a high body temperature, everything in the body worked faster and body temperature could be maintained independently of how cold or hot the environment was. Heat was produced by the cell's normal energy machinery only there was much more of it and consequently it was more leaky. If the aim of the energy machinery is to produce heat, it does not need to be efficient. It needs, on the contrary, to be inefficient, to leak energy all over the place. And this is the situation today: warm-blooded animals (mice and men) are very inefficient energy users, in comparison to cold-blooded animals (lizards and crocodiles). An analogy can be drawn with a car: in cold temperatures when it is not being used, the engine temperature falls and it may not start well, working sluggishly until it warms up. This problem could be overcome by allowing the engine to run all the time (even when not moving) to maintain an engine temperature perpetually at an optimum level. This strategy's obvious disadvantage is that it is very inefficient in terms of fuel consumption. This seems the strategy of warm-blooded animals. However, it is virtually impossible to prove the evolutionary function of a biological process, so we may never solve this mystery.

Mitochondria are old, older than the hills. The modern cell, found throughout our bodies, arose a billion years ago from the fusion of two different cell types: one big and many small. The big one swallowed or was invaded by the smaller, and they ended up living inside it. Over time the small cells lost their independence, handing over most of their DNA and molecular machinery, but gaining a safe haven inside the much larger cell. The small cells eventually became mitochondria and the big one the modern cell. Of all living organisms the mitochondria most resemble ancient bacteria. Mitochondria are the same size as bacteria, they are bounded by two thin walls similar to bacterial membranes, and inside both their machinery and DNA are alike. These similarities are no coincidence, since mitochondria almost certainly evolved from bacteria engulfed by larger cells.

Life itself began long before mitochondria, perhaps three and a half billion years ago, when the flows of energy, molecules, and information were somehow twisted together to form the first living cell. What the first energy source was, we do not know, but within half a billion years cells had evolved the machinery to harvest the light of our nearest star, the sun, ultimate source of all energy on earth. The light was used to split water (H_2O), producing oxygen, which was released to the air, and protons and electrons, which when combined with carbon dioxide from the air, was used to build the complex molecules of life. This simple yet powerful process of photosynthesis enabled life to succeed and rapidly expand. The first global pollution and ecological disasters started two billion years ago, when oxygen, that toxic by-product of photosynthesis, started to build up in earth's atmosphere.

Oxygen, the quintessential molecule of animal life, is a relatively unstable and toxic molecule. In fact it is itself a kind of free radical and can rip electrons off other molecules, pulling them apart to form even more toxic free radicals. That's why butter and other foods go rancid, why iron rusts and why some animals die in an atmosphere of pure oxygen. This could well be the reason why our body tries to maintain the oxygen level in our cells at about one tenth of the atmospheric level. Until two billion years ago, there had been no significant oxygen, but from then on oxygen released as a by-product of photosynthesis slowly built up in the atmosphere reaching the levels present today about a billion years ago (one fifth of air is now oxygen). When oxygen first appeared in significant amounts, many cells must have been killed off, just as many types of bacteria are killed by it today. Those that survived evolved defence strategies against oxygen. One strategy, still used by bacteria today, was the evolution of enzyme machines that could consume oxygen as fast as possible, so its level in the cell and surroundings was kept low. The first respiration may have evolved from these oxygen-consuming machines. Respiration produces energy by reversing the processes of photosynthesis – the complex molecules of plants or other animals are taken apart and the electrons fed to oxygen, forming water – but instead of the excess energy being released as light or heat, some is used to do useful work in the cell. This process depends on oxygen, and thus oxygen's appearance in the atmosphere presented both a problem and an opportunity. Those cells that evolved respiratory machineries reaped the opportunity, and thrived. One to one and a half billion years ago some of those respiring cells were engulfed by larger cells, forming mitochondria and the ancestor of the modern cell. However, this may have been a Faustian bargain, as the very machinery using oxygen to produce energy (the electron transport chain) also leaks electrons to oxygen, producing superoxide, the first of the toxic free radicals. Thus the modern cell bought a greatly enhanced energy supply at the expense of maintaining a toxic sitting tenant.

Mitochondria retain their identity within the modern cell by virtue of retaining their own DNA, the only DNA outside of the cell nucleus. But it is a small amount of DNA, only enough to code the absolute essential components of the mitochondria: the energy-generating machinery. Most of the mitochondria's machinery is coded in the nucleus, built in the rest of the cell and then imported into the mitochondria, but some crucial components are coded by mitochondrial DNA and built inside the mitochondria. DNA is essential because it provides the plans, the blueprint for the machineries and without it nothing can be built. Mitochondrial DNA divides, evolves and is inherited separately from nuclear DNA. Essentially all the mitochondrial DNA in our bodies comes from our mothers. This is because when the father's sperm penetrates the mother's egg cell during conception, it delivers a full load of nuclear DNA but only a few or no mitochondria, whereas the huge egg cell contains tens of thousands of maternal mitochondria. Thus each newly fertilized egg cell, from which every human develops, contains thousands more copies of maternal mitochondrial DNA than paternal. This maternal inheritance is important in a number of ways. For example, it means that defective (or super-efficient) mitochondrial DNA is inherited only down the maternal line. Thus if you are lethargic (or hyper-energetic) you can blame your mother's genes. But there are many contributing factors to lethargy apart from mitochondria, and many components of the mitochondria are coded by nuclear rather than mitochondrial DNA. Although, we now know of many diseases of mitochondrial

DNA, causing chronic tiredness and more serious symptoms – all of which are maternally inherited.

It seems strange that mitochondrial DNA is maternally inherited if we consider the process of sex and sperm selection. The act of sex puts about three hundred million sperm into the vagina, and each sperm carries a different version of the paternal DNA. They compete in a race against each other up the vagina, uterus and fallopian tubes attempting to reach and penetrate the egg. This race is essentially a rigorous selection process for the most energetic sperm and thus for the DNA coding for energetic functions. Any defects or inefficiencies in paternal mitochondrial DNA are selected out by this race, because any sperm carrying defective mitochondrial DNA will be unable to reach the egg first. Yet, when the victorious, superfit sperm reaches and fertilizes the egg, this paternal DNA plays no significant role in forming the child. The maternal mitochondrial DNA forming the new individual's mitochondria, is not similarly selected. Defective maternal mitochondrial DNA is simply passed on to the child, unless, of course, the defect is sufficient to kill the cell or embryo. However, many mitochondrial and non-mitochondrial components involved in energetics are coded for by nuclear DNA, and will therefore be selected by the sperm race. And this race for life is even more poignant when the sperm of two or more males compete to fertilize the egg of a single female.

On the other hand, mitochondrial DNA is selected by women's lives. If a woman lives, reproduces and brings up her daughters to reproduce successfully, her mitochondrial DNA will be passed on. If the DNA codes for efficient mitochondria that provide for the energy needs of women then the spread of this DNA will be favoured, but if not, the DNA will eventually die out. Mitochondrial DNA is not directly selected by men's lives (or only to the extent to which they benefit women) because men do not pass on their mitochondrial DNA to their progeny. Women are the vessels and shapers of mitochondrial DNA.

Mitochondrial DNA differs from nuclear DNA in another important way: it mutates and evolves at ten times the rate of nuclear DNA. This means that the message and blueprint for energy production are slowly changing, both in the germ cells passed down from generation to generation, and in our body cells as we get older. Most mutations of mitochondrial DNA are harmless, but some are damaging, compromising energy production in the cell. A few harmful mutations in the trillions of mitochondria inhabiting our body may have little effect on our energetics, but these mutations accumulate with age. Few cell mutations are detectable before the age of thirty or forty, but after that they rise exponentially, so in old age the proportion of mutant mitochondrial DNA may significantly damage our ability to generate energy. We do not yet know what causes human ageing, but one promising theory suggests it arises from dysfunctional mitochondria. The mitochondrial theory of ageing proposes that our mitochondria continually produce toxic free radicals that inexorably attack our mitochondria, mutating its DNA. And this mitochondrial damage may cause an even greater production of free radicals, in an increasingly vicious circle. For mutant mitochondrial DNA is associated with a frightening range of progressive degenerative diseases, including Alzheimer's, Huntington's, and Parkinson's, diabetes, atherosclerosis and, of course, ageing itself.

But mitochondrial DNA mutations are not all bad. Most mutations have little or no effect on the mitochondria's ability to produce energy, and the spread of these mutations down generations means that most people not genetically related have slightly different sequences in their mitochondrial DNA. This enables biologists to trace the genetic relatedness of different human populations. Comparing the mitochondrial DNA sequences of two individuals, similar or identical sequences indicate the individuals are closely related, whereas if they are widely differing that indicates that the two individuals are only related by a distant ancestor. The more differences there are in the sequence, the further back in time the common ancestor of the two individuals must have existed. Thus comparisons of mitochondrial DNA have been extensively used to trace the relatedness and origin of different human races. Analysis of the diversity of DNA in modern human races has led scientists to propose that all modern humans arose from a single population located in Africa roughly one hundred and fifty thousand years ago. Some biologists have gone further, suggesting all mitochondrial DNA in modern humans is derived from a single woman, the mitochondrial Eve living in Africa about two hundred thousand years ago. If this were true it would mean that this mother of all mothers is the ancestor of everyone living today. In a sense, we are all her children. Every human mitochondrial DNA molecule existing today would be derived from those in the body of that anonymous woman walking the plains of Africa two hundred thousand years ago. However, her existence is now in doubt because the statistical analysis used in the original research was flawed. It still seems likely that some woman or small group of women were the common ancestors of all modern mitochondrial DNA, but we do not know where or when. The mitochondrial Eve, if she existed, remains anonymous.

Mitochondrial DNA can also be used to trace our more recent history. By extracting mitochondrial DNA from corpses, bones and mummies, and comparing it to living DNA, we can determine the genetic relatedness of the dead to the living. Mitochondrial DNA is more abundant and robust than nuclear DNA, and in cases where human remains have decayed, mitochondrial DNA is often used for identification. For example the remains of the last Tsar, Nicholas II (killed by Bolsheviks with his entire family) and Jesse James, the American outlaw, were positively identified by comparing their mitochondrial DNA with that of known, living relatives – in the case of Tsar Nicholas, the Duke of Edinburgh. More recently the remains of Anastasia, star of the Disney movie, were also tested against the Duke's DNA, showing that she was in fact a fraud, rather than the daughter of Tsar Nicholas, as she claimed.

So, mitochondria can contribute to the death of the cell by producing toxic free radicals, damaging mutations and the slow decline in energy production leading to the inevitable demise of the cell. But recent research suggests that the mitochondria may play a more active role in killing cells. Mitochondria are indeed the assassins of the cell.

Cells die in two differing ways: controlled suicide or chaotic explosion. The former is known as apoptosis, the latter as necrosis. Necrosis could be compared to a frenzied, savage murder. The mitochondria and other parts of the cell blow up like balloons and explode, releasing their contents first inside the cell and then, outside, as the whole cell explodes. This kind of cell death causes huge problems for the rest of the body, because the entire contents of the cell, including toxic chemicals and enzymes are released, which causes damage to surrounding cells, and general inflammation. Apoptosis, or 'programmed cell death' as this is more generally known, is a much more controlled process whereby the cell is gradually killed and digested from within. Nothing is released, the cell is disassembled from inside, gradually shrinks, and is finally engulfed and digested by white blood cells. A silent shrinking into invisibility, rather than a violent explosion. This is all very well but *why* would a cell want to commit suicide? Usually it is because the cells are no longer needed (such as excess brain cells during development, or the womb lining at menstruation); or because they are diseased (such as a cell that is cancerous or infected by a virus). So apoptosis can play a vital role in shaping and protecting the body. Although, it is obviously essential that this suicide programme does not get out of control: too much suicide and the body will fall apart, too little and cancers and disease will spread unchecked. This control of the cell death programme is central to some of the most feared human diseases. Neurodegenerative conditions such as Alzheimer's and Parkinson's disease and stroke cause excessive death of brain neurons because apoptosis is over-activated; while one of the key mutations allowing cancerous cells to survive is the deactivation of their apoptotic machinery.

Mitochondria appear to play a central role in initiating both apoptosis and necrosis. They pronounce the death sentence of the cell. This is probably no coincidence since mitochondria are the main target for many noxious stimuli, such as toxins, free radicals, excessive calcium and lack of oxygen. Mitochondria are damaged by these and the consequence of this damage is that the energy supply to the rest of the cell fails, and without energy the whole cell spins out of control. The stupendous juggling act that is cell life depends on a continuous supply of energy: without it the cell literally falls apart. Without energy the molecules, meant to be kept outside the cell, cannot be prevented from coming in, and those meant to be inside cannot be stopped from leaking out. But since mitochondria are sensitive to the lethal events causing necrosis, it makes good biological sense for them to be triggers of apoptosis too. Because if a cell is exposed to a lethal event (such as a toxic dose of radiation), it would be better for the rest of the body if the cell killed itself quickly by apoptosis before necrosis takes hold and explodes the cell, causing damage to neighbouring cells. Apoptosis is not always quick enough to preempt necrosis, and if the damage is severe enough there will not be enough energy to power apoptosis. The self-immolation of apoptosis is executed by molecular machines called 'caspases'. These are molecular scissors that once activated, go around the cell cutting up other molecular machines. Caspases are activated by being cut by other caspases, so once one is activated the caspase cascade snowballs into an avalanche of molecular snipping, the molecular death-toll is as high and as bloody as the finale of a slasher movie. Damaged mitochondria can set off this avalanche by releasing factors, normally kept safely inside the mitochondria, which once released activate the caspases, and set the course for cell death. In 1996, the new but rapidly expanding field of apoptosis research was agog when Xiaodong Wang of the University of Texas reported that this fatal avalanche was initiated by the release of cytochrome c from mitochondria. Cytochrome c is a small, venerable protein, discovered by Keilin in 1933 and known to be central to energy production in almost all forms of life. What was it doing initiating cellular suicide? Nobody at the time believed it to be true. However, here, the unbelievable turned out to be true. Cytochrome c normally is safely tucked away in the mitochondria, performing the vital task of passing electrons down the mitochondrial respiratory chain. But if the mitochondria are punctured, then it is released into the rest of the cell, where it activates the deadly caspases.

So, the caspases are the executioners of apoptotic cell death, but the irreversible trigger, appearing to control both necrotic and apoptotic cell death is a huge hole or pore in the mitochondrial membrane, known as the 'permeability transition pore'. This is normally kept closed, otherwise mitochondria could not function to provide energy to the rest of the cell. But the pore is very sensitive to lethal stimuli, such as free radicals or too much calcium, and in these conditions opens up, like a giant hole in the centre of the mitochondria. The opening of this pore has dire consequences for the cell, as mitochondria are then incapable of producing energy, seemingly condemning the cell to necrotic death, and the opening of the pore causes mitochondria to release cytochrome c, which activates the caspases and triggers apoptotic death. The pore is thus the trigger for a double dose of death. This seems to be what happens to our cells in a heart attack or stroke. Cardiac arrest or stroke is caused by a blockage of the blood vessels supplying the heart or brain, so the cells of these organs cannot obtain sufficient oxygen to supply their mitochondria. In these unhappy circumstances, the mitochondria suicidally open the pore, resulting in either necrotic or apoptotic cell death. After a heart attack or stroke, some cells die by necrosis (probably those most damaged by the blockage), while others die by apoptosis (and are rapidly cleared away). The race is now on for drug companies to develop drugs that block apoptosis or pore opening, which may be of benefit in a wide range of diseases. However, it is as yet unclear whether blocking apoptosis would be beneficial, as a damaged cell may then be diverted to necrosis, causing further damage. Or even if necrosis is blocked, a damaged cell may function abnormally or produce free radicals, causing delayed damage and dysfunction.

So, our cells agreed a somewhat Faustian bargain when first embracing the mitochondria a billion years ago. In return for the greatly increased capacity to produce and use energy, the cell also accepted a suspended death sentence. We have already seen that the energy-producing capacities of the mitochondria inevitably create damaging free radicals, which may be responsible for ageing and many diseases. It has even been suggested that a billion years ago the ancestors of our mitochondria already contained a toxin, deterring the larger cell from destroying the smaller cell inside it. Over time the larger cell, which became our cells, gained some control over the release of this toxin and thus programmed cell death evolved. Playing with death is a dangerous game and inevitably sometimes goes wrong, with fatal consequences.

The revelation that our mitochondria, these ancient monsters we thought were tame and benign, are in fact our silent executioners, has reinvigorated the field of mitochondrial research, putting it at the forefront of biological and medical research. Are the mitochondria our friends or foes? As one death researcher (Richard Miller) recently put it: 'Mitochondria – the Kraken awakes! When left alone in their deep evolutionary slumber they are certainly our friends. But, please – don't disturb them!'

Below the thunders of the upper deep;
Far, far beneath in the abysmal sea,
His ancient, dreamless, uninvaded sleep
The Kraken sleepeth: faintest sunlights flee
About his shadowy sides: above him swell
Huge sponges of millennial growth and height;
And far away into the sickly light,
From many a wondrous grot and secret cell
Unnumber'd and enormous polypi
Winnow with giant arms the slumbering green.
There hath he lain for ages, and will lie
Battening upon huge sea-worms in his sleep,
Until the latter fire shall heat the deep;
Then once by man and angels to be seen,
In roaring he shall rise and on the surface die.

['The Kraken' by Alfred, Lord Tennyson, 1830]

Chapter 7

THE PACE OF LIFE AND DEATH

There appears to be a mysterious but fundamental relation between energy and time. As individuals, when full of energy, time seems to pass quickly, but when lacking in energy it drags along slowly, sometimes too slowly. Comparing different species, animals such as turtles, that use very little energy, live life very slowly and survive to a ripe old age; whereas animals such as shrews, requiring vast amounts, live life at a frantic pace, but die very early, as if burnt out. These facts support the idea that different individuals and species can live life at a different pace, but that a faster pace or rate of living inevitably leads to a more rapid death. This is the 'rate of living' theory, which has a long history and many dubious applications.

The total energy production of a human or animal over a set period of time is called the 'metabolic rate', and can be measured by the heat production or oxygen consumption of the body. The metabolic rate is a very fundamental characteristic of an organism, because it determines how much energy the organism has to spend on processes like muscle use, growth, and reproduction, as well as how much energy it must acquire as food from the environment each day. The metabolic rate of an individual or species is analogous to someone's salary or the GNP (Gross National Product) of a country. It tells you the total resources and this has a fundamental impact on structure, behaviour and lifestyle.

Most wild animals experience periods of energy limitation, when the amount of food energy they can get limits what they can do, in terms of movement, growth, reproduction and heat production. The amount of food energy coming in must balance the amount of energy being used; if this delicate balance is upset by insufficient food energy or by too much energy expenditure then death is sure unless a balance can be rapidly regained. The evolution of most species of animal and plants has been dominated by the necessity to balance their energy budget or die. Consequently, animals have evolved to allocate their limited energy resources economically between the various energy-consuming necessities of life: growth, reproduction, movement and heat production. A small bird in winter must somehow assess the energy costs of flying to find food, and exposing itself to cold, relative to the constant energy requirement for food energy. It has to assess its energy income relative to how much it can afford to spend on growth; how many and how large eggs it can produce; how much time it can spend looking after its young. Even sitting still uses energy. Of course the bird does not assess these things consciously, but evolution has endowed it with instincts and behaviours, balancing the energy equation. And because all animals and plants within an eco-system either compete for or eat each other for energy, the whole web of life is linked by a series of energy exchanges, which must be optimized if individual species are to survive. The amount of time and energy that we humans devote to work, rest, play, sleep, sex and reproduction has been determined long ago during the evolution of our species while battling to balance our own energy equation.

Our energy production measured when resting is known as the 'resting metabolic rate', and when, in addition, we are not cold and have not eaten anything for twelve hours the rate is known as the 'basal metabolic rate' (because it is the minimal or basal rate when we are awake). In a resting adult, no energy produced is used to do any net work and none of the energy is conserved, all is released as heat. The basal metabolic rate of an adult human is between sixty and a hundred watts. That means that an adult human at rest uses the same amount of energy and produces the same heat as an ordinary light bulb. However, during peak exercise, the energy and heat production is ten times higher; equivalent to ten light bulbs. Our metabolic rate also goes up (about twenty per cent) after a meal, because we use energy to process and store the food. The rate also increases when we are excited or frightened, because adrenaline (and stimulation of the sympathetic nervous system) can increase energy use by up to one hundred per cent. It goes up when we are cold, because we release adrenaline and shiver to keep warm. It would be easy to imagine our energy use would go up when we are thinking hard, but in fact it hardly changes, and indeed only drops by ten per cent when we are asleep.

The average amount of energy we use during a normal day of real life is known as the 'field' or average daily metabolic rate. The average daily metabolic rate is larger than the basal metabolic rate, because it averages periods of rest and periods of exercise, feeding and shivering. However, the field or average metabolic rate for most people is only about fifty per cent higher than the basal metabolic rate. This seems at first somewhat surprising, as it implies that living life takes little more energy than doing absolutely nothing. But from another point of view, this is simply a reflection of the fact that our bodies (and minds) have such a huge resting or basal energy consumption. This resting energy consumption is used to maintain the structure of the body, power our information processing and to keep us warm.

The average daily metabolic rate varies according to who we are and what we do. If we were to do absolutely nothing the average rate would be equal to the basal rate, which is about 1600 calories per day. An office worker or housewife in the developed world has an average rate fifty per cent higher than the basal rate, roughly equivalent to 120 watts, or 2400 calories per day. So, to replace this energy they need to eat about 2400 calories of food energy per day. The most extreme manual work, such as manual mining or lumbering, has an average metabolic rate three times higher than the basal rate (up to a maximum of 4800 calories per day in men), and requires three times the food and air. Domestic animals, such as sheep and cattle, generally have an average rate twice their basal rate, while wild animals usually have an average rate three times their basal rate. These differences reflect the greater muscle use and need for heat generation in the wild, and the relatively sedentary lifestyle of domestic animals and of most people in the developed world.

The basal metabolic rate of small animals is less than that of a large animal, because, of course, there is less of the small animal. However, the basal metabolic rate per gram of body weight of small animals is greater than that of large animals, it is for example twenty-five times greater in mice than in elephants. Which means that a one gram chunk of mouse is working twenty-five times faster than a one gram chunk of elephant. There is in fact a mathematical relationship between the size of all species of mammals and birds and their metabolic rate. This was first described by the distinguished Swiss-American physiologist Max Kleiber in 1932 and takes the form of a biological law relating body weight to basal metabolic rate. Although this relation has been confirmed for many animals, the reason for it has caused great controversy. Why do small animals use more energy per gram than large animals? The most important reason appears to be that small animals need to produce relatively more heat per gram to give the same body temperature as large animals. Or expressed differently, an elephant needs to produce less heat in the centre of its body than a mouse, because the heat has further to travel to the surface and less surface area relative to its weight to get rid of the heat. So if an elephant produced heat at the same rate as a mouse it would rapidly cook inside.

The heat requirements of warm-blooded animals do not, however, fully explain the form of the relation between body size and metabolic rate. A second reason for this was alluded to by Galileo in 1637. Galileo pointed out that the bones of large animals need to be much thicker than those of small animals, in order to support the extra weight. If the body plan of a small animal was simply scaled up in proportion, for example every dimension multiplied by ten, the scaled-up animal would not only cook inside but would also collapse under its own weight as its bones were crushed. A more modern, mathematical version of this theory was proposed by McMahon in 1973, who analysed the forces exerted on the skeletons of different sized animals during rest and running and the amount of muscle and supporting metabolism required to move that skeleton. He concluded that the relation between body size and metabolic rate could be explained exactly if the primary constraint on body design was the need to keep the forces on the skeleton the same. So apparently the reason large animals have a lesser metabolic rate per gram than small is partly due to the heat requirements and partly due to the skeleton's structural requirements.

The necessity for small animals to have a faster metabolic rate per gram than large animals has dramatic implications for their function, physiology, behaviour, lifestyle and ecology. Smaller animals have a faster heart rate, breathing rate, metabolism, food acquisition, growth rate, maturity, and consequently a shorter life span. Their whole life is lived faster and this is a direct result of their faster metabolic rate. A shrew (the smallest mammal, weighing roughly three grams) has a heart that beats a thousand times a minute, while an elephant's heart beats just thirty times a minute. An awake shrew is difficult to see clearly because its restless movements are so rapid. It is living at a different speed. Because of its frantic metabolism, a shrew needs to capture and eat its own body weight in food every day. In fact a shrew cannot afford to sleep for more than an hour or two, otherwise its body energy reserves run out, and it would wake up dead! So instead the shrew rushes between short periods of sleep and frantic searches for food, about ten to twenty times a day. It is living 10–20 'days' per earth day. By contrast the Blue Whale (the largest animal on earth, weighing about one hundred and fifty tons) is able to swim regularly from one side of the world to the other, not eating for several months, because its energy use relative to the size of its energy stores is so low. Also the whale's relatively low metabolic rate enables it to dive below the surface for up to an hour, since the stores of oxygen in its body are able to supply its low energy use.

The radically different rates at which various animals live their lives have led to the concept of 'physiological time'. This is that different animals live at different rates and the time scale on which an animal lives should be measured in terms of its physiological cycles, such as the heartbeat, rather than clock time. The mouse's heart beats six hundred times per minute, and its maximum life span is about three years, so that it may beat eight hundred million times in its lifetime. Although the elephant's heart only beats at thirty times a minute, because it lives longer, the total number of beats per lifetime is similar to that of the mouse. A thirty gram mouse that breathes one hundred and fifty times a minute will breathe about two hundred million times in its three year life span. While a five-ton elephant breathing six times a minute will take roughly the same number of breaths during its forty year life. Although mouse and elephant live at very different rates, the total amount of energy, food and oxygen is roughly the same per gram in a lifetime. If time is measured in terms of heartbeats rather than clock time, then the metabolic rate, molecular activity, breathing rate, growth rate, maturity rate and life span of all mammals are roughly the same.

Exceptions to the general rule that the total amount of energy used in an average lifetime is roughly equal include humans, who live up to four times longer than they should according to body size and metabolic rate. The reason for this relative longevity is unknown, but may reflect the relatively long childhood of humans and the transmission of knowledge from generation to generation, so that evolution favoured the survival of older members. But overall, for all species of mammals, and many other animals, the relationship between body size, metabolic rate and maximum life span is impressive. Any serious theory of life span and how ageing occurs needs to account for the fact that small animals with high metabolic rates have much shorter maximum life spans than large animals with low metabolic rates (per gram). The general theory that a fast pace of life or metabolic rate somehow causes rapid ageing is known as the 'rate-of-living' theory of ageing.

The rate-of-living theory has a long history, but one of its most enthusiastic supporters and the man who gave it its catchy name was Raymond Pearl. Pearl (1879–1940) was a prolific scientist and popularizer of science at Johns Hopkins University, Baltimore. Unusually tall and intelligent, he towered over his peers, both literally and figuratively, and has been described by some as uncommonly arrogant and overbearing. In his lifetime, he published seventeen books and more than seven hundred scientific papers; he also wrote for newspapers and literary journals, on many subjects ranging from fruit flies to the link between smoking and cancer. Following the rate-of-living theory, with all this frenetic activity we might expect him to have died young, but in fact he reached the respectable age of sixty-one, significantly older than the age (fifty) at which he thought people became too foolish or senile to vote. Pearl believed that ageing was an inevitable side-effect of a rapid energy metabolism. He wrote an article for the *Baltimore Sun* in 1927 headlined 'Why Lazy People Live the Longest'. He even attributed women's greater longevity to the fact that they supposedly performed less physical labour. Pearl collected data on people's longevity in differing occupations and professions with different amounts of physical labour and thus various metabolic rates. He found, perhaps unsurprisingly, that people working in occupations with high physical labour, such as miners, had on average shorter lives than those doing little physical work, such as academics like Pearl himself. Of course, many other explanations of this finding are possible, including the effects of poverty, nutrition and health care, but Pearl saw it as strong evidence for the rate-of-living theory of ageing. If this theory were true, it would have the startling implication that exercise shortens your life, while being a couch potato prolongs it. Unhappily (or happily for the puritans among us), we now know that this is not true: professional athletes, who use considerably more energy than the average person, live just as long as the rest of us.

So, the rate-of-living theory of ageing is dead, but we do need some explanation why the rate-of-living, measured by metabolic rate, is related to life span. Many, if not most, researchers into ageing now believe that ageing is in some way connected with accumulating damage due to free radicals: that animals with a higher metabolic rate may produce more free radicals as a side product of their metabolism and thus have a shorter life span. The amount of free radicals produced by an animal may be roughly proportional to the amount of energy produced, so if an animal produces and uses a lot of energy it also produces many free radicals, and this may shorten its life. The moral is that you can choose a short, fast life, or a long, slow life, but you get the same amount of living either way.

But do people live at different rates? Babies and children have higher metabolic rates (per gram) than adult humans. Children have faster heart and breathing rates, have more mitochondria and use more energy (per gram) than adults. This could partly explain why children appear to have more 'energy' and to live at a faster pace. Children rush around faster and more frequently, frenetically changing between different activities, topics of thought and moods far more rapidly than adults. Children also need to eat more often and sleep longer in order to maintain their higher energy levels. But they do appear to be living at a faster pace than adults and within their own frame of reference to time the world must appear to be going very slowly. Thus in childhood, minutes and days seem to pass at a slow pace and the adult world must appear relatively dull and static. The metabolic rate (per gram) of humans and other animals inexorably declines with age, from birth to death. So old people have a slower metabolic rate than people in their twenties. Thus old people eat less but tend to put on more weight, sleep less and are less active. There are other reasons for these changes in old age but the decline in metabolic rate contributes. The pace of life in general gets slower as we get older, our activities, thoughts and moods change less frequently, we do less and do new things less often. Within this slower reference frame, the rest of the world seems to be going faster – hours, days, and years speed past.

Could the differences in apparent energy of different adults (life's speed freaks and couch potatoes) be due to different metabolic rates? It's not that simple: social, psychological and neurophysiological factors all play a role in determining the energy and pace of life. Two hormones in particular, thyroid hormone and adrenaline, have dramatic effects on both our metabolic rate and feelings of energy. Different people produce quite different levels of these hormones, resulting in varying subjective feelings of energy and pace of life. People with hyperthyroidism produce too much thyroid hormone in their bodies, while those with hypothyroidism produce too little. Thyroid hormone does many different things in the body, but basically increases the metabolic rate, by increasing the number of mitochondria and other components of energy metabolism in both body and brain. Increasing the thyroid hormone in the body can double the metabolic rate, while decreasing the hormone can half the metabolic rate. People with hyperthyroidism not only have a high metabolic rate, but they also have a faster heart rate and reaction time, as if they were continuously 'excited' or 'energized'. Sufferers from hypothyroidism not only have a low metabolic rate, but also have a reduced heart rate and slowing of all intellectual functions, leading to a feeling of profound lethargy. Thyroid hormone also causes weight loss, due to the increase in metabolic rate and has in the past been used as a slimming drug, but there are a variety of unpleasant side-effects. Differences in the amount of thyroid hormone released are also part of the reason that animals have different metabolic rates. We all produce slightly different amounts of thyroid hormone, dependent partly on our genes and regulated by unconscious centres in the brain, gauging our energy needs. But thyroid hormone is not the only messenger regulating our energy level and metabolic rate. Adrenaline and noradrenaline, released during excitement, arousal or fear, are also important controllers of metabolic rate and energy level in the body and brain. Differences in people's tendency to release these hormones may underlie the difference between a high-energy achiever and a low-energy couch potato. They also partially determine how rapidly we live our lives, and the subjective sense of how fast time is passing. When we get excited or afraid, noradrenaline and adrenaline are released into our body and brain, resulting in a speeding up of our actions, reactions, and thinking – we get faster while the world around us slows down.

The rate at which time appears to pass is not an objective property. There is no such property in physics, indeed time does not flow at all in physics, and many philosophers have pointed out that it makes no sense to measure the rate at which time flows. However, there is such a *subjective* property – the sense of time passing quickly or slowly – and this is determined by the organism. So it is certainly possible that either your neighbour or your cat experiences time as passing more quickly than you. However, it is impossible to experience someone else's subjective sense of time, so we cannot say definitively that the subjective rate of living of different people or animals differs – but it does seem likely.

Energy and time are intimately related. When we are full of energy, enthused, scared, or excited our body and mind are flooded with chemicals making them go faster, and consequently the external world seems slow relative to our racing mind. Drugs, such as LSD and cocaine, that stimulate the brain's own arousal system, also massively distort the subjective sense of time, so a 'trip' can seem to last forever. Driving into a car crash, the world seems to go into slow motion, as the mind races into overdrive. But when we lack stimulation or excitement, the mind is starved of its natural 'speed' drugs so the external world and its hours, days and years appear to flit by rapidly. This may be a reason why time seems to go faster as we get older – for a child everything is new, producing excitement or fear, whereas as we get older less and less is really new experience and we learn to hide from stimulation in a blanket of security. Hence, a little girl rushing around is either buzzing with excitement, or bawling her eyes out with fear and fatigue, so an hour is an eternity, and a day stretches out forever. An old man may have turned his life into a set of endless routines, blocking out all novelty, there is no need for adrenaline in his life. In comparison to the many years he has already lived, each hour seems to pass faster than the last.

The subjective sense of time may also be related to how much we remember. People who have lost the ability to lay down memories, as can occur in certain types of brain damage, live in an eternal present. If we remember everything then sixty minutes are filled with an infinite number of happenings, but if we remember nothing then it appears nothing happened in that hour. When we are aroused or excited we remember more, because adrenaline and noradrenaline stimulate the formation of memories. That is in part why significant or traumatic events are remembered in such detail, while boring days are so easy to forget. Jim McGaugh of the University of California at Irvine has shown if rats are given a shot of adrenaline directly after learning something, they then have an enhanced ability to remember it later. When humans were given a drug blocking the actions of adrenaline, then read an emotional story, they were less able to subsequently remember its details. This demonstrated that even the mild arousal of reading something emotional was sufficient to enhance the laying down of memories through the increased adrenaline levels. So excitement can speed us up, and slow down the external world, partly by enhancing our memory.

The pace of our lives changes from moment to moment, as we encounter the stimulation of new situations and people or the boredom of routines, and we know how to change that pace by taking stimulants (such as caffeine or nicotine) or by adding more excitement to our lives. Different people have different levels of intrinsic mental arousal and tension (life's adrenaline junkies or timid introverts) and this affects how much external stimulation they seek. The pace of life seems to slow inexorably with age, but we can resist this, to some extent, by staying active and seeking out stimulation.

Chapter 8

GETTING FAT AND
STAYING THIN

Today, practically everyone worries about their weight – and with good reason, as it is clear people are getting fatter. The World Health Organization and International Obesity Task Force have stated that there is a global epidemic of obesity, which 'poses one of the greatest threats to human health and well-being as the twenty-first century approaches'. The proportion of the UK population classified as obese increased from seven per cent in 1980 to sixteen per cent in 1994; by more than double in under fifteen years. Over the same period, obesity increased from fourteen to twenty-two per cent in the US population; fifty-four per cent of the American population are now overweight (meaning that their weight is a significant threat to their health). If current trends continue then, within a few more decades, the majority of the British and American populations will be obese. It is not just in the developed world where waistlines are ballooning; countries such as Brazil and Mauritius have also reported increased obesity, and then there are troublespots such as Western Samoa, where between 1978 and 1991 urban obesity rates went from thirty-nine to fifty-eight per cent in men, and from fifty-nine to seventy-seven per cent in women.

What has gone so wrong with our bodies or brains that we can no longer control our own weight? Americans spend about forty billion dollars a year on weight-loss treatments, which, in the long-term, are almost completely useless. However, recent research has brought us much closer to understanding why it is we get fat and why it is so hard to become thin again. Obesity research has even become sexy. But before discussing the causes of fatness and thinness, we need to understand some of the basics about the body's fuel supply, because obesity is caused by a mismatch in the body's fuel supply, storage and utilization.

THE FUEL SUPPLY

Sugar and fat are the two alternative fuel sources powering the body. The switch between these fuel sources is an essential process in feeding, hunger, exercise and fatigue, as well as in the more extreme conditions of starvation, diabetes and obesity. Switching is controlled by two hormones: insulin and adrenaline. The ebb and flow of sugar and fat, insulin and adrenaline within the body underlie our everyday experiences of tiredness, hunger, excitement, hyperactivity, stress and satiety. These are the key players in body energy.

As all schoolchildren once knew, Julius Caesar famously said: 'All Gaul is divided into three parts.' Justus von Liebig and the other nineteenth-century chemists and physiologists divided all complex organic molecules, all the substances in food and the body, into just three types: carbohydrate, fat and protein. And although France's geography has changed somewhat since Caesar, we still recognize this tripartite division in nutrition. Carbohydrate, fat and protein are complex molecules made from simple components. Carbohydrate is made from sugars, fat is made from fatty acids and protein is made from amino acids. This is the basis of the distinction between the three types of molecule. By arranging the simple components in various ways, different types of carbohydrate, fat or protein can be made, but when stripped to their components (as they are in the gut) they have a similar nutritional value to the body. However, inside the body, carbohydrate, fat and protein play very different roles. Their components can all be burnt by the mitochondria to produce energy, but protein is only used as a last resort in starvation. Proteins provide the nuts and bolts of the cell: all the machinery and most of the structure. Fat acts as a long-term store of energy in the body, fats also make up the membrane of the cell and fatty acids are the main fuel for the resting body. Carbohydrates act mainly as a short-term energy store (stored in the form known as 'glycogen'), and the sugar 'glucose' is a major body fuel. The sugar that we put in our tea or on our cereal is one type of sugar called sucrose, used by plants to store energy, but within our bodies, it again gets converted to glucose or glycogen.

The human brain exists on a metabolic knife-edge. Although the rest of the body can use glucose or fat as energy fuels, the brain can only use glucose – and lots of it. Roughly one hundred and fifty grams of glucose a day is burnt by the brain to supply its energy needs. But there is no store of glucose in the brain, thus its energy supply depends entirely on a continuous supply of glucose from the blood. If the glucose level in the blood falls from its normal range (about 0.8 gram of glucose per litre of blood) to half, the brain begins to malfunction. When it falls to a quarter of its normal level (as it can in diabetes) the brain goes into coma; without any glucose it suffers irreversible damage in minutes, and death rapidly follows. The total amount of glucose in the blood is only about five grams, enough to supply the brain for less than an hour. The liver is the only organ in the body that stores glucose (as glycogen) and can replenish the blood levels of glucose. Although glucose is also stored in muscle, this glucose can only be used within the muscle and cannot be released to the blood. In the absence of a glucose supply from digested food in the stomach and guts, the liver is the only source for replenishment of blood glucose, and thus brain energy. However, the liver only stores roughly seventy-five grams of glucose and can supply the brain only for about twelve hours, in the absence of food. In fact our livers become depleted of glucose overnight, because we are not feeding, but our brains continue consuming energy while we sleep. So what happens if we skip breakfast? Do our brains begin to malfunction? Do we fall into a coma and die? Well, no. Although we may feel a bit groggy and hungry, our liver comes to the rescue again in the early morning by starting to make glucose from protein. But this protein is not coming from some handy surplus store, but from the proteins making up the machinery of our muscles. When we fast for more than twelve hours, our muscles start to be broken down into amino acids, supplying the liver for the production of glucose, which in turn supplies the brain to keep it working. This is a strange arrangement because the body has a huge energy store, enough to last over three fasting months. The problem is that this energy store is in the form of fat, which the brain cannot use, nor can fat be converted into glucose. This really is odd: the brain needs a continuous supply of glucose, but the body only stores sufficient glucose to last overnight, and when it runs out it starts tearing the muscles apart.

Why doesn't the brain use fat as an energy source like the rest of the body? We don't yet know the answer to that question. It has been suggested that fat might mess up brain functions, but that idea doesn't really work because the brain contains lots of fat, used for many different things, but not as a source of energy. For whatever reason the brain is dependent on glucose, it may well be that this addiction is only a problem for humans because we have such large brains. Most mammals have much smaller brains relative to the size of their bodies and consequently a smaller demand for glucose.

Why doesn't the brain store glucose? And why does the body use fat as its major energy store, rather than glucose? Well, fat is a much more concentrated way to store energy than glucose (or protein). Fat produces about nine calories of energy per gram when burnt, whereas glucose and protein produce roughly four. Glucose and protein also bind a lot of water, which must be stored with them, and fat does not, so weight for weight a fat store can supply ten times the energy of a glucose or protein store. An obese human may carry one hundred kilos of fat, but if he had to carry the energy equivalent of this in glucose, he would need to find room for a thousand kilos. Thus, when our food intake exceeds the body's energy requirements, the excess energy is stored as fat. And there is fifty to a hundred times as much fat stored (eight to twenty kilos in a lean human) as glucose (seventy-five grams in liver and one hundred and fifty in muscle).

Because the human brain has such a voracious appetite for glucose, it is essential the blood sugar level is kept constant however much sugar is put into the blood, and however much is taken out. During maximal exercise, the glucose consumption of our muscles may increase up to a thousandfold. Under these extreme circumstances, it is essential firstly that the liver produces glucose flat out and secondly that fat is mobilized from its stores so it can serve as an energy fuel for muscle and the rest of the body. This is achieved mainly by the release of adrenaline. Adrenaline is released into the blood during exercise, excitement or whenever the blood glucose level falls and acts to mobilize fat from the fat stores, and to stimulate the liver's glucose production. If adrenaline was not released during exercise, the blood would be rapidly depleted of glucose and the brain would go out like a light. At the other extreme, after a good meal, when we are sprawled out on a sofa, glucose is flooding into the blood from the guts and it is vital that our glucose stores in the liver and muscles are replenished. It is the hormone insulin that pushes the body into storing glucose when the blood sugar level is high after a meal or sweets, and we can see the consequences of this not occurring in insulin-dependent diabetics.

Insulin-dependent diabetics produce no insulin, and consequently when glucose floods into the blood after a meal it is not stored, and the blood sugar level rockets. To prevent the blood becoming thick with glucose, the kidneys start dumping the excess glucose into urine. Sweet urine is one of the classic symptoms of diabetics and doctors used to taste the urine before more modern tests became available. Nowadays you are defined as a diabetic if your blood glucose is more than two grams a litre at any time (normal level is 0.8 grams a litre). However, because diabetics fail to store glucose and the excess is lost in urine, blood glucose levels may later plummet and the diabetic exhibits all the classic signs of hypoglycaemia (low blood sugar), such as craving for sugar, nervous hyperactivity, distracted thought, heightened emotion, and cold sweats. These symptoms are mostly due to an activation of the sympathetic nervous system and the release of adrenaline, occurring when blood sugar is low, acting to stimulate glucose production and mobilize fat stores. If the glucose level falls further, mental confusion, dysfunction and coma may ensue. Today's insulin-dependent diabetic has his own supply of insulin to inject, enabling the sugar released into the blood during a meal to be stored. This self-administered treatment prevents most symptoms of diabetes, and enables these diabetics to live a normal life, impossible just twenty years ago. Many diabetics do eventually suffer from damage to their blood vessels which causes circulatory problems and blindness. The surprising reason is that high blood sugar is actually damaging to the body. Glucose is mildly toxic and can produce free radicals, attaching itself to proteins in the blood and cells, causing malfunction and further free radical production. This, then, is yet another reason why it is essential to keep blood sugar level constant; too low and the brain malfunctions, too high and the body is damaged.

Insulin-dependent diabetes is relatively rare, but ten times as many people suffer from non-insulin-dependent diabetes. About six million people are currently diagnosed diabetic in the United States, and a further four to five million are estimated to be undiagnosed or border-line diabetics. Non-insulin-dependent diabetics differ from those who are insulin-dependent in that they usually have plenty of their own insulin, but their bodies do not respond to it for reasons still unclear. The surge of glucose after a meal results in an increase in insulin levels, but the body does not respond to the insulin by removing glucose from the blood. Thus the blood glucose level rockets, and may plummet later if the stores of glucose are depleted. The body appears deaf to the pleas of the insulin to store the glucose and these patients are called 'insulin-resistant'. The high blood sugar level causes damage to the heart, blood vessels, eyes and kidneys. So diabetes is bad for you: it is the third most common medical cause of death, and the second most common cause of blindness in the United States. And the most common cause of non-insulin-dependent diabetes is obesity.

WHY DO WE GET FAT?

There can be no doubt that we, in the developing world, are getting fatter at an alarming rate. It is not easy to define obesity, but it is at present defined as a Body Mass Index (calculated as the weight in kilos divided by the square of the height in metres) greater than thirty, or a weight more than twenty per cent greater than the 'ideal'. The ideal is 126 pounds (57 kg) for a 5' 4" (1.63 m) woman, and 154 pounds (70 kg) for a 5' 10" (1.78 m) man, giving a Body Mass Index of about twenty-one. According to these criteria, eighty per cent of the American population is heavier than the 'ideal', fifty-four per cent is classified as 'overweight', twenty-two per cent is clinically obese and this proportion is growing. Obesity is associated with a greatly increased risk of diabetes and heart disease, so obese people die younger as well as suffering from a variety of disabilities. Being fat is not a good idea.

So why do we get fat? There was a theory that fat people have a slower metabolism: their bodies burn less food and thus from the same food intake they store more food as fat. In effect, fat people have more efficient bodies, wasting less energy, and storing more for emergencies. This 'too-efficient metabolism' theory can still sometimes be found loitering in magazines or the occasional doctor's head and it has been a popular one with fat people themselves. Recent research has shown, however, that the theory is fallacious. Measurements of metabolic rate, both in the laboratory and during normal life, have shown that fat people have a higher metabolic rate than those of average weight. That means fat people use more energy and burn more food than thin, so if they ate the same amount of food as thin people, they would gain less weight or lose weight faster. The reason fat people have a higher metabolic rate is unsurprising: they are bigger, have both more fat tissue and more non-fat tissue (lean mass). Because they have more lean mass (such as muscle) their bodies consume more energy, but per kilogram of lean mass, both fat and thin use the same amount of energy, their cells have the same energy use. The fat also require more energy to walk and exercise than thin people because they have to move more weight. The theory of a too-efficient metabolism partly originated from studies of fat people recording their food consumption over a period of time, which showed that they were eating the same or less food than thin people. However, more recent investigation of these studies has found that fat people consistently under-report their food intake, compared to thin people, and in properly controlled studies fat people definitely eat more than thin.

If we don't get fat because we use less energy, then why do we get fat? The reason is again obvious: most fat people get that way because they eat more than thin people. But why do they eat more? People generally start eating because they are hungry, and stop because they feel 'full up' (satiated). Appetite and satiety are controlled by nervous centres in the brain, particularly in the hypothalamus. Damage to these appetite centres in humans or animals causes obesity. The appetite centres receive information (via nerves and hormones) about both short-term and long-term food intake. When you eat a meal, expansion of the stomach causes sensory nerves in the stomach wall to send nerve impulses to the appetite centres in the brain, which then stop

feelings of hunger, inducing satiation. Similarly the fed stomach produces hormones that signal the brain to stop feeding. Sugar and fat
entering the blood from the gut after a meal directly or indirectly
(such as by increasing insulin levels) act on the appetite centres to
maintain satiety and prevent hunger. Hunger itself seems to be partly
induced by a slight fall in blood sugar level. If you crave a biscuit or
sweet drink mid-morning or mid-afternoon, you are probably
detecting a slight fall in your blood sugar level. But appetite does not
just respond to short-term factors, such as feeding, but also to long-
term trends, in particular the amount of fat tissue in the body. So if
an individual becomes fatter, a message is sent from the fat to the
appetite centres in the brain. The brain can act to decrease fat levels
by two different means: it can decrease appetite or it can increase
energy expenditure. In general it does both. The appetite is controlled
by a large number of brain hormones (called neuropeptides) via mechanisms that are not yet well understood. But one of these, neuropeptide
Y, if injected into the brain causes a voracious appetite; levels of this
neuropeptide are suppressed by glucose or insulin, thus decreasing
appetite. How energy expenditure is increased by the brain's appetite
centres is again unclear, but apparently results from stimulation of
the sympathetic nervous system, causing mobilization of fat and sugar
reserves and the stimulation of energy expenditure by muscle.

So appetite centres in the brain monitor short- and long-term fuel
levels, and if fuel levels are too high they act to decrease them both
by suppressing appetite and stimulating fuel consumption. The centres
defend a particular 'set-point' (or target level) for fuel levels in the
body. If fuel levels exceed this set-point then appetite centres act to
decrease them back to this point, whereas if fuel levels are below the
set-point then the centres act to increase them. The 'set-point theory'
of obesity suggests that fat and thin people have different set-points
operating in their appetite centres. Fat people defend a higher level of
fuel reserves in their body because the set-point in their brain is set
to a higher level. This resembles the thermostat on an air-conditioning
or central heating system: if the thermostat detects the temperature is
below the set-point, it increases the heat; if the temperature is above
the set-point it lessens the heating and may increase the cooling.

Evidence for the set-point theory is convincing. Body fuel stores are regulated remarkably tightly in most people; in fat people as much as thin. If you were to change your food intake by a small but consistent amount per day, dramatic changes in body weight would accumulate over a period of time. For example, increasing your food intake above the normal amount by only a hundred calories a day (one slice of bread, about five per cent of normal food intake) could in theory increase your weight by about five kilos over a year. Weight gain at this rate is very unusual, so body and brain must be regulating food intake very tightly, gauging the amount consumed to within the equivalent of one slice of bread per day. Fat people appear to defend a higher set-point than thin people do; as soon as they come off a diet, they rapidly return to almost exactly the same weight. After losing weight on a diet, people generally have a decreased metabolic rate, are persistently hungry and intolerant of cold. Conversely, experimental overfeeding of both fat and thin subjects results in a higher metabolic rate and decrease in appetite. Thus the set-point theory seems attractive.

Whether a person's set-point for weight is at the skinny or obese end of the range is determined by their genes. Indeed obesity is partly a genetic disease. The prevalence of obesity among children of slim parents is less than ten per cent; with one obese parent the figure rises to thirty per cent; and with two obese parents it is greater than sixty per cent. This may of course reflect both upbringing and genes, but studies of adopted children have proved there is a large genetic component. That is not to deny the importance of environmental influence on obesity, which is obviously significant as well. The dramatic increase in obesity over the last thirty years, with no significant change in genetics, demonstrates that environment is important. Many people who move from the developing world to the developed show an increase in obesity. Diet and exercise are thought to be the main environmental factors responsible for this. Probable culprits are the high calorie, high fat diet and low exercise lifestyle of the developed world. But environment and genetics interact in many complex ways. If we hear that some human trait is eighty per cent genetic (as has been claimed for obesity), this does not necessarily mean that the environmental influence is low. A different set of genes may make you more, not less, sensitive to the environment. For example, the Pima

Indians of Mexico and New Mexico (USA) are genetically similar to one another, but differ from other American Indians. The Pima Indians of New Mexico have an extremely high incidence of obesity, whereas their cousins in Mexico have a much lower incidence. The factors precipitating obesity in the Pimas of New Mexico are again diet and lifestyle, but it is their genes that have made them particularly susceptible to these environmental factors.

The Pimas are said to have thrifty genes: genes beneficial in their Mexican environment, where the calorie and fat intake is low, physical work is hard and long, and occasional fasting or even famine has occurred. In these conditions, genes that enable fat to be laid down rapidly in periods of plenty would be beneficial if the periods of plenty were often followed by those of famine, where the stored fat could be mobilized to survive starvation. But in New Mexico's changed conditions, these genes cause severe pathology, including a greatly increased risk of heart disease and diabetes. Thus genes beneficial in one set of environmental conditions, turn out to be detrimental in others. The Pima Indians may just be a more extreme case of an evolutionary paradox which everyone in the developed world suffers from. It has been cogently argued that humans evolved in just those conditions that would favour thrifty genes. Before agriculture, people lived by hunting and gathering with little or no food storage, which inevitably led to periods of famine and plenty. The men and women who could endure long periods of famine would survive to pass on their genes, while those whose genetic inheritance did not enable them to survive would die and their genes with them. A person of average weight has eight to twenty kilos of fat reserves and can survive roughly a month of starvation, whereas an obese individual may carry over 100 kg of fat, enabling survival for over four months. In the conditions of human evolution, this ability may have been vital and would have led to the selection of genes that favoured fat storage. Only relatively recently, where food is plentiful and continuously available, has an ability to lay down fat become a curse rather than a boon. The type of diet and exercise level of early humans may also have prevented obesity, although this is more difficult to assess.

Recently a key component of the set-point mechanism has been discovered – the hormone 'leptin' – and with it an entirely new perspective on obesity. Obesity research has been revitalized, and there is new optimism that an effective treatment for obesity is close. The breakthrough came when Jeffrey Friedman and colleagues at the Rockefeller University in New York found that a strain of obscenely obese mice were failing to make an unknown protein, because they had a mutation in the gene coding for it. By testing which tissues the gene was normally expressed in, researchers found that the product of the gene was only produced in fat tissue, but was released into the blood. Maybe the new protein could be a hormone produced by fat tissue? Researchers made and isolated as much of the protein as they could, then injected it into the obese mice. Once they were treated with the protein the mice began to lose weight, and within a few weeks they were down to a normal size. The scientists had found the Holy Grail of obesity research, a natural hormone, regulating the set-point for body weight. The new protein was named 'leptin' (Greek for thin), because it made the fat mice thin. Leptin was the missing link in the set-point theory of body weight control. It acted as a signal from fat stores to brain. If the fat stores were high, more leptin was produced by the fat and released into the blood. From the blood, leptin went to the brain's appetite centres, and there it both suppressed appetite and stimulated energy usage. The appetite suppression was partly due to leptin decreasing levels of neuropeptide Y, which acts as a stimulant of appetite. The stimulation of energy usage was due to leptin stimulating the sympathetic nervous system (the fight-or-flight response). Thus leptin acted as a feed-back signal between the body's fat stores and the brain's set-point; when fat stores were too high, leptin levels increased and reset the brain's set-point, causing us to eat less and burn off more fuel.

But was leptin present in humans and did it play the same role in regulating body weight? Testing for the gene and protein showed that the same protein was indeed present in humans and other mammals. Injecting leptin into rats, made obese by overfeeding, caused them to lose weight, but injecting it into those of normal weight had little effect. This was a perfect property for an obesity drug to have, as it would reduce body weight to normal but no further. But before the researchers could break out the champagne, they needed to test levels of leptin in obese humans. If human obesity was caused by lack of leptin, there should be abnormally low levels of leptin in the blood of obese humans. Unfortunately, it turns out that blood leptin levels in obese humans are higher (by about four times) than in people of normal weight. And this leptin was of the normal type: human obesity was not caused by a mutation in the gene, or a failure to produce leptin. It rather appeared that obese humans were resistant to the effects of leptin. Their body fat was producing more leptin, signalling that there was too much fat but the signal was not being received in the brain, or was being ignored. People have been discovered with a mutant leptin gene, on occasion, and are, as expected, spectacularly obese, but the vast majority of the obese have no problem with leptin production, but their brains appear to ignore its signal.

Leptin signals the size of the body's energy stores and the body normally responds by altering its expenditure on various energy-expensive processes. For example, during a period of starvation, leptin levels fall and this suppresses the immune system, saving vital energy but making the body more vulnerable to infection. That may well be why starving people often die from infections rather than from the starvation itself. During starvation or excessive exercise, the fall in leptin levels also suppresses women's fertility, reducing the chances of an energy-expensive pregnancy.

So where does that leave us? People apparently get fat because they eat too much. They eat too much because the fat in their body fails to suppress their appetite as much as it does in the thin. This appetite suppression has both long- and short-term components. Acting in the long-term through the fat tissue and leptin; and in the short-term through the levels of fuels (and hormones) in the blood after a meal. Both sugar and fat in the blood can suppress appetite, causing us to stop eating. Calorie for calorie, fat is less able to suppress appetite than carbohydrate. When presented with high fat or high carbohydrate foods, people presented with high fat foods consumed thirty per cent more calories a day, presumably because these were more palatable and suppressed appetite less. Moreover, obese people are satiated more slowly by fatty foods than lean people, and continue to eat them longer because the fat fails to stop their appetite. Apparently the body uses the carbohydrate content (rather than fat) of a meal to gauge when to stop eating. This may again be due to the human brain's overriding need for glucose, and that the body's carbohydrate stores are small and thus rapidly refilled.

How can all this new knowledge help us get or stay thin? If getting fat is due to eating more, the only sure way to get thin is to eat less. Undoubtedly dieting makes fat people thin. But fat people on a diet are always hungry and go back to their previous weight as soon as they come off the diet. Either we need to accept our set-point weight, or to accept being perpetually hungry. Exercise can help because it burns off calories. But it requires a lot of exercise to burn off a little fat. Three hours of exercise a day for twenty-five days is required to lose roughly one kilo of fat. And fat people are less tolerant of exercise than thin. Nevertheless, when coupled with a diet, exercise can and does help reduce weight.

When we overindulge at Christmas, some of us put on weight and some of us don't. Why? Perhaps it is because the latter burn off the extra calories by fidgeting. This was the surprising conclusion of a recent study by Michael Jensen and his colleagues at the American Mayo Clinic. They overfed sixteen volunteers by a fixed amount (a thousand calories a day for eight weeks) and tried to track down what accounted for the variability in the consequent weight gain, which varied from 1.4 to 7.2 kilos. There was little difference in the volunteers' resting metabolic rate or exercise (which was kept constant). But they found a significant increase in the activity-dependent metabolic rate in those volunteers who resisted weight gain. They suggested that this was due to increased 'fidgeting' (by which they meant all movements other than walking, exercise or work). Those volunteers who failed to increase these 'futile' activities significantly (this included the four women in the study) put on the most weight. One might assume fidgeting does not consume much energy, but in fact measurements have shown that it accounts for about an eighth of our total energy expenditure. Different people fidget to varying extents, depending on the activity of their sympathetic nervous systems causing the release of noradrenaline and adrenaline, and this variability may well be mainly genetically determined. Whether consciously increasing our fidgeting would reduce weight gain is unclear. But when your mother told you to stop fidgeting at the dinner table, she was perhaps giving you the wrong signals.

The pharmaceutical industry has long sought the perfect slimming drug. Amphetamines ('speed') have been used to stimulate the nervous system and adrenaline release, increasing basal metabolic rate and causing weight loss. However, this is equivalent to worrying yourself thin and can result in nervous exhaustion and psychosis. Thyroid hormones occur naturally in the body and regulate the basal metabolic rate. If your thyroid gland is too active in making hormones you end up thin and hyperactive, whereas people who do not produce enough are slow and fat. So thyroxin (the main thyroid hormone) has been used successfully to treat obesity, but unfortunately it has several nasty side-effects. Drugs have been developed to act on the brain's appetite centres to induce satiety, thus suppressing appetite. But again most have psychological side-effects, such as excessive dreaming.

A slimming drug was discovered during the Second World War, and although it turned out too toxic for general use, it contributed eventually to the discovery that our cells are powered by proton electricity. Workers in munitions factories found themselves becoming excessively thin with a very high metabolic rate. Official investigation discovered that the workers were made hypermetabolic by dinitrophenol, a chemical used to make high explosives. Dinitrophenol was found to be a mitochondrial uncoupler, carrying protons across the mitochondrial membrane and short-circuiting the generation of proton electricity. The amount of food burnt by the mitochondria massively increased, but the energy was wasted as heat. These unfortunate munitions workers were literally burning up inside. Dinitrophenol found its way into a number of slimming treatments but there were obnoxious side-effects, of which not the least was, because dinitrophenol is itself coloured, slimmers turned slightly yellow.

A high-carbohydrate low-fat diet suppresses appetite more quickly, resulting in a lower calorie intake than a high-fat diet. Cultures where such a diet is usual have low obesity rates, whereas in the West, where the fat content of the diet has increased to over forty per cent in the last century, obesity has become common. A recent survey of adult British men found obesity was almost absent in men normally eating a high carbohydrate diet. This suggests that if you want to get thin or avoid getting fat you need to change to a high-carbohydrate low-fat diet. High-carbohydrate foods like pasta, bread or potatoes rapidly make you feel full, so you do not eat excess calories. Sugar suppresses appetite even more rapidly; this explains why we snack on sweet food or drinks when hungry; why we don't eat sweets before a meal; and why a sweet course ends a meal, not begins it. But sugar is rapidly metabolized, so cannot suppress appetite for long. Whereas carbohydrate (particularly 'complex' carbohydrate such as 'fibre') is only slowly broken down in the gut, releasing sugar, and suppresses appetite more slowly, but for longer.

But man cannot live by bread alone. In our enthusiasm to pursue the genetic and mechanistic aspects of obesity, it is easy to forget the undoubtedly important social and psychological perspectives. Obesity is more common in women, older people and the lower classes. Thinness correlates with anxiety and smoking. Obesity often leads to a life characterized by general inertia and sexual inactivity, but is associated with low anxiety levels and the relative absence of depression (at least in men). Our culture partly determines what is an 'acceptable' body weight and what is 'unacceptable'; this varies with gender, class, country and historical period. In the end, it comes down to how individuals balance their different wants in the terms of food, body weight and lifestyle and – if a change is required – how much motivation there is.

Health experts have recently played down both the risks of being moderately overweight and the benefits of dieting. Early surveys indicated any weight above the ideal (which includes most people in the developed world) significantly increased the risk of premature death. More recent research has suggested that being moderately overweight may not pose a significant health risk. It depends partly on where the fat is: fat people who are pear-shaped (with the fat stored in their lower body) are at less of a health risk than those who have most fat in their upper body. The health risk also strongly depends on the individual's fitness level. A recent survey of 21,856 American men found that unfit, lean men were at twice the risk of mortality than fit, overweight men. As fat people tend to be less fit than thin people, the apparent health risk of fatness itself may have been overestimated. These conclusions are disputed, however, and do not mean that fatness poses no health risk. They mean rather that the strong benefits of fitness can override the risks of being overweight. Fitness, as we shall see in the next chapter, is one of the most important determinants of health.

Chapter 9

EXERCISE, FATIGUE AND STRESS

What are the limits of body energy and what happens when we try to go beyond them? This chapter will examine the limits of physical exercise and athletic performance and how they have been pushed back. We will explore the nature of motion and limits and discover what happens when those limits are exceeded. Finally we will look at the key regulators of body energy and how they span the gap between the mind and the body to control everyday feelings of energy, stress and fatigue.

THE SPEED LIMIT

By mistake you have been entered for the Olympic ten thousand metres final. Get ready! You enter the stadium and the crowd roars. As you approach the starting block, adrenaline surges through your veins. Your mind is racing, your stomach and guts clench; blood drains from your face and skin; muscles twitch and freeze, you are panting and start to sweat. This is all preparing you for the race ahead. The starter gun goes off: impulses ripple through your nervous system, and a wave of neurotransmitters hits your muscles. Channels open all over the muscle wall, calcium floods in and the muscles contract. All in a fraction of a second. You're off! Contraction of the muscle fibres is causing massive ATP use – enough to deplete the complete supply in a few seconds. Luckily ATP can be replenished from a storage form – phospho-creatine – but unluckily this only lasts another ten or so seconds. You had better start breaking down your muscle glycogen into glucose and using that to make more ATP. Now the high carbohydrate breakfast you had, stuffing your muscles full of glycogen, stands you in good stead. However, breaking down glycogen and glucose to lactate, to produce ATP without recruiting mitochondria, only supplies sufficient ATP for a minute or two. Fortunately, a twenty-fold increase in blood supply to the muscles provides sufficient oxygen and fuel to kick the mitochondria into life. The body's total oxygen consumption, energy turnover and heat production increases ten-fold. You're speeding out in front of the pack. You're on a high, your veins are full of adrenaline and opium-like drugs flood your brain. Your entire metabolism is turned upside down: adrenaline is high and insulin is low, causing fat to flood out of the fat stores and be burnt in preference to glucose throughout the body, while glucose is produced for the brain by the liver using lactate and amino acids supplied by the muscles. But hold on, you are starting to tire. Your muscles just won't work at the same rate, are starting to hurt and lactate accumulating throughout your body is causing 'burn'. The other runners are passing you. The winning line recedes into an impossible dream, where this pain and fatigue might eventually stop. You reach it last – and collapse. You abandon yourself to your body, which immediately starts on the long job of repaying the metabolic debts built up during the race and repairing any damage done.

What stops us from going faster? Why do we tire? How can we overcome these barriers? These are questions that have haunted athletes for thousands of years, and perplexed scientists for hundreds of years. As Lavoisier and Séguin discovered in the eighteenth century, the body's oxygen consumption increases with the intensity of exercise. But if we keep on increasing the intensity or work required, we eventually reach a limit: the body's maximal oxygen consumption, which corresponds to the highest energy production or metabolic rate of the body. This rate is ten times the resting rate in the untrained, but is up to twenty times in trained athletes. But what limits this rate? Which process in the body prevents it being higher? The maximal metabolic rate might be limited either by the muscles and the rate they produce and use energy for contraction and relaxation; or by the heart and the rate it pumps the blood around the body; or by the lungs and the rate they bring oxygen into the blood and expel carbon dioxide.

The lungs are not the problem, since even during maximal exercise when the amount of air breathed increases twenty-five times over the rest level, they could still work fifty per cent faster. The lungs thus appear to have excess capacity and probably do not limit the maximal metabolic rate. This is supported by the finding that blood levels of oxygen and carbon dioxide are remarkably constant, even at the maximal exercise rate. If the lungs' oxygen intake limited energy production, then the level of oxygen in the blood would go down when we start strenuous exercise, but in fact it changes very little. Exercise training has little effect on the lungs. In complete contrast, training for endurance exercise (such as marathon running) increases the rate the heart can pump blood by about forty per cent. The heart increases in size and the chambers inside also expand, so that for each beat the heart can pump more blood. This is why you can tell someone's fitness level from their heart rate or pulse. At rest, a fit and a non-fit person have about the same metabolic rate and thus require the blood to circulate at the same rate. But the fit person's heart is larger, pumping more blood per beat, so to maintain the same blood circulation, a lower number of beats per minute is required. Thus an untrained person's heart rate averages about seventy-five beats a minute at rest, while an athlete's is about fifty.

But does the heart limit maximal exercise? Does the human heart limit the Olympic ten thousand metres record and your capacity to sprint a hundred metres to catch the bus? These are, in fact, two entirely different modes of exercise (endurance and power exercise), which use different body fuels and are limited by distinct factors. During maximal exercise in endurance sports, the heart works at ninety per cent of its maximal capacity. The limit of human performance in endurance sports is very close to the heart's limit and it appears to be the heart that restricts that performance. Looking at this problem in another way, we can examine the effect of exercising different limbs on the body's oxygen consumption. If you maximally exercise one limb, say, your leg on a bicycle, your oxygen consumption increases to roughly two litres a minute. If you now exercise both legs, then your oxygen uptake almost doubles. But if you exercise both arms and legs together, there is no further increase in oxygen consumption. It remains at four litres a minute, moreover exercising legs and arms together reduces the amount of work each limb can do individually. Thus if you are cycling at maximal speed and then have to exercise your arms also, your legs' capacity to cycle would decrease. This indicates that, when you use two or more limbs, maximal oxygen consumption and thus energy utilization is not limited by the muscles but by other body processes, most likely the heart's ability to circulate blood. However, the blood's ability to carry oxygen to the muscles would be improved if the amount of haemoglobin in the blood could be increased, because it is the haemoglobin that actually carries oxygen. It has been found that increasing haemoglobin can up the maximal energy production of the body by five per cent or more. This is the basis of 'blood-doping' used by some athletes: one litre of the athlete's blood is removed and over the following few weeks the body adapts by making more haemoglobin. The blood is then reinfused, so that, at least for the next few weeks, there is a higher than normal level of haemoglobin in the body. Alternatively, the determined athlete can take a type of natural hormone called 'erythropoietin' (or EPO), which stimulates the body to make more red blood cells. This was the 'drug' that disrupted the 1998 Tour de France, when it was discovered in the van of the Festina cycling team. It is almost impossible to detect whether cyclists are taking EPO because it is naturally produced by the body. The most single-minded athletes have now resorted to surgery to increase their blood supply by increasing the size of major arteries and opening out the heart's valves. The effectiveness of all these treatments indicates that the rate oxygen can be supplied to muscle does, indeed, limit maximal energy production.

Races are, on the other hand, won not so much because of the winner's higher maximal metabolic rate but because of greater endurance – that is less fatigue. Training can increase our maximal metabolic rate by five to twenty-five per cent, but can increase our endurance, the time we can sustain the maximal rate before fatiguing, by five hundred per cent. This appears to result from an increase in the amount of mitochondria in muscles during training. Mitochondria generate ATP much more efficiently than glycolysis from glucose and glycogen, and enable the muscle to generate energy from fat rather than carbohydrate. Endurance training changes the fuel utilization used to power exercise: the rate carbohydrate is burned decreases and the amount of fat burned increases. This enables the carbohydrate stores, so vital for both brain and muscle, to last longer. It is the depletion of the carbohydrate stores that causes exhaustion during endurance exercise. This is why athletes eat a high carbohydrate diet before a taxing event, filling up the stores of the muscles and liver. On a high fat diet, carbohydrate depletion and exhaustion occur after ninety minutes of running, whereas with a high carbohydrate diet this may not occur until after four hours. Marathon runners call carbohydrate depletion 'the wall' because the feeling is like running into a wall: all the muscles feel extremely weak and heavy, the legs shake and the brain becomes confused.

Most muscle use and exercise are powered by phospho-creatine and carbohydrate. Although, at rest, our main fuel is fat, during high-intensity exercise ninety-five per cent of the fuel is from carbohydrate. We only start burning fat again when the carbohydrate stores run down. Carbohydrate can be used to generate ATP and thus energy, in two radically different ways. The first way is to burn it in the mitochondria. This produces lots of ATP, roughly thirty ATP molecules per glucose molecule burnt. But it is relatively slow, and requires lots of oxygen to be supplied from the blood. The second way is to convert the glucose into lactic acid. This method, called 'anaerobic glycolysis', only produces two ATP molecules per glucose molecule, but is much faster and does not require oxygen. This is thus one of the main means used to generate ATP during intense exercise. Glucose is derived from glycogen in the muscle, so that, at first, nothing is required from the blood to supply the hugely increased energy consumption of the maximally contracting muscle. During a hundred metre sprint the energy requirements of the body may increase by thirty times and the muscles' total ATP content (about fifty grams) is consumed and needs to be remade each second. But the athlete hardly breathes at all in the race's brief time span and no extra oxygen is required, because half the ATP is remade from phospho-creatine and half from anaerobic glycolysis. The problem with this energy generation is that it cannot last long. The glycogen is rapidly depleted and the lactic acid produced rapidly builds up. Lactic acid is indeed an acid, and at high concentrations it 'burns', causing the unpleasant sensation of 'stitch' across the chest of unfit runners. The acid is also one of the main causes of fatigue.

Muscle fatigue during exercise or work has multiple causes, depending on the exercise involved. This is hardly surprising seeing that different types of exercise, such as weight-lifting, football, sprinting and marathon running, use different muscle types, for various times, different energy sources, making variable demands on the body. A common cause of fatigue is a failure of energy supply, due either to depletion of energy reserves (phospho-creatine or glycogen), or the build-up of the end products of metabolism (lactic acid or phosphate). But fatigue may also be caused by a failure of signals telling the muscle to contract. This may occur inside the muscle, when metabolic end-products inhibit calcium signals normally activating muscle contraction. Or it may occur outside if the brain fails to send the muscle nerve impulses: a failure of will. Muscle fatigue is normally reversible, although replenishment of muscle glycogen stores after a run to exhaustion normally takes at least forty-eight hours on a high carbohydrate diet. However, fatigue from constant muscle contraction against a weight, such as in weight-lifting or rock-climbing, may result in subtle muscle damage which is only slowly reversible. Damage to muscles, tendons and joints is common to many sports. Fatigue is certainly a complex process and one still not fully understood.

So, how can these barriers to performance be overcome? How can we break through the human body's physiological limits to new levels of achievement in sport and life? Or are the limits of human physical performance fixed, and we are destined to battle over fractions of seconds in our world records for the rest of human history? Athletes have been stretching the limits of metabolic rate and endurance for thousands of years. The ancient Greeks used an extract of asses' hooves, ground and boiled in oil with roses. The Aztecs used cactus extracts to support runs which could last up to seventy-two hours. The Incas used coca (from which cocaine is extracted) to increase stamina. As already mentioned, the main modern methods to improve performance limits are training, lifestyle and diet. Training increases maximal metabolic rate and endurance: by increasing the size of the heart, number of blood vessels, muscle mass and density of enzyme machines and, not least, the amount of muscle mitochondria. The type of muscle fibre can also be changed by training, as well as type of fuel used. There are two main varieties of muscle fibre: fast, but rapidly fatiguing and slow, with high endurance. A muscle that has mainly fast fibres, is white (like chicken breast). This is because it contains very few mitochondria and blood vessels and relies on anaerobic glycolysis to supply ATP rapidly but at an unsustainable rate. Whereas muscles with mainly slow fibres are red, brown or grey (like a chicken leg), because they are packed full of mitochondria and blood. Training can change the proportions of the different fibres in your muscles. A sprinter or weight-lifter may have eighty per cent fast fibres, twenty per cent slow, whereas a marathon runner has the opposite proportion. Thus, it is important to do the correct training or you can end up with the wrong fibre type. In high-intensity power sports, it is important to also increase the *amount* of muscle as this is directly related to power output. This can be achieved by strength training, a diet rich in protein and carbohydrate and by taking anabolic steroids. Anabolic steroids are drugs, related to testosterone, the male sex hormone, that increase muscle mass. They are banned in competitive sport, partly because of the competitive advantage but also for their damaging side-effects, which include acne, impotence and sterility. Ben Johnson was deprived of his one hundred metres Olympic gold medal in 1988, when his urine tested positive for anabolic steroids; these are still the main culprits of drug abuse in sport. Anabolic steroids can be detected, but natural hormones which increase muscle mass, such as Human Growth Hormone, are much harder to control. When the star of the Chinese swimming team arrived in Australia for the world championships in 1998, a customs official found more than just a swimming costume and a pair of goggles in her bag. She had thirteen phials of Human Growth Hormone, enough to supply the entire Chinese team with the hormone, which would be indistinguishable from the body's own. However, although a large amount of muscle is essential for sports which require strength, this is not true for endurance sports, as is evident from the slim physique of long-distance runners.

Although training for strength, power and endurance are important, technique is just as important to performance. When we use muscles to perform work, such as weight-lifting or cycling uphill, only twenty-five per cent of the energy used to power the muscle is converted into work, seventy-five per cent is wasted as heat. Increasing this efficiency, we can increase performance. If you think about it, running is a strange means of locomotion, involving bouncing up and down, as well as moving forward. This bouncing is aided by the elasticity of the ankle's Achilles tendon, which acts like an elastic band, stretching when we put our foot downwards and pulling back to its relaxed length to propel us upwards. A considerable amount of energy is thus conserved during running, raising the energy efficiency from twenty-five per cent to forty per cent or more. Training increases the tendon's elasticity, while ageing decreases it, making running less efficient. Kangaroos are the ultimate masters of this pogo-stick effect, enabling them to increase from five kilometres an hour to twenty without using extra energy, just more bounce.

Training can re-engineer the body, moulding it to the requirements of a particular sporting activity. One of the biggest developments in training technique was the introduction of interval training. This consists of repeated periods of exercise and rest. For middle distance runners, this might involve ten seconds of sprinting, then twenty seconds' rest, repeated for one to two hours. It is hard to see why this improves performance, but it does. Interval training was developed by Dr Reindell, a German cardiologist, in the 1930s to strengthen his patients' hearts. He tried different regimens, making careful cardiac measurements: his results showed that the most effective method was the running of repetitive short distances spaced by short rest periods. This resulted in the heart's size and the amount of blood pumped per beat increasing. Reindell also discovered that there was a marked increase in the body's total oxygen consumption during exercise (the maximum metabolic rate), so changes induced by the interval training were not restricted to the heart, but occurred throughout the body. It turned out the most dramatic changes were occurring in the skeletal muscle. So these medical findings were rapidly applied to top-class athletes in pre-war Nazi Germany. Woldemar Gerschler was the most notable coach to systematically apply interval training and Rudolf Harbig, his star pupil, took almost two seconds off the eight hundred metres' world record in 1939, soon afterwards breaking the four hundred metre world record as well. Harbig was to die in the Second

World War, but interval training survived, soon spreading around the world.

Although interval training works, it is not so clear why. In exercise of varying intensity and duration, different parts of the body limit performance, whether lungs, heart, blood supply, amount or type of muscle or mitochondria. If in a particular type of exercise, one part of the body is especially limiting, then it is that part alone which is stressed, adapting to the exercise by increasing its size or performance. To increase the amount and performance of muscle mitochondria it is important, therefore, to make the mitochondria limiting for exercise. But in middle distance running, for example, mitochondria only partially limit performance, because the supply of oxygen and fuels by heart and blood vessels also act as curbs. Thus training for middle distance races by doing middle distance runs can only have a minor impact on improving the amount and efficiency of the mitochondria. But, during very short bursts of exercise, muscle mitochondria are not limited by the supply of oxygen through the heart or blood supply, because a small amount of oxygen is stored inside the muscle itself. Thus for a short period at the beginning of exercise (until the oxygen runs out) the mitochondria work flat out and are stressed to an extent that the muscle cell realizes that it must make more mitochondria. Lactate and other fatigue-inducing molecules are made during the intense exercise and the period of rest allows time for these to be flushed out of the muscles, thus preventing fatigue. Different periods and intensities of exercise in the intervals stress different parts of the body and thus more effectively train them.

Diet and athletic performance have been linked since ancient Greece but the link is often poorly understood. For example, many modern athletes still believe, as did those of ancient Greece, that a high-protein diet is an essential preparation for competition. Modern research has shown to the contrary that even those who require a large muscle mass only need moderate protein levels; it is rather carbohydrate-rich foods that provide the fuel essential for prolonged, heavy exercise. The biggest breakthrough in the nutritional enhancement of endurance performance has been 'carbohydrate loading', developed by the Scandinavian Eric Hultman among others. This is a regimen designed to pack the body with as much carbohydrate as possible before a race, to increase endurance. The regimen starts a week before the race, consisting of rest (only light training) and a high carbohydrate diet (seventy per cent of calories from carbohydrate). This increases the carbohydrate stored in the muscle (as glycogen) by up to one hundred per cent, and although increasing the maximum running speed, more importantly it increases the time the maximal speed can be maintained (endurance) by about fifty per cent. That's because, in endurance sports, once the glycogen is depleted, fatigue rapidly ensues. Carbohydrate loading is one of the few regimens that actually works, but it only works for endurance sports lasting longer than one hour.

Dehydration, as a result of excessive sweating, can hasten fatigue more rapidly than carbohydrate depletion. This is because it reduces our capacity to sweat and this reduction in heat loss results in an intolerable rise in body temperature. Drinking is vitally important in endurance sports. Nowadays sports drinks are supplemented with carbohydrate and salts, as these have been shown to increase endurance more than water alone.

Recently 'creatine' has been widely used as a supplement, since it is taken into the muscle and converted to phospho-creatine, which then acts as a rapid source of ATP in the first ten seconds of high-intensity exercise. Creatine is the most important discovery to hit sports nutrition since carbohydrate loading and is widely touted as a fatigue panacea. The first clue to its usefulness came from Roger Harris, a physiologist at the Animal Health Trust in Newmarket. In 1984, he tried to give creatine to a horse: when the horse balked he took the dose himself. Soon afterwards he found the creatine in his blood, thus demonstrating that it could move from the gut to the blood. This was an important discovery since most complex substances, such as ATP and protein, are broken down in the gut and can never enter the blood intact. Next, Harris (and his colleagues Hultman, Soderlund and Greenhaff) tested whether creatine could enter the muscles, increasing the normal levels. This again was a crucial breakthrough because cells are highly selective about what they take from the blood, normally regulating their contents very tightly indeed. They (with colleagues) found feeding people with high doses (twenty-five grams a day) of creatine increased muscle creatine levels by twenty per cent, but even higher levels were obtained when this was coupled with high-intensity training. Higher creatine levels enabled the resting phospho-creatine levels in the muscle to increase, but, more importantly, it enabled phospho-creatine levels to be restored more quickly after depletion by exercise. Performance in intermittent high-intensity exercise was marginally but consistently increased by a creatine supplement. Tests on ten trained middle-distance runners performing four three hundred metre or thousand metre runs with a three to four minute rest period between runs, showed that the creatine-supplemented runners performed better than the runners receiving a placebo in the last of the four races. The best three hundred metre and thousand metre times were also faster (0.3 and 2.1 seconds respectively) in the creatine-supplemented runners. Since then, other trials have shown creatine can marginally increase high-intensity performance. The only side-effect of these huge doses of creatine so far known is weight gain, but the long-term effects are as yet unknown.

Several stimulant drugs are used to improve performance: they generally work by enhancing the action of adrenaline and the sympathetic nervous system. Amphetamines ('speed') and cocaine act in this way and can increase performance, but are illegal and have multiple side-effects. Caffeine is a legal alternative, long used by athletes. Recent studies suggest that the equivalent of two to three cups of coffee enhances both high-intensity exercise and endurance.

The options available for increasing human performance thus all have rather marginal effects. These can be very important for an individual in a race, but do not have dramatic implications for the record books. World-record times in running have been slowly decreasing ever since records have been kept, and the average speed in races has been correspondingly increasing. If there were a physiological limit or maximum to human running speed we could expect as we approached it that improvements in times and speed would become rarer and slower, until there was no further improvement possible. Remarkably, this does not appear to be true; world-records for running have increased linearly over the last century, with no decrease in their rate of improvement. Thus if there is a limit, we are not in sight of it yet. Also, rather unexpectedly, women's world-records are improving faster than men's. This rate of improvement was extrapolated by Brian Whipp and Susan Ward of UCLA in a *Nature* article, 'Will women soon outrun men?' They predicted that if the rates of improvement continue as they have over the last fifty years, then in most events women will outrun men by 2035, considerably sooner in endurance events such as the marathon. Most observers, however, believe these rates of performance improvement, both male and female, cannot be sustained. We may have to wait until 2035 to find out.

Exercise is not just the concern of the athlete, it should be everybody's. The general decline in exercise and fitness over the last fifty years in the developed world, resulting from a sedentary lifestyle, has contributed to the modern epidemics of obesity and heart disease and possibly to depression and anxiety as well. Exercise can help to prevent or reverse each of these disorders. But the 1992 UK National Fitness Survey found that seven out of ten men, and eight out of ten women, do not take sufficient exercise to benefit their health. Frequent exercise of medium to high intensity changes the way the body handles fat and carbohydrate, so they are cleared more rapidly from the body, thus reducing the risk of obesity, diabetes and damage to the blood vessels. Exercise also soothes anxiety and depression, probably by changing the levels of neurotransmitters in the brain. Exercise is as close as we get in the modern world to a panacea, but the rapid decline in fitness in modern times indicates that exercise is not nearly as popular as popping pills.

THE MIRACLE OF MOTION

How is willed movement possible? How do I move my arm just by willing it so? This is the central question of the ancient mystery of life. For the ancient Greeks and other cultures, the ability to initiate motion was what separated life from death, and indicated the presence of souls, gods or devils. Today, we would divide the question into three separate problems: how does a muscle contract; how does the message pass from brain to muscle; and how is the message initiated in the brain? Only in the last fifty years have we found answers to the first two questions, while the answer to the third remains as elusive as ever.

Almost all willed motion is due to the contraction of multiple muscles in the body. If you move your hand towards your shoulder, this is due to the contraction of the biceps muscles which lie on top of your upper arm. If you move your hand away, this is due to the contraction of triceps muscles on the bottom of your upper arm, while the biceps relax. Muscle relaxation is entirely passive: the muscle stops contracting and may lengthen if other muscles are contracting so that it is pulled at either end. Complex hand and finger movements, say, to pick up a cup, are due to the co-ordinated contraction and relaxation of dozens of different muscles. Breathing movements and motion of the eye are similarly co-ordinated by multiple muscles. Internal movements of the heart, stomach, gut and uterus (womb) are due to rhythmic contractions of cylinders of muscle: the walls of the cylinder are made of muscle and when this contracts, the diameter narrows, pushing the contents out.

The only significant body movement not due to muscles is the erection of the penis, brought about by the penis becoming engorged with blood. The reason the penis does not use muscle is probably because the required movement would be difficult using muscle. All large movements are brought about by muscles attached to bones, anchoring the muscle and amplifying the movement caused by muscle contraction. Even if a bone were present in the penis (and it is in some animals such as the armadillo), it would be difficult to pull on it in such a way as to erect the penis and the bone's presence might hinder the penis from changing size and shape. However, if the penis had used muscle it certainly would have given rise to quicker erections!

So how does an individual muscle contract? Muscles contain vast numbers of tiny 'filaments', like minute ropes, running the length of the muscle, packed parallel to each other within the huge cells. Half of these filaments (called 'thick filaments') have many little arms along their length, sticking out to the side of the thick filament, which can grab hold of and attach to the neighbouring filaments (the so-called 'thin filaments'). Each 'arm' is a little protein machine, permanently attached to the thick filament at one end (the shoulder), while the other end (the 'hand') may attach to or detach from neighbouring thin filaments. When attached to a neighbouring filament the arm may contract or bend, and this causes the two filaments to move slightly relative to each other or rather slide over each other in opposite directions. The arm can then detach from its neighbouring filament, relax and then reattach further up, then repeating its cycle of attachment, contraction, detachment and relaxation, up to five times a second. This cycle is powered by ATP: one ATP molecule binds to the part of the arm that bends, and the ATP splitting powers the contraction and cycle. The ATP acts like a spring-loaded gun. The arm binds the gun (ATP) inside its structure and pulls the trigger, causing the arm to change shape (a kind of rocking movement of the hand according to current models), and this powers the contraction.

There are many 'arms' on each thick filament (about three hundred) and each is independently pulling on neighbouring filaments, causing the filaments to slide over each other at a rate of up to fifteen millionths of a metre per second. Some of the filaments are indirectly attached to bones at either end of the muscle, and thus when they slide over each other the muscle contracts. It resembles a tug-of-war, except in the game of muscle contraction all the tuggers of one team are tied to one rope (their common thick filament). Half the team face one way and the other half the opposite direction, with their backs to each other. They do not pull on the rope tying them together, but on two other ropes (the thin filaments), which are not tied to anyone, but are also being pulled in the opposite direction by two further teams. Many teams and ropes may be joined in this way in a long line, and if one end is attached to something immovable and the other to a movable weight, it will contract and do work by pulling the weight. This model of muscle contraction is known as the 'sliding filament model' and was proposed independently by Cambridge biologists Hugh Huxley and Andrew Huxley in 1953 and 1954.

Although this model tells us how a muscle contracts, it does not show how this is controlled. As with most of biology, it is essential to not just know how to do it, but also when to start doing it, and when to stop. Movements such as running require the alternate contractions and relaxations of many muscles, which must be precisely and strictly co-ordinated in time. This requires a signalling molecule to carry the message from the nerve impulses coming from the brain to the contractile machinery inside the muscle cells. Within muscle cells, this message is carried by calcium. Calcium binds to the thin filaments and allows the cyclic interaction between neighbouring filaments powering contraction. In the absence of calcium, the thick filaments' arms cannot attach to neighbouring thin filaments, and the muscle relaxes. Thus, when the calcium level is high in the cell the muscle contracts, relaxing when it is low.

But how is muscle contraction linked to the brain willing it so? The brain and muscle are connected by a motor neuron, which ends next to the muscle. When the motor neuron fires, an electrical impulse passes down the neuron right to its end, causing a chemical (a neurotransmitter called acetylcholine) to be released from the neuronal ending onto the muscle cells. This neurotransmitter then binds to specific pores in the muscle cell membrane, causing the pores to open and allowing electrical charges to cross the membrane. This provides a spark, triggering an electrical signal to rapidly explode along the cell membrane and throughout the muscle. The electrical signal, in turn, sparks pores in the muscle cell membrane to open, allowing calcium to enter the cell. Calcium entering through the pores activates the release of further calcium from internal stores and the explosive increase in the level of calcium inside the cell, triggers muscle contraction. When the nervous signal stops, calcium no longer enters the cell and is pumped out and back into stores, causing the cell level of calcium to fall, and thus the muscle to relax. The pumping back of calcium requires a lot of energy in the form of ATP. In fact about a third of the energy used in muscle contraction and relaxation is used simply to pump the calcium out of the muscle cell, allowing it to relax.

So that's it. That is how motion is possible. No pneumatic spirits or vital forces are necessary – only a vast number of molecular machines inside an incredibly complex structure, which are all choreographed to produce a co-ordinated motion, such as a ballerina's pirouette.

WHO CONTROLS THE ENERGY?

Having energy is not the same as being able to use it. A fat man may carry one hundred kilos of high-energy fat, but may have some difficulty in mobilizing the energy to get up the stairs. A chronically fatigued woman may have all the machinery of energy production intact, but is unable or unwilling to use it. An athlete may have stuffed himself with enough pasta to power ten marathons, but cannot win the sprint gold. Why is this? What is the problem?

This is, after all, a very familiar and crucial problem in every walk of life. The economy may have the capacity to produce the goods we want, but we don't have the ready cash to buy them. The motorway may have eight lanes from where we are to where we want to go, but there are road works blocking the route halfway. We may have sufficient money to buy that house, but it's stuck in a chain of buyers and sellers. Although there may be enough sun in the Sahara to grow a rain forest, there is no water.

Some things limit a process and some do not. In the examples above: the economy was limited by consumer cash and consumption, but not by the production of goods; your journey time was limited by the number of lanes operating through the road works, not the number in the rest of the motorway; how soon you can buy that house is limited by how soon some other seller can find another house, not by your cash's availability; and the growth of forest in the Sahara is limited by water, not sun.

In the same way, how energetic we feel may be limited by some things, but not by others. Having energy is not the same as being able to use energy, because how fast we use energy for moving or thinking is usually not limited by the availability of energy fuels, but rather by other factors. How fast or strongly we can operate can be limited by the amount of glucose or other fuels in some circumstances, such as starvation, but usually not. So, popping a glucose pill or a chocolate bar, is in most circumstances going to do you no good and will in fact often do you harm for reasons we will see later. Nor will swallowing a jar of ATP improve your energy levels, although jars of ATP have certainly been sold for this purpose. There are three reasons: firstly, that ATP will not be absorbed into the blood from the gut; secondly, if it got into the blood, it can't be transported from the blood into the cells; and thirdly, even if it got into the cells, the ATP supply does not normally limit its usage. Even if the ATP supply did limit usage, as it might do in running a marathon, the quantities required are huge, about 10 grams of ATP per second for a marathon runner, or about one hundred kilos a marathon.

Health shops and health magazines are stacked with products that will apparently 'energize' you, because they have something to do with energy metabolism. In fact, ninety-nine per cent of these products will, in normal circumstances, do absolutely nothing, because your energy economy is not limited by these factors.

If the fuel supply does not normally limit our energetics, then what does? Usually it's the cell machinery that transforms that energy into ATP or the machinery using that ATP to perform work such as muscle contraction or nerve impulses. This machinery has a maximal rate and however much fuel you give it, it will not go any faster. However, the rate at which this machinery works is regulated by hormones and nerves, while the amount of machinery in the cell is regulated by the DNA. Thus, for example, if we regularly exercise, the machinery for energy production (mitochondria) and use (the muscle fibres) slowly increases within our muscles, because messages are sent to the DNA, causing it to up the amount of these proteins in the cell. So there are things we can do to increase our energy level, but they are not as obvious as eating more fuel.

A process consisting of a chain of jobs is generally as slow as the slowest component job; not the fastest or the average, but the slowest. We all know this from our experience of bureaucracy. A production-line manager knows it is no good producing one hundred car bodies a day, if only ten engines are produced a day. So why doesn't he get one hundred engines made a day? Well, perhaps he only needs to make ten cars a day, or can only get hold of sufficient parts to make ten engines a day. In which case, it would be best to make ten lots of everything, ten engines, ten bodies, ten sets of wheels, etc. Otherwise the factory would rapidly fill up with unused car parts.

The same kinds of problems occur in the body. Energy is produced by burning food, and is used to maintain the cells and to do things like grow, reproduce, contract muscles and keep warm. But this overall process involves hundreds of different smaller jobs. The food has to be acquired, eaten, digested, absorbed, distributed in the blood, absorbed by the cells, broken down step by step by metabolism, burnt step by tiny step by mitochondria, converted to electron electricity, converted to proton electricity, converted to phosphate electricity, distributed throughout the cell and then either converted to sodium electricity on the membrane or used to drive the muscles or other machines, or whatever. The point is that there are very many individual steps, which all have to go at exactly the same rate, otherwise the whole process will get massively out-of-step very rapidly.

This wouldn't be such a big problem if we had one fixed rate to produce energy. Then we could arrange for all the hundreds of tiny steps in the process of energy production to work, all at the same rate, and everybody would be happy. Unfortunately, this is not the case. The body is continually challenged by two kinds of change: change in the amount of energy required and change in the availability and type of fuel. When we speed from rest to maximum sprint to escape a marauding rhinoceros, our muscle cells increase their energy use one hundred times and the whole body increases its energy use ten to twenty times. If we didn't we would be impaled on a rhinoceros's horn. When we just manage to escape by climbing a eucalyptus tree, we need to turn our energy production down to rest levels. Failing to do that, all energy reserves would be used up in a few hours. However, if the persistent rhino stays at the bottom of the tree all night, we are going to be in trouble unless we switch our fuel supply from glucose to fat. If we don't, our glucose store will run out by dawn, our brains freeze and we will fall out of the tree. Again if after being stuck, foodless, for three days in the tree, we are rescued by a prince or princess on a magic carpet and swept away to a sumptuous banquet of roast rhino, we need to be able to switch our metabolism back to the storing of glucose and fat. If not, we may be embarrassed by our lack of fuel reserves when thrown out of the palace in the morning.

If the rate of energy and fuel metabolism has to be changed, then we have to find somewhere inside this metabolism where the whole complex process can be controlled from – a master switch to start and stop energy production. In the 1950s and 60s it was thought each process in the body had a single rate-limiting step, a key step slower than all the rest, acting as a 'bottleneck' or 'pacemaker' and setting the pace for all the others. And it was at this regulatory step that hormones acted to change the process' rate, because the overall rate of the process could only be changed at the rate-limiting step, and thus regulated. However, in the 1970s a revolutionary new theory, 'Metabolic Control Analysis', was simultaneously proposed by Henrik Kacser and Jim Burns in Edinburgh, and by Reinhart Heinrich and Tom Rapoport in Berlin.

The essence of their idea was simply that the extent to which differ-ent steps were rate limiting should be measured, and then we could decide whether pacemakers existed in cells. No one had previously bothered to measure the extent different steps were rate-limiting, partly because they didn't know how and partly because the previous theory had assumed only one step was limiting and that therefore there was no point in measuring how limiting the other steps were. Metabolic Control Analysis provided a means to measure how limiting a step within a process was and also provided a theory that explained how limitation, control and regulation worked. For example, it showed that if you decreased the extent to which one step limited a process, then a different process must become more limiting. So, if your energy level is limited by vitamins, when you take a bucket-load, the vitamins will no longer be limiting, but something else will have become so.

When scientists started using Metabolic Control Analysis to measure the extent to which the different steps (for example within ATP pro-duction) limited overall rates they found to their surprise that most metabolic pathways did not have a single rate-limiting step, but rather several steps were partially rate-limiting. Moreover, the distribution of rate-limitation between different steps changed in various con-ditions. This has important implications for our energy level, and the rate at which we can do things. There is no single step inside our bodies or cells limiting our performance, but rather a number of different steps or processes that partially limit it, and which steps they are depends on conditions. There is no single, central, all-powerful step or regulator inside the body that limits and controls our perform-ance and energy level in all conditions. Therefore, there is no single vitamin, drug, or treatment that can target this regulator to massively improve our performance or charge up our energy levels. There are rather a large number of processes, each limiting our performance slightly, and if we do or take something to improve one process then the overall performance will be a little improved but something else will now limit it.

Kacser compared the concept of the rate-limiting step to the politics of a dictatorship: where one person tells everyone else what to do, since a rate-limiting step can tell all other steps what rate to go at. He suggested that cellular processes operate much more like a democracy, where most steps have a small but significant say in how fast the overall process runs. Time, and the application of his theory, have shown that he was right.

If the cell is to change its fuel utilization and energy production according to the body's fickle requirements, it needs to know how much fuel is available and how much energy is required. But how is the lowly cell to know this, without a brain of its own? And who is going to tell each of the trillions of tiny molecular machines, constituting thousands of metabolic steps, scattered between a dozen different organs, about all these changes? If the muscles start sprinting, who is going to tell the liver to start making more glucose? If we gorge ourselves on ice cream, who is going to tell the muscles and fat tissue to store excess fuel? The organs and their myriad molecular machines do not know intuitively what the needs of the rest of the body are, they need a messenger to tell them. There are two main routes this message comes: via hormones in the blood and via neurotransmitters released by nerves. Hormones are the master messengers orchestrating the response of different organs to the body's changing needs. But nerves, radiating from the brain, also penetrate every organ in the body and when the need arises, release neurotransmitters locally into the organs to control their function.

Although the means of transport of the message is different for hormones (through the blood) and neurotransmitter (through nerves), its reception by the cells is similar. Somewhere on the cell surface there needs to be a detector, which can recognize the presence of that messenger outside the cell, broadcasting the message to all the molecular machines inside. The detector is called a 'receptor' and there may be thousands or millions on the surface of a single cell. The receptor is a protein machine, which binds the hormone or neurotransmitter. This causes the receptor to change shape, passing the message through the cell membrane to machinery inside the cell. Once activated by binding the hormone or neurotransmitter, the receptor needs to produce a second message within the cell to pass from the membrane to all the molecular machines inside, which will carry out the message by doing whatever is required. This second message is in fact usefully known as the 'second messenger'. Many different types of molecule or change are used as second messengers. They may be a simple molecule, such as calcium or involve a protein machine that switches on or off the molecular machines that are the message's target. Alternatively, the message's target may be the cell's DNA, and the second messenger may switch on particular genes within the DNA, causing new proteins to be made inside the cell which result in new activities. Thus, the information in a message may pass through a myriad of molecular interactions, within the body and its cells, when passing from signal to target.

But the cell is not entirely passive in receiving this message. It is not slave to a single message. It receives hundreds of different messages simultaneously, via different hormones, neurotransmitters and a multitude of other signalling molecules. So the cell needs to integrate all this information and decide what to do based on its own genetic make-up, which depends on what kind of cell it is and what its history has been. Information processing by a single cell is far from simple and the task becomes mindboggling when we consider that our brain and body consist of billions of cells. The transfer and processing of information is one of the three main cell functions (the other two are the transfer and processing of matter and energy). The cell devotes a large fraction of its machinery and energy to this important task. Roughly half of all the human body's energy use may be related to information processing, although it is often difficult to disentangle the processing of matter, energy and information within the body.

It is important to keep in mind the distinction between energy and information. A burst of adrenaline will increase our capacity for generating and using energy, but adrenaline itself is not energy, nor can it produce it. Adrenaline is a signal, part of the flow of information between organs, and acts via cellular receptors and second messengers to regulate the flow of energy through the cell machinery. Energy comes from food and oxygen, not adrenaline. Nevertheless, day to day we are concerned with boosting our energy levels, and for that adrenaline is at least as effective as food or oxygen, usually considerably more effective. Thus adrenaline (and many other hormones and drugs) are energy regulators, without actually providing any themselves.

Another level of control resides inside the brain itself, acting through nerves and hormones. Whether a muscle functions depends ultimately on the brain sending a message down a nerve to tell the muscle to start or stop contracting and how strongly to contract. Sometimes fatigue is caused by the muscle not working hard enough, sometimes by the nerves not working fast enough and sometimes it is the brain itself that is fatigued (so-called 'central fatigue'). The body may have plenty of energy and capacity to perform an action, but if the brain is tired, sleeping, or lacking sufficient motivation to carry it out, it may not happen. The brain can control some things directly by nerves and others indirectly by stimulating the release of hormones such as adrenaline. The nerves that go to the muscles are under your conscious control, but other nerves (part of the 'autonomic nervous system') going to the rest of the body, and are controlled by your unconscious brain. These nerves, partly regulated by the emotional brain, can accelerate or slow down some processes in the body, such as digestion or the heartbeat and can also cause the release of adrenaline or other hormones. There are, however, many important processes in the body, such as growth, over which the brain has little or no control.

So different factors limit energy production in different conditions and the whole process is regulated by hormones, the brain and complex cellular machinery. But how does this affect our lives? To increase our energy level it is important to know what is limiting that level in our particular circumstances, because most of the processes involved are not actually limiting, and therefore most of the drugs, vitamins, supplements and treatments will have minimal effect. If we are depressed or fatigued, then taking glucose or any other supplement won't solve our problem, because glucose is not normally limiting for our energy level. Similarly, if we want to improve sporting performance, we need to know what limits that performance. Training programmes can be designed to work on that particular limiting factor. But when we are ill or fatigued a new set of factors may limit our activities; we need to know what they are and how they are controlled before we can treat them.

ADRENALINE AND STRESS

You wake up suddenly in the middle of the night. You are alone in your bed, it's completely dark, and it sounds like someone is trying to break into the house. Is it a burglar creeping into your bedroom?

You are petrified and trapped: frozen into immobility. Your heart is racing. Blood drains from your skin and guts to supply the muscles tensed for flight. Your mind races over every possibility at breakneck speed. Is this a dream? The light goes on and it's Father Christmas standing at the end of the bed. And you remember you are Mrs Christmas. Every muscle fibre relaxes. Perhaps it *was* a dream.

How is it possible for an idea or emotion to have such a profound effect upon the body? For example, the heart rate of athletes preparing to start a race has been found to more than double, from sixty-seven to one hundred and forty-eight beats per minute, as the starting commands are shouted out, but before the race has actually begun. This dramatic change in body function was brought about by an idea, the belief the race was about to begin. How is this possible?

The alarm response to a demanding or frightening situation is known as the 'fight-or-flight' response, a term coined by the American physiologist Walter Cannon in the 1920s. Cannon was investigating the process of digestion in the gut of animals and used X-rays, then only recently discovered, to look inside the living body and visualize the process as it happened. He noticed that any stress caused digestion to stop abruptly, and became fascinated by how and why this happened. Alarm or danger caused a common set of responses throughout the body, including the gut, heart, blood, muscles and skin. All of the bodily responses were found to be controlled by a common system of nerves and messengers: the sympathetic nervous system which produced noradrenaline and adrenaline. The fight-or-flight response prepared the body for a demanding situation requiring a large energy expenditure. Cannon proposed that animals had two basic ways of dealing with threats: they fight or they flee. A rabbit depends on its ability to run away, while a lion depends rather on its ability to fight to stay alive and to obtain food. Whether we attack or retreat, our body needs a large amount of extra energy, and this needs to be redistributed away from the guts, skin and other organs to the muscles and brain, required for action. The alarm is triggered by a perceived threat or need as judged by the brain, and in humans the type of threat that triggers the response has expanded to include psychological and social stress. And this is not only triggered by emergency situations – adrenaline levels are rising and falling throughout the day in response to our situation, thoughts and feelings. For example, a mildly stressful situation such as public speaking doubles the adrenaline level in the blood, while laughing, the antithesis of stress, can lower the normal level of adrenaline. But this system was only designed to meet the needs of a short-term situation, which required large amounts of energy. It was subsequently discovered that chronic stimulation resulted in several debilitating effects on the body and this long-term response to demanding situations is called 'stress'.

The sympathetic nervous system is a network of nerves sending messages from the base of the brain to virtually all parts of the body. A parallel system of nerves, known as the parasympathetic nervous system, has essentially the opposite effect. It is activated at the end of the fight-or-flight response and results in its reversal. The two systems (the yin and yang of body energy) are collectively known as the 'autonomic nervous system' (ANS). The sympathetic system is the body's alarm system; when the brain detects a threatening situation it sends a message through this system to all parts of the body, telling them to get ready for action. Impulses arising in the brain rush through a network of tiny nerves, which branch off into the furthest recesses of the body. At these nerve ends, a messenger molecule is released: noradrenaline. Noradrenaline, and the related chemical adrenaline, are the alarm messengers of body and brain. Together they tell the body to prepare for strenuous physical activity, while noradrenaline also alerts the brain to prepare for intense mental activity. As we shall see in the following chapters, these chemicals may literally be the 'buzz' of excitement and fear. Noradrenaline and adrenaline then are the keys to unlocking body and mind energy. Normally, most of the body's energy is locked away to prevent wastage, but when the brain detects a need, it activates the sympathetic nervous system and uses its two keys, noradrenaline and adrenaline, to unlock the energy stores.

How does this work? One of the sympathetic nervous system's first actions is to stimulate the adrenal glands (located on top of the kidneys). This causes the glands to release adrenaline into the blood, which then circulates around the body. Noradrenaline and adrenaline are very similar molecules and their effects on the body are much the same. But one big difference is that noradrenaline is rapidly and locally released and speedily removed after its message is received by a tissue;

whereas adrenaline is released more slowly, circulating throughout the body, and is more slowly removed, so its action is longer lasting. Noradrenaline is classified as a neurotransmitter and adrenaline as a hormone, but their actions are the same. They both tell the heart to pump faster and harder; act on the blood vessels to redirect the blood from the skin and gut to the muscles and brain; tell the liver to release glucose; the fat stores to release fat; and the muscles to mobilize their energy stores, and prepare to contract.

You will recognize many of the physiological effects of noradrenaline and adrenaline release from symptoms of excitement, fear, sex, stress or hypoglycaemia. The heart beats harder and faster (in preparation for activity). The skin becomes pale, cold and sweaty (due to the blood being diverted away from the skin and increased sweating to keep you cool during potential activity), thus someone who is scared may look 'white as a sheet' and may break into a 'cold sweat' or have 'cold feet'. The muscles become tense (a 'freeze' response to avoid detection) or start shaking (due to increased sensitivity to contraction). There are 'butterflies' in the stomach and guts (due to diversion of blood and relaxation of the gut muscles, which may result in a messy expulsion of its contents). The halting of digestion saves blood and energy for the muscles, but also requires we stop eating, and appetite is suppressed (hunger vanishes when you're excited or afraid); the swallowing reflex is inhibited (it's difficult to swallow food); and production of saliva stops (you get a dry mouth). The bladder also relaxes, resulting in a need to urinate, annoying in excitement, but embarrassing in extreme fear. Possibly the emptying of the bowels and bladder evolved to aid running by rapidly reducing weight. The lungs breathe deeper and faster (to get more oxygen into the body). The mind races (to speed thinking) and becomes more sensitive ('jumpy' or 'nervous') to external stimuli (to detect threat).

It's a familiar idea that the rational, conscious mind can control the body through motor nerves acting on the muscles. But it is rather a surprise that the brain can also control the functions of the rest of the body, heart, liver, guts, skin, blood and immune system, through the sympathetic nervous system. On the other hand, this system is not controlled by the conscious mind, but by the emotions. They constitute an alternative control centre inside the brain regulating body functions.

People can, however, be trained to control the autonomic nervous system consciously using techniques such as biofeedback or yoga, and these techniques can be helpful managing both stress and relaxation.

Stress apparently is an unavoidable consequence of life, with a profound effect on energy levels. Many types of 'stressor', both physical and psychological, disturb the equilibrium of the body or mind, initiating a common 'stress response'. 'Stress' as a concept was invented by the Canadian scientist Hans Selye in the 1930s and 1940s. He found that certain challenges to an animal's equilibrium, such as cold, heat, infection, toxins or shock, if prolonged, always produced the same response. This included a decrease in the size of the thymus and other immune system organs, ulcers in the stomach and gut and enlargement of the adrenal gland. Selye argued that there was a common response to many types of stress and this stress response normally acted to defend the body, but chronic stress was harmful and caused the onset of disease. The stress response is mediated partly by adrenaline and the sympathetic nervous system, just as the 'fight-or-flight' response. But the harmful effects of stress are due to the long-term effects of chronic stimulation of this system, plus the actions of a separate stress system, known as the HPA (hypothalamus-pituitary-adrenal) axis and the hormone cortisol.

Selye divided the stress response into three phases: alarm, resistance and exhaustion. The alarm phase is identical to the fight-or-flight response, arising from an external or internal threat to the normal state of the body or mind. Normally the situation would then be rectified and the threat removed, so that all the changes caused by the response could be reversed by the parasympathetic nervous system. But if the threat remained and became a chronic stimulus, then the body made a number of adaptive changes – Selye called these 'resistance'. Finally if the threat still failed to recede after weeks, months or even years, the body entered a phase of exhaustion, when multiple organs of the body failed, causing characteristic stress-related diseases and possibly death. The threat sparking the response may be physical as in exercise, cold, and injury, or may be psychological as in the failure of a long-term relationship. The sympathetic nervous system is stimulated, noradrenaline and adrenaline are released and all the physiological responses already outlined occur. In addition another hormone, cortisol, is also released by the adrenal glands. Cortisol is a vital stress hormone, which complements the actions of noradrenaline and adrenaline, by both boosting their production and by making the body more sensitive to these hormones (stimulating cells to make the receptors that detect noradrenaline and adrenaline). Cortisol also stimulates the liver to produce glucose and the fat tissue to release fat, thus releasing energy for the body to use. Cortisol acts on the brain to enhance memory, and increase sensitivity to incoming information from the senses. Cortisol can also damp down the immune system and inflammation, and is used by physicians for this purpose. However, this is partly why chronic stress can decrease your resistance to infection and disease. Continuous stress leads to chronically high levels of cortisol, suppressing the immune system, and thus leaving you vulnerable to passing infections.

Another hormone involved in the stress response is beta-endorphin, which is released inside the brain, acting in the same way as opium or morphine, elevating mood and suppressing pain. This may be one source of 'runner's high', and more generally the reason that excitement can be pleasurable. Noradrenaline and adrenaline, cortisol, and beta-endorphin together co-ordinate the stress response.

In popular usage, the word 'stress' has a negative connotation, but Selye used it in a neutral sense to mean any challenging situation and our response to that, so stress could be good ('eustress') or bad ('distress'). Stress can be accompanied by positive emotions, the 'buzz' of excitement, or negative emotions, which are typically anxiety, fear and anger, as shown in the fight-or-flight response. The type of emotion engendered depends largely on whether the person involved sees the situation as controllable and predictable or out-of-control and unpredictable. For example, the physical stress of a voluntary run is entirely under the runner's control, but when pursued by a tiger the outcome may be neither predictable nor controllable, and thus results in very different emotions. During a roller-coaster ride, types of emotion may alternate, depending on how controllable and predictable the situation is perceived to be. More recently, stress has been categorized as either a reaction of defence or of defeat. A defence reaction occurs when the subject still believes the situation is controllable or is seeking to regain mastery of the situation (such as running from the tiger). By contrast, the defeat reaction occurs when the situation has gone out of the subject's control but the outcome is still unknown (such as being trapped or pinned down by the tiger). Again emotional and physiological responses are different in these situations. Negative, distressful emotions during stress cause much higher levels of cortisol, whereas stress accompanied by positive emotions causes little or no change in cortisol levels. As cortisol suppresses immunity, this is one way that a chronic negative mood can lead to infection and disease. In the next chapter we will see the many other ways the body and mind interact.

Stress is not all bad news – in the short term, whether in the form of excitement, anxiety or challenge, stress can be a Good Thing. The rise in adrenaline and noradrenaline boosts our energy levels and increases our physical and mental performance. Thus, if we fail to get excited, challenged or stressed by a difficult situation, we may not perform so well. It has been found that among those taking exams, the students who exhibit the largest adrenaline level increase tend to get the best exam results. And among Norwegian trainee paratroopers, those who had the largest adrenaline and noradrenaline increase when they made a trainee jump, also performed best when jumping from an aircraft, and in written tests. So as Nietzsche said: 'Believe me! The secret of reaping the greatest fruitfulness and the greatest enjoyment from life is *to live dangerously*!' (*Die fröhliche Wissenchaft*, 1882).

Chapter 10

MIND ENERGY

What on earth is 'mind energy'? It sounds like a touchy-feely, Age-of-Aquarius kind of idea. Can such a concept survive in the hard-headed, and hyper-technological twenty-first century? However we do know that the essential qualities required to succeed in work and life are motivation, spunk, drive, dynamism, ambition, sparkle, confidence, the ability to concentrate and work without rest, to think fast and coherently, in short 'energy'. Every head-hunting agency is searching for that elusive quality of energy within the heads it hunts to energize a corporation or enterprize. All around us, everyone is looking for that sparkle in friends and lovers to 'make things happen'. But even more, this search has internalized as everybody looks for that positive energy inside themselves, the motivation, drive and power to get up and do something; the endurance, stamina and resolve to complete the tasks we need to do, and the courage and will to change direction, to break out of the old routines, when necessary. We may know how to do something, but without the will and the energy, it is not going to happen. Without mental energy, there is no joy, excitement or enthusiasm. Mental fatigue is almost a modern invention; depression and mental exhaustion now appear epidemic in our society. We are surrounded by people crying out for more mental energy. But does this concept make sense in the light of the modern science of the brain? And if so, how can we use this new knowledge to inform our quest for mental energy?

THE ORIGINS OF MIND ENERGY

The conceptual split between mind and body seems older than history, originating in the distinction between the soul/spirit that survived death and the material body which did not. As history evolved along its unsteady course, the spirit gained an ethereal quality and retreated into the brain. The triumph of mechanical explanation in science emboldened its champions to attack the brain itself, attempting to evict the spirits of mind from the body's citadel. The birth of the energy concept in the mid-nineteenth century presented an opportunity for reconciliation between the ideas of dead matter and vital spirit. It was inevitable that this energy concept, so successful in physics and biology, would before long be applied to the mind itself.

The modern concept of mind energy originated with Sigmund Freud at the close of the nineteenth century, so our story of mind energy starts appropriately by following Freud's own story. *Fin-de-siècle* Vienna was a stage set for an epic scientific struggle. All the essential ingredients for a blockbuster are there: sex, ambition, drugs, embittered friendship and tragedy turned to triumph. Our three protagonists are a young, ambitious doctor, Sigmund Freud (1856–1939) and his older, more cautious friend, Josef Breuer (1842–1925), plus the enigmatic, young and beautiful Fräulein Anna O. The chemistry between these three produced a whole new science (or art); psychoanalysis; a new dimension to the mind – the unconscious; and two new forms of energy: mind and sex energy.

Freud started as a neurologist, studying the anatomy of the nervous system, under the great German physiologist, Ernst Brücke. Brücke was a founder (with Hermann Helmholtz) of the Berlin School of Physiology. Their movement sought to sweep the vital force out of biology and replace it with a deterministic science purely based on known physical and chemical forces. Helmholtz himself was one of the founders of the energy concept, and had used the concepts and techniques of physics to study the nervous system and perception. He had been the first person to measure the speed of signal conduction by nerves in frogs and men, and his finding that nerve conduction was actually rather slow (closer to the speed of sound than the speed of light) startled the scientific community. This implied that the brain itself was slow and that the world, as we perceive it in the mind is delayed, relative to the real, external world. Thus Helmholtz believed that the world as we perceive it is constructed by the brain. We start with the raw sense data supplied by the eyes, ears and skin, and this is then moulded into a perceptual form using 'unconscious inferences' supplied by the brain. Most of the brain's hard work is therefore unconscious and not open to conscious inspection. Freud was trained in this rigorous school of biological thought, based on hard physical materialism. Although his later ideas were based on psychological concepts not easily interpreted in terms of brain mechanisms, Freud always believed that his psychoanalytic concepts would and should be replaced eventually by physiological explanations in the terms of networks of neural excitation in the brain.

Giving up physiological research, Freud underwent medical training at Vienna General Hospital, and then went into private practice specializing in the treatment of hysteria. Hysteria was an interesting psychological disorder not generally recognized today, but seemingly prevalent in *fin-de-siècle* Vienna. Hysteria was in fact an ancient diagnosis of neurotic women. Hippocrates attributed it to the womb (in Greek, '*hystera*') moving into other parts of the body. For example, the hysterical symptom of a constricted throat was thought due to the womb's becoming lodged in the throat. Later, when the wandering womb theory was shown to be unfeasible anatomically, hysterical women were said to have an 'attack of the vapours' and these were thought to be noxious vapours from the womb that affected the brain. Unsurprisingly, in Viennese scientific circles dominated by Helmholtz's School of Medicine, hysteria was not regarded as a suitably scientific subject for study. However, Freud went to Paris to study with Charcot, a brilliant neurologist, who had made the study of hysteria and the use of hypnosis fashionable and almost scientifically acceptable.

Freud tried all the latest medical fads, including massage, hydrotherapy and electrotherapy, but they were all of little use in treating hysteria. Hydrotherapy is a medical treatment by external or internal application of water, originating in ancient Greece and Rome. It was particularly popular in the eighteenth and nineteenth centuries, when health spas sprang up throughout Europe. Darwin used hydropathy extensively to treat his disposition to 'excitement and fatigue' which was accompanied by vomiting, tremors, depression and spots before the eyes. He built a bathhouse and every day steamed himself into a sweat, then showered in cold water; this was followed by a cold bath in the garden and scrubbing with a cold, wet towel until his skin became red and raw. Darwin certainly believed that this radical regimen was essential to maintain his energy levels. Hydropathy is not so popular now for medical purposes, but most people still use hot and cold showers, hot and cold bathing, swimming and saunas to lift their spirits and boost their energy. Why such treatment should be effective is not clear, but the sharp drop in body temperature when going from hot water into cold causes the release of adrenaline and stimulation of the sympathetic nervous system, major controllers of body and mind energy.

Freud also tried electrotherapy on his first patients. Electricity was a very popular panacea in the 1880s and 1890s for all kinds of ailments, both physical and mental. But its origins are as ancient as those of hydrotherapy: the shock given by the electric torpedo fish was known to Hippocrates, and later Greek physicians applied the torpedo to the affected part of the body. This treatment was apparently particularly effective at curing headaches. In the eighteenth century, Volta's methods for generating and storing electricity enabled it to be applied to patients either in a static form or as a shock. Electricity, it was claimed, could cure all kinds of ailments. In 1729, a London surgeon, John Birch, treated a hospital porter suffering from melancholia by passing six small shocks through his brain on three successive days. The porter regained his spirits and went back to work, remaining well for several years. Thence ECT (electroconvulsive therapy) was born, although it was not widely used until the late nineteen-thirties. It remains today an effective treatment for severe depression, although no one really understands how it works.

Freud himself was not a well man. He suffered chronically from fatigue, nervousness, depression and other psychosomatic symptoms, such as diarrhoea. In the late nineteenth century this constellation of complaints was called 'neurasthenia', and was one of the most frequent psychiatric diagnoses. Asthenia is Greek for weak or listless and neurasthenia is a chronic weakness or listlessness of neural/psychic origin. Both name and diagnosis were devised by George Beard in the 1860s, who regarded neurasthenia as nervous exhaustion brought on by the pressures of modern civilization. Energy's recent discovery in physics and biology led to new concepts of physical and mental fatigue, rapidly becoming the obsessions of the late nineteenth century. Humans were thus seen to have a limited store of mental or nervous energy (known as *vis nervosa*) which was dissipated by modern life. The recommended cure was usually bed-rest and isolation; thus genteel women with 'nerves' were confined to their darkened bedrooms.

The diagnosis of neurasthenia is still used occasionally today for mildly neurotic depressives, but has mostly been replaced by 'chronic fatigue syndrome' or ME. Freud found cocaine relieved his own neurasthenic symptoms and recommended it as the treatment of choice for neurasthenia. Cocaine (and amphetamines) can indeed relieve some symptoms of depression and fatigue, but with long-term treatment larger doses are required, and the withdrawal of the drug causes an even deeper depression. Freud's enthusiastic advocacy of cocaine led to its widespread use: the subsequent discovery of cocaine dependency caused him acute embarrassment.

Freud also used hypnosis, a technique that can be traced back to Franz Mesmer, the controversial Viennese physician (1734–1815), whose name inspired the term 'mesmerism'. Mesmer used a type of hypnotism or suggestion on his patients, but attributed his powers to a hitherto unknown physical/psychic force, 'animal magnetism'. He described this force or fluid as permeating the universe and suggested that the human nervous system was somehow attuned to it. But an imbalance in animal magnetism inside the body could bring on nervous illness. Mesmer treated his patients directly by channelling animal magnetism through his own body to the affected part of the patient with a kind of laying-on of hands, and indirectly by 'magnetizing' iron bars or other objects, by touching them himself and the patient then used these objects to 'magnetize' themselves. In pre-Revolutionary Paris, Mesmer's treatment was highly fashionable, particularly with women. Patients were treated in groups, sitting around a large barrel full of water and magnetized iron filings, from which protruded iron rods, which each patient grasped. Mesmer, dressed as a magician, would magnetize his patients, to the accompaniment of soft music. So, there are striking parallels with both the modern laying-on of hands by psychic healers (such as in Christian Science), and the use of 'psychic energy' by new-age, esoteric therapies.

The scale of Mesmer's success caused a stir among conventional doctors and scientists, and the French Government eventually appointed a royal commission to investigate both his treatment and the existence of animal magnetism. This was chaired by Benjamin Franklin, and included Lavoisier and Guillotin (whose invention was later to claim Lavoisier's head), so clearly Mesmer's ideas were taken very seriously, although sceptically. The commission's 1784 report concluded that animal magnetism did not exist, and the success of mesmeric treatment was due to the power of human imagination. mesmerism was discredited and Mesmer himself vanished into obscurity. But the success of mesmerism did demonstrate the importance of 'powers of the imagination' and hypnotic suggestion for both medical and psychological treatment. Much of the success achieved by both the witch doctor and the modern doctor depends on the patient's belief that the doctor will cure him. This belief is aided by the modern doctor's white coat, medical terminology and scientific equipment, just as belief in the witch doctor is by his outlandish appearance, spells and religious paraphernalia. This powerful psychological factor in medical treatment is known today as 'suggestion' or the 'placebo effect', and gives a strong example of how the mind can heal the body, rather than the body the mind. The effectiveness of psychoanalysis may also be due largely to suggestion or the placebo effect, but if this were so, whether this would invalidate psychoanalysis is highly controversial. Freud would probably argue that the effectiveness of placebos in treating both physical and mental disorders presents further powerful evidence supporting his concept of the unconscious directing our lives.

Freud realized that knowledge of the brain's physiology and chemistry was advancing far too slowly to ever reach into its hidden depths. Confronted by the immediate problem of treating his patients, he used another route into the brain, which was to explore the psyche with the patients themselves. But as the patient's consciousness had limited access to the psyche, Freud developed various tricks, using hypnosis, free association and dreams to dig deeper into the murky world of the unconscious. He rapidly found the most effective treatment was the 'talking cure' (or 'cathartic method') developed by Breuer and his hysterical patient, Anna O.

Breuer's career had been similar to Freud's, only somewhat earlier. A successful Helmholtzian physiologist, then one of the most sought-after private physicians in Vienna, Breuer had always retained a wide interest in science. In 1880 he began the treatment of an engaging and beautiful twenty-one-year-old woman. Although her real name was Bertha Pappenheim, she has gone down in history as Fräulein Anna O, because her case history was reported under that name in Breuer and Freud's *Studies on Hysteria*, the work that launched psychoanalysis. She had developed a veritable museum of hysterical symptoms, including a nervous cough, disturbances of sight and speech, an inability to take food and the paralysis of three limbs. She also had a split-personality, one normal, the other a naughty child who existed in an altered, semi-hypnotic state of consciousness. In talking to her, Breuer realized each symptom was connected to a past traumatic experience. These symptoms could be resolved if she relived the experience and its emotions in a hypnotic or semi-hypnotic state. Anna O was highly intelligent and developed a technique of talking through her past experiences to relieve her symptoms, one by one. Thus the 'talking cure' (or 'chimney sweeping' as she called it) was born and remains the basis of psychoanalysis today. But Anna O's was a long and intense treatment requiring vast quantities of emotional energy from both patient and doctor. Breuer and Anna O never discussed sex or sexual matters and Breuer even believed her to be asexual. However, they clearly became engrossed with one another and Breuer's wife became morosely jealous. When Breuer realized the root of his wife's moodiness and the extent of his own emotional involvement with Anna O, he abruptly terminated the treatment. He announced to Anna O their relationship was over as she was ostensibly cured. Later that evening he was called back to her house in crisis. She had regained all her old symptoms and was in the throes of a hysterical childbirth, apparently caused by Breuer's attentions. Breuer calmed her down under hypnosis, and then fled the house. The very next day, he and his wife escaped to Venice for a second honeymoon. Or, at least, that is the story as told by Freud.

Freud and Breuer developed the theory that hysteria and other psychological disturbances were largely caused by repressed sexual drives or experiences. This was not received well in late nineteenth-century Vienna, mostly meeting with stony silence from the scientific community. Breuer bowed to the times, and it was only with great effort that Freud persuaded him to publish their mutual findings on hysteria. Freud was spurred on by the opposition, championing the sexual theory with ever increasing enthusiasm. Frustrated by Breuer's timidity and their relationship complicated by the many debts he owed him, Freud and Breuer fell out. Breuer then retired completely from psychoanalytic research.

Freud's emphasis on sex energy as an unconscious force led to him giving it a separate name – libido – the psychic drive derived from the sex instinct. The libido continuously charges experiences, day-dreams, and actions with a sexual edge. The evolutionary reason for this all-powerful psychic drive is obvious: the spreading of genes. But in a culture as sexually repressive as 1890s Vienna, the repression of the libido causes psychic havoc, as most thoughts and experiences charged with libido cannot discharge, festering instead in the unconscious, disrupting the conscious mind. Freud saw sex as the basis of most psychic disturbances. Hysteria thus was due to the repression of early sexual experiences: while neurotic anxiety was attributed to a failure to relieve an unbearable amount of sexual excitement, due for example to the practice of *coitus interruptus*, or the long engagement of a chaste but passionate couple. Similarly, neurasthenia was due to inadequate relief of sexual tension by autoerotic methods, such as masturbation.

Freud's interest in sex alienated many, including his two ablest pupils, Adler and Jung. But it had the opposite effect on the Austro-American, Wilhelm Reich, who made sexual energy the centre of his analytic philosophy. Reich declared that the discharge of sexual energy during orgasm was key for a happy, fulfilled life, but psychic blocks to the discharge of energy were manifested as muscular tension inside the physical body. Reich claimed to actually see this energy, which he called orgone energy, as blue particles under a microscope. He designed and built boxes, 'orgone energy accumulators', which people could sit in to accumulate and enjoy this energy. Reich inevitably became increasingly isolated and paranoid as his theories were rejected, and the FBI's investigation of his accumulators led to his imprisonment for fraud. He later died in prison. Reich's ideas live on, transmuted as 'Bioenergetics', a therapy devised by his American pupil, Alexander Lowen. Bioenergetics seeks to remove psychically-generated blockages of energy flow by treating muscular tensions in the body, to allow the full flow of orgasmic energy. Although Lowen's therapy has not been a particularly popular one, there has been increasing recognition of the utility of physical treatments for psychological problems, such as the use of exercise, massage and yoga to treat depression, anxiety and stress. Of course, as we have already seen, this idea of treating the mind through the body is a very old one, originating in ancient Greece, India and China.

Freud and Breuer's theory of psychic function and motivation was based on mind energy. According to this theory there are a number of unconscious drives, principally for food and sex, which provide motivation for all mental and physical actions. When a drive is active it motivates the person, causing a discomforting tension in association with the idea of the object of that drive. For example, when the body is short of food, the food drive causes a tension in association with the idea of food and we experience that tension as hunger pangs. We then seek to relieve that tension by hunting and eating food. These actions relieve the tension and we experience that relief as pleasure. This is what pleasure is: the relief of tension set up by the drives. The basic motivation for animals and humans is the pursuit of the pleasure we derive from relieving the tension, set up by the unconscious drives. Freud called this theory 'the pleasure principle'. The drives act as a *source* for the tension, which may be thought of as an excitation, charge or energy. The drive sources are located in unconscious parts of the brain (ultimately a group of neurons), or possibly the body (for example, the hungry stomach). But the *object* of the drive is a conscious idea (ultimately a different group of neurons in a conscious part of the brain). When the drive is operating it transfers a tension from the source to the object. Once this is conscious, the organism attempts to relieve the tension by discharging it, either externally or internally. Thus, when the sex drive is active, it acts as a source of discomforting tension that charges up some (sexual) idea. Relief of this tension can be obtained by sexual activity. The relief of tension is experienced as pleasure.

When an unconscious drive charges a thought, experience or area of the brain with energy, the process is known as 'cathexis', and when an area is overcharged, this was associated with discomfort. While 'catharsis' was the process of discharging that energy, associated with the feeling of pleasure. Normally the energy or emotional charge associated with an experience would be discharged by actions or thoughts prompted by it. But if the memory were repressed or the experience received in an abnormal state (such as hypnosis or fatigue) where it could not be discharged by the usual conscious processes, then the experience would remain charged in the unconscious, acting as a latent source of energy to excite and disturb conscious processes. Thus the therapeutic method invented by Breuer and Anna O and elaborated by Freud, of recovering and discharging emotionally charged experiences from the unconscious, was known as the 'cathartic technique'. This method and approach are the mainstays of today's psychotherapy and popular psychology.

Ultimately Freud and Breuer wanted to ground their psychological theory in the terms of biology and physics and talked initially of their drives and ideas in the terms of neurons and of the tension in terms of 'energy' or electrical excitation. Freud invented a law for this energy to follow, in analogy to the First Law of Thermodynamics. The principle of constancy asserted that the brain tries to keep the level of excitation constant (or at a minimum). However, Freud and Breuer's use of the concept of mind energy is an obscure and ambiguous one. In different contexts it refers to different things: metabolic energy, nervous excitation, emotional affect, attention, arousal and mental activity. Ultimately, their theory of drives, tension and catharsis is a psychological theory of motivation. It could not be grounded in terms of metabolic energy or electrical excitation: their use of the term 'energy' simply functions as a metaphor for psychological tension.

However, since Freud, two energy concepts have evolved in psychology: arousal and tension. Arousal is the general level of mental activity, waxing and waning with alertness or tiredness. Tension is variously described as anxiety, distress, psychological stress or negative affect, but is basically derived from Freud's theory of tension. Anxiety has been described as an acquired drive, as it can function as a Freudian drive producing tension, but is acquired by learning or experience. For example, I might be anxious about an exam and relieve the tension produced by revising, but this anxiety was not derived from the internal drives for food, water, or sex, it was rather acquired externally from my peers and society. Society has a rigid code for appropriate and inappropriate behaviour and we acquire a sense of what is approved and disapproved of at an early age from our parents and peers. Freud called this the 'superego', inducing anxiety and guilt when we violate society's standards or contemplate doing so, but also pride or satisfaction at 'doing the right thing' in society's eyes. Its partly conscious and partly unconscious nature made the superego potentially problematic as we may well be unaware of the source of our anxiety or guilt. Anxiety or tension, however, can be a good thing. Anxiety is the most important motivator to do things in society. Without it we might do very little, apart from fulfil our basic drives for food and sex.

To conclude then, we have two concepts of mind energy, neither directly relating to the body's metabolic energy, although, as we shall see, there are some connections. The arousal concept relates to the general alertness, sensitivity and vigour of the response of the nervous system. Arousal is well characterized at a psychological level and is firmly based in the brain's biology. The concept of tension is less well characterized, but refers to the stress, distress or anxiety brought about by a particular stimulus or drive.

AROUSAL AND TENSION

In a deep, dark valley beside a silent lake at the base of the brain, there is a small chamber, the hypothalamus, in which all the raging passions of mankind are contained and harnessed to drive us on. This small smudge of neurons, less than one per cent of the brain, is the drive centre of the mind. In the driver's hands are the two sets of reins (known, rather unpoetically, as the autonomic nervous system and the reticular activating system) by which it controls the body and the brain. These two systems are the central controls over body and mind energy respectively. They do not produce energy but rather aim to control it, as reins control a horse, sometimes spurring it on and at other times reining it back. When we are spurred on, body and mind are flooded with energy and we give full vent to anger or anxiety, fight or flight, passion or drama. When the reins are relaxed, we unwind and rest. And when drawn in further, we may fall asleep or into a depression.

The reticular activating system (RAS) is the brain's arousal system. When activated by the hypothalamus or incoming sensory information it alerts the brain, making it attend to the incoming information. It is an alarm system telling the brain 'Wake up, pay attention, something is happening'. But it also actively energizes the brain by spraying it with stimulant chemicals, making all the neurons more excitable, sensitive and faster responding. Without the activation of RAS, the brain hardly pays any attention to incoming information; with extra RAS activation the processing is faster and more focused. RAS wakes the brain and keeps it awake, controlling the sleep/wake cycle. RAS drives, and motivates, and is involved in compulsion and addiction. RAS regulates emotion, mood, excitement and euphoria. RAS is the system targeted by drugs such as amphetamines, cocaine, Ecstasy, LSD and Prozac. RAS is the mind energizer.

As we have seen before, the autonomic nervous system (ANS) is the arousal system of the body. It has two arms: the sympathetic nervous system, which energizes the body, preparing it for fight-or-flight, and the parasympathetic system, which relaxes the body after the passing of the threat. Activation of the sympathetic system causes the 'fight-or-flight' response, while chronic stimulation of the sympathetic system causes the stress response. Part of the stress (or rather distress) response is mediated by a separate system, the hypothalamic-pituitary-adrenal (HPA) system. This is a third rein by which the hypothalamus controls body energy and is particularly active in anxiety and depression. In distress, the hypothalamus sends a message to the pituitary, a tiny gland below it, and this relays the emergency message to the adrenal glands, which then release the stress hormone, cortisol.

Arousal is a key concept used by psychologists to refer to the generalized activation or energization of the nervous system resulting from some stimulus. Myriads of sensory messages continually enter the brain from the eyes, ears, nose, tongue and skin, generally passing through the brain relatively unattended. If the message is particularly strong, new or unexpected, then it sets off an alarm inside the brain, causing both generalized arousal and focused attention. The concept of arousal evolved from several different lines of research. The English neurophysiologist, Sir Charles Sherrington (1857–1952), found that pricking a dog's foot with a pin not only caused the reflex withdrawal of the foot, but also sensitized the dog to a whole range of other reflexes. A similar effect could be demonstrated in humans. People vigorously using their muscles responded more rapidly to a signal. It appeared that stimuli (such as a pin-prick) both evoked a specific response (such as a reflex withdrawal) and more generally alerted the whole nervous system, so it became more sensitive, responding much more vigorously to many (or all) other stimuli. The nervous system was thus aroused. And this arousal both increased responses to external stimuli, and enhanced sensitivity to the internal drives. Thus a rat given an electric shock would not only get annoyed, but also mate and eat more frequently than it would do otherwise. Similar sensitizing effects can be shown in humans. For example, many people who are stressed eat more. Both women and men were found to be more sexually aroused by an erotic film if, immediately before, they watched a vivid, gory film about car accidents. While the first film had no sexual content, its shock value caused general arousal, spilling over into sexual arousal when the second film was shown. J. G. Ballard's notorious book, *Crash* (and David Cronenberg's equally notorious film) are in fact based on just this auto-erotic premise – that car crashes and their victims become, and are seen as, sexy. Some kinds of sexual foreplay involve biting, pain or other forms of stimulation, which can lead to greater sexual arousal. Sadomasochism and auto-eroticism are well-known pursuits of those within our culture who find the elements of pain or humiliation essential for sexual arousal.

An ingenious, but infamous, test of the arousal concept was devised using two bridges spanning a river and one pretty woman. One bridge was five feet across, four hundred and fifty feet long, swaying danger-ously with a two hundred foot drop to the rocks below. Crossing this bridge was a high-anxiety, arousal experience. The other bridge, further up-river, was solid, only ten feet above a shallow river. Crossing this bridge was easy. The male subjects, who happened to cross one bridge, were met at the other side by a woman who asked them to help her with a psychology project. The men filled out a questionnaire and responded to a test, later scored for sexual imagery. Finally, the female experimenter gave every subject her telephone number, with the excuse that she would be willing to discuss the experiment if he wished. The men who crossed the low bridge scored low on sexual imagery, and only twelve per cent rang her. Whereas men who had crossed the high bridge scored high on sexual imagery, and a much more impressive fifty per cent rang. The interpretation of these results was that the frightening experience of crossing the high bridge had heightened physiological arousal, enhancing sexual arousal and resulting in the men being more attracted to the woman experimenter. Perhaps this research has relevance to the sex-lives of politicians. Henry Kissinger once said that power was the greatest aphrodisiac; and the experiences of some recent American Presidents tend to confirm that a high-adrenaline life can lead to a more highly sexed life.

Arousal increases attention, concentration and performance and can arise from many sources, for example anger. Martin Luther King once said:

> 'When I am angry I can write, pray, and preach well, for then my whole temperament is quickened, my understanding sharpened, and all mundane vexations and temptations gone.'

Supporting evidence for the existence of a generalized arousal system in the brain came from the electrical stimulation of the base of the brain and from recording the electrical activity (brain waves) from its surface. Electrical stimulation of the RAS in the brain stem resulted in generalized arousal in animals: they would wake up (if asleep), raise their heads, open their eyes and look around alertly. If this system was damaged, the animals were drowsy, lethargic and unresponsive. Thus, this part of the brain is a general arousal or alarm centre, telling the rest of the brain 'Wake up! Pay attention! Something interesting is happening! Prepare to investigate and do something about it!'

The effect of arousal centre stimulation on the higher areas of the brain can be monitored using an electroencephalogram (EEG). EEG is an almost magical method for listening to the brain waves coming from the surface without having to open the skull. Electrodes are painlessly attached to the scalp's surface and record the electrical activity below. EEG was first used on humans by the German psychiatrist Hans Berger in 1929. He was very excited to discover various types of brain waves coming from his subjects' brains in different states, from relaxation and sleep to full arousal. Berger thought that these were due to a new form of psychic energy, or as he called it, P-energy. He believed he had discovered the secret of ESP (extrasensory perception) and worked in great secrecy for five years. Eventually, he was dismissed by the Nazis and became clinically depressed, finally committing suicide. Although Berger was wrong about P-energy, he had discovered something of great importance to brain function. The waves of electrical activity he observed were due to the synchronized oscillation of millions of neurons at the surface of the brain. All these neurons were firing in synchronized bursts or waves, so when all active at the same time, they produced a large electrical signal that could be detected on the scalp's surface. This was not so in all psychological states. When the subject was asleep or awake but relaxed the brain waves were large and slow, but when the subject was aroused or attending to something they became small and rapid. It was as if, when the brain was occupied with a task, all the various neurons had to do different things, so their activity was no longer synchronized. Whereas, when the brain was relaxed and not doing much, all the neurons went back into synchronicity once more because they were not separated by their own tasks of information processing. Stimulation of the arousal centre at the base of the brain causes the synchronized oscillation to break up into small rapid waves. Thus, the arousal centre does seem indeed to act as an alarm telling the rest of the brain to wake up and get cracking.

So, can we have too much or too little arousal? Several lines of evidence suggest that too much or too little arousal can both make us unhappy and make us carry out various tasks poorly. Extremely high levels of arousal, such as for example with high levels of fear, noise or pain, impair mental performance, thinking becomes chaotic and there is a high level of anxiety. There may well be an optimal level of arousal for any particular circumstance or task. Too little arousal, and we have insufficient mental alertness to perform well. For example, early in the morning or late at night it can be difficult to focus on and process relevant information. Too much arousal, and the increased sensitivity to stimuli and increased rate of thinking may lead to mental overload and an inability to concentrate. Flight controllers monitoring incoming flights at an airport have, for example, been known to suffer from a type of sensory overload, causing a loss of attention and concentration on the task at hand. The same equally applies to sportsmen, actors, soldiers, businessmen and secretaries: a certain level of arousal is essential for optimum performance, but an adrenaline overload will inevitably cause problems.

We might expect people to feel relaxed and happy when their arousal level is low, but the opposite appears to be the case when people are deprived of all stimulation for any extended period. Donald Hebb and his students at McGill University in Canada first studied the effects of sensory deprivation in the 1950s. Students were paid a substantial sum of money to lie in bed and do nothing for as long as they could. This might seem like a student's idea of heaven, but they were also sensorially deprived so they could not see, hear or feel anything. The students were fine for about a day, but then lost the ability to think straight or concentrate. After forty-eight hours they could not do simple mental arithmetic, began to see vivid images and hallucinations and were desperate for any form of stimulation, however banal. All found the experience very unpleasant, and though paid substantial sums of money for each day, most were desperate to escape after a maximum of two or three days. Hebb concluded from this and other studies that we have an innate drive for arousal and stimulation – we find under-arousal or boredom unpleasant and so seek out potential stimuli to arouse us. But over-arousal can also be unpleasant, and Hebb proposed that our response to increasing arousal followed the shape of an inverted U – hence the inverted U-curve of arousal. If feelings are plotted against level of arousal, then at low arousal we feel bad (bored), we feel better as arousal increases, and feel happiest at an optimum level of arousal, but as arousal continues to increase beyond the optimum we start to feel bad and anxious. This inverted U-curve of feelings versus arousal is also found for performance versus arousal.

Our drive for arousal seems innate. If the arousal level is too low, we experience unpleasant feelings of boredom and frustration: whereas when arousal is optimal it stimulates reward pathways in the brain, making us feel good, even euphoric. Arousal stimulates neural pathways, releasing neurochemicals that make us high: the same pathways that are stimulated by cocaine, amphetamines and heroin. This is why we like being excited. Evolution appears to have primed us to seek out stimulation. This is part of the reason we find ourselves reading books and newspapers, going to movies, socializing, snowboarding and climbing mountains. If, say, we are bored on a Sunday, we will seek out anything to tickle our neurons, even if it's yesterday's newspaper, read twice already.

Just as chronically low levels of arousal and stimulation are unpleasant, so are chronically high levels, but in a different way. Chronically high arousal is linked with anxiety. Anxious people are in a chronic state of high arousal. This does not mean they are always highly aroused, but that they are more sensitive than others to real and potential situations or threats, causing them to be aroused more often, to a higher level, and stay so for longer. Anxiety is not just a state of hyperarousal, however, it also involves seeing the world negatively. A very high level of arousal is not necessarily unpleasant – it depends how it is viewed, in particular on whether the situation is thought under control or out of control. Imagine a roller-coaster ride: you are looking down a particularly vertical drop – you can anticipate the fall but your fear is under control; when you begin to drop – the situation and your fear are massively out of control – both body and brain are flooded not just with adrenaline and noradrenaline, but also with the stress hormones cortisol and endorphins, which prepare you for disaster; eventually (seemingly a million years later) you hit the hill's bottom and the tension is released as laughter, the situation appears to be under control again and the remaining adrenaline and endorphins produce a rush of euphoria – until the next time. A similar emotional roller-coaster ride can be provided by rock-climbing or a horror movie. Arousal may be continually high, but we can switch abruptly from euphoria to intense anxiety and back again, depending on whether we perceive the threat as controllable or not. If we perceive the threat to our well-being as out of our control, we become anxious, releasing the stress hormones so damaging to long-term health. Chronic anxiety is like living permanently on a roller-coaster with an uncontrollable fear of heights.

Not everybody seeks out the same level of arousal. Some people are sensation seekers – so-called adrenaline junkies. They have an apparent need of a higher level of arousal to feel good and seek it out in social contact, sex, sports and more dangerous pursuits. Sensation seekers may start from a lower arousal baseline and are thus seeking more or may be less anxiety-prone and consequently can sustain a higher level of arousal. For whatever reason, the sensation seeker attempts to maintain an arousal level higher than the average person, and considerably higher than that of the sensation avoider. The sensation avoider is the inverse of the adrenaline junkie. They have a low optimum arousal level, where they feel happiest, and this is either because their arousal baseline is already high or because they are anxiety-prone, so even moderate levels of arousal promote anxiety. So sensation avoiders evade situations and social contact that may push arousal levels above their low optimum.

Background arousal and the level of arousal people seek, is one of the more fundamental aspects of human personality. The controversial British psychologist Hans Eysenck argued in the 1960s that the essential difference between extroverts and introverts was that extroverts start from a lower background level of arousal and thus seek much more stimulation to maintain themselves at a higher optimum level of arousal. Introverts start from a high arousal baseline and seek minimal stimulation or eschew stimulation completely in order to maintain a low optimum arousal level. Since social contact is a key source of arousal, extroverts seek social contact, while introverts may avoid it or seek less arousing or anxiety-provoking types of contact.

Hans Eysenck's life was one full of sensation, and, from his own criteria, it seems likely that he was a sensation seeker. Born in Berlin during the First World War, Eysenck left Germany for England on the Nazis' rise to power. He became a professor of psychology at London University studying the basis of personality and intelligence. An outspoken critic of psychoanalysis, he was one of the pioneers of behavioural therapy. He also believed that intelligence was almost entirely genetic, and therefore that racial differences in intelligence were genetic too. This, understandably, caused intense academic and public controversy, which continues today. However, his contributions to the theory of personality and the central role of arousal remain intact.

Eysenck's theory was extended by Gray and Kagan in the 1980s to elucidate the biological basis of anxiety. Gray proposed that there was a pathway in the brain, which he called the behavioural inhibition system, functioning during a perceived threat to inhibit ongoing behaviour and redirect attention towards the potential danger. The behavioural inhibition system of people with chronic anxiety had a higher activity, and thus they were chronically inhibited with their attention focused on potential threats. The brain pathway involved in this system overlaps partly with that of the RAS and is activated by arousal, but also includes brain areas controlling behaviour, attention and emotion and so has more specific effects on the brain. It has often been argued that arousal is intimately connected with attention. With low arousal, the mind is relaxed, brain waves are slow and deep and thinking is broad and diffuse, but when arousal is high the mind becomes focused, concentrating on the task at hand. A certain level of arousal is necessary to concentrate as is obvious when we need to read and understand something late at night. But very high levels of arousal cause a reorientation of attention, away from thinking, towards the perception of potential threats, and result in a hypervigilant state accompanied by intense worry. This may have been an advantage for our caveman, where threat detection was more important than general thinking, but it can be a nuisance for the overloaded modern executive lying awake at night, contemplating potential threats in the urban jungle.

Jerome Kagan, a Psychology Professor at Harvard, has studied the nature of timidity in children. He discovered that some children are inclined to approach unfamiliar objects and people, and others are not. He called these uninhibited and inhibited children. These children are not two ends of a spectrum of behaviour, but two distinct types of people, each with a distinct genetic origin. A major difference between inhibited and uninhibited children is their level of autonomic arousal (ANS and adrenaline); inhibited children have a higher arousal level, just as Eysenck's theory predicted. Kagan argues that inhibited and uninhibited children possess different thresholds for excitability of the brain's emotional centres (the so-called 'limbic system' and in particular the 'amygdala'). Inhibited children have emotional centres more easily excited, and activate the hypothalamus to alert the ANS and

RAS, thus causing arousal, which in turn may activate the behavioural inhibition system resulting in inhibition. In short, inhibited children are more nervous. And in the main inhibited children start as inhibited babies and grow up to be inhibited adults. Inhibition is the basis of shyness, introversion and timidity. Kagan believes timidity is a genetic disposition, although learning and thought alter its expression. There is, in fact, considerable evidence indicating anxiety is, at least in part, inherited. For example, one study found the level of anxiety much more similar in identical twins (sixty-five per cent) than in non-identical twins (thirteen per cent). The upshot of this is that anxiety is closely related to arousal and different people have varying levels of arousal and anxiety due partly to how sensitive their emotional or arousal systems are.

Your hypothalamus is located just above the roof of your mouth. The multiple smudges of neurons that make it up lie on either side of a dark lake, the third ventricle, within which in Classical times the animal spirits were thought to swim. The hypothalamus is the drive centre of the brain, controlling hunger, thirst, lust, anger and arousal. But it does not evoke these passions arbitrarily like a Greek god. The hypothalamus rather resembles Blake's vision of Isaac Newton as a cold scientist, measuring and taking the measure of everything, and calculating how much 'what is' deviates from 'what is desired', then producing the appropriate amount of drive to correct the gap between 'how things are' and 'how things should be'. The hypothalamus does indeed take the measure of almost everything occurring in body and mind: it measures the food, fuel, salt and water content of the body by monitoring the contents of the blood. It compares these values with predefined target values and adjusts the drives of hunger and thirst to nudge the real values closer to the target. It measures the body temperature, and like a thermostat, sends messages to regulate our heat production or dissipation appropriately. This body thermostat can be adjusted slightly by conditions such as illness, hence body temperature can increase in fever, as the hypothalamus also monitors illness through chemicals released by the immune system. The hypothalamus contains a clock, the body clock, to keep track of what time of day it is, and adjusts our level of arousal and our sleep/wake cycle to keep time. But the hypothalamus doesn't just monitor the body, it also keeps track of the mind. In particular it is connected to the brain's emotional centres, which surround it like a pair of cradling hands. The hypothalamus sees the world through a fog of emotion. Sensory information from the eyes, ears and body passes through the thalamus (the gateway through which the sensory information enters the mind), and then either goes on up to the rational mind in the cerebral cortex on the brain's surface, or to the emotional mind surrounding the brain's core. Within the emotional centres (once called the limbic system), sensory information is compared to emotional memory to determine whether it has any relevant emotional content, such as 'scary', 'delicious' or 'sexy'. This emotional labelling will often require the rational mind's help, so there is often a lot of to-ing and fro-ing of information before a label is settled on: but if rapid action is required the emotional centres can decide for themselves. If body and mind need to be alerted and aroused, if for example the emotional centres perceive a dangerous threat, then the hypothalamus is activated to raise the alarm through the ANS in the body and the RAS in the brain. In a sense the hypothalamus works by monitoring the brain's emotional tone, just as it monitors the body's physical tone, acting to correct any deviations from the norm by sending signals to other areas of the brain. The hypothalamus is the drive centre of the brain, managing all the passions, but these passions are not blind.

THE PSYCHOLOGY OF ENERGY

How do body or mind energy relate to *feeling* energetic or tired? Does the feeling of being energetic actually correspond to the body or brain having more energy? We might know all there was to know about the mechanics of energy supply in body and brain, but this will be useless unless it can impact on our feelings of energy, arousal, tiredness and fatigue. This is vitally important because if we knew what feelings of energy and tensions corresponded to in our body and brain, we would be better able to interpret their message, or to combat them better. In this section we will look at the extremely practical but apparently nebulous subject of everyday emotions and moods. Recent psychological research has indicated that feelings of energy and tiredness are central to everyday moods, and has come up with some very practical ways of regulating our psychological energy level.

So what do you mean when you say you feel energetic, or lack energy? You could be referring to a subjective feeling; or to your capacity to do things; or even to your desire to do things. And for each category you might be referring to either your body or your mind. An energetic body and mind is and feels different to one that is tired. The body, including our muscles, skin, gut and heart, is full of sensory nerves telling the brain how it is feeling. These detect the local tension, stretch, pressure, pain and chemistry, and continually inform the brain about the tone of the body. And we in turn interpret these signals in the terms of feeling energetic or tense, or tired and fatigued. But feelings are not all there is to feeling energetic – we may also mean our capacity to do things: such as, our capacity to run up a flight of stairs without weariness, or to concentrate, thinking rapidly and clearly without fatigue, or to work, play or socialize. This is our capacity to do things now, irrespective of any learned or innate ability. So we are not talking about skill, but energy. Our ability to achieve these things waxes and wanes during the day, and through our lifetime: when we assess that we can do them we say we have lots of energy, when we think we can't we say we are tired or lack energy. But the capacity to do something is not all that is necessary, we also need to want to do it. Energy often refers to our general level of motivation or drive. If we are full of energy then we are enthusiastic, full of plans and desires, we want things and we want to do things. When we lack energy, then we don't want anything, and don't want to do anything, except perhaps to go to bed and turn out the light.

The nature of emotions and feelings, and their relation to bodily arousal has been central to the history of psychology. The father of psychology, William James (1842–1910), proposed the astonishing hypothesis that emotion simply is our bodily behaviour and our perception of that behaviour. James, brother to the novelist Henry James, was one of the greatest American psychologists and philosophers. He explained his counter-intuitive hypothesis thus:

'Common-sense says, we lost our fortune, are sorry and weep; we meet a bear, are frightened and run; we are insulted by a rival, are angry and strike. The hypothesis here. . . is that we feel sorry because we cry, angry because we strike, afraid because we tremble . . . Without the bodily states following on the perception, the latter would be purely cognitive in form, pale, colourless, destitute of emotional warmth. We might then see the bear, and judge it best to run, receive the insult and deem it right to strike, but we should not actually *feel* afraid or angry.'

Carl Lange proposed a similar theory at about the same time, emphasizing the arousal-induced changes in the circulatory system, for example, increased blood pressure, and our perception of these. Consequently, the theory that emotion is our perception of our body's responses became known as the James-Lange theory of emotion. Their hypothesis suggests that what we feel as emotion is simply the perception of our own behavioural and physiological responses to arousing stimuli. More modern versions of the theory emphasize the responses of the sympathetic nervous system, which produce sweating, the pounding of the heart, and tension in our stomach and guts. We feel these, and that feeling *is* the emotion. When your stomach churns before an important exam, it is part of the feeling of anxiety, as is your clammy skin and pounding heart. Tension in neck and jaw muscles is an essential part of feeling 'tense'. Feeling our muscles contracting while we run forms part of the sensation of being energetic. The sense of fear is made up by the accumulation of our pounding heart, churning stomach, trembling limbs, dry mouth and clammy skin. When we feel these things then we know we are afraid.

This really is a counter-intuitive theory because it suggests that emotion comes *after* our response to a situation. We see a threat, our sympathetic nervous system is automatically activated causing a pounding heart etc., and the emotion comes then as we perceive these responses. So emotion does not make these things happen – it is rather the awareness that they are happening or have happened.

Modern versions of the James-Lange theory have also emphasized the face. Charles Darwin analysed the evolution of emotion partly in terms of facial expression, showing that humans and other animals adopt a characteristic expression for each emotion. Thus the expression of emotion is, at least in part, a product of heredity, rather than culture. Modern researchers have made the surprising discovery that simply by adopting a particular facial expression, we experience the corresponding emotion. Thus, if we adopt a sad face we become sad, if we put on a snarl we become angry and if we smile we become happy. This seems too ridiculous to be true, but this finding has been repeated many times. It has even been suggested that people can learn to regulate their subjective feelings by controlling their facial expressions. It's hard not to feel cheerful when you are smiling. Try it now.

The James-Lange theory was subsequently severely criticized by Walter Cannon. An American physiologist, Walter Cannon (1871–1945) became head of Harvard's Physiology Department at about the time that James retired. Cannon pointed out a number of experimental findings inconsistent with the James-Lange theory. Firstly, that people continue to feel emotion even after the nerves connecting the stomach and guts to the brain are cut. The sensations from the organs are lost, but the emotions of anxiety remain. Secondly, that the response of the body's organs is simply too slow to account for the immediate emotions we experience in threatening or anger-arousing situations. Thirdly, that although our emotions vary widely, the response of the sympathetic nervous system to all kinds of arousal is very similar. Fear and anger both activate the sympathetic nervous system, producing a stereotyped response in the body. But if emotion is just sympathetic arousal or our perception of its effects, how do these different emotions feel so different?

Since Cannon made his objections it has been discovered that actually slightly different bodily responses do occur in association with different emotions, thus partly undermining Cannon's final objection. But direct experimental tests of the James-Lange Theory have also been made. Subjects were injected with adrenaline, the fight-or-flight hormone, which causes most of the physiological responses to sympathetic activation. If fear or anger were the reactions to these physiological responses, then adrenaline injection should also produce fear and anger. But although the subjects reported sensing the physiological responses, they felt little or no feeling, except a kind of 'cold' emotion – as if they were afraid or angry. But none of the subjects mistook the cold emotion for the real thing.

The theory that Cannon proposed to replace the James-Lange theory located emotion in the neuronal circuits of the brain, rather than in the body. He suggested that emotion-provoking stimuli activated emotional centres located in the base and centre of the brain. These centres then did two things: they activated the sympathetic nervous system and thus the body, and secondly they activated higher brain systems, which evoked emotional experience. The emotions were not actually located in the emotional centres, rather these centres acted as drive sources activating neuronal circuits in the cerebral hemispheres on the brain's surface, and these circuits evoked the conscious experience of the emotion. Different emotion centres could activate different circuits, and thus produce different emotional experiences. Thus, according to Cannon's theory, arousal caused emotional experiences in the brain, differing according to circumstances.

Later scientists altered his theory by suggesting that generalized arousal might contribute a dimension of intensity to the emotional state, or the behaviour that expresses it. Thus arousal did not correspond to a particular emotion of 'arousal' but rather to the increased intensity of whatever emotion was involved. So an aroused state of sex, fear or anger did not share a common feeling of arousal, but rather the fact that they were high intensity states, which were felt or expressed strongly.

Many of today's psychologists accept a compromise between the James-Lange and Cannon theories of emotion. They see emotion as consisting of both perception of and sensation from the body, including the face, and the perceptions and sensations derived from the brain itself. However, modern theories also emphasize the roles of motivation and thinking in emotion.

So is anxiety merely a more extreme form of arousal? Probably not. A variety of evidence indicates that positive and negative emotions are entirely different systems. Psychologists analysing people's descriptions of their emotions have concluded that positive and negative emotions are entirely different dimensions of feeling. There is also evidence from the emotional effects of drugs. Anxiety can be effectively treated by benzodiazepines and other drugs that act on GABA (gamma-aminobutyric acid) receptors in the brain, but these drugs have relatively little effect on arousal or alertness. This suggests that anxiety is not simply an excessive level of arousal. However, it remains true that excessive arousal often causes anxiety and that there is a close relation between these two states.

An emotional state of tension is accompanied by tenseness of the body, as the sympathetic nervous system, reticular activating system and adrenaline all cause the muscles of the body to increase their tension by contracting slightly. Stress results in a prolonged state of tension, which can damage our muscles and cause headaches. Part of what we mean by being tense is the perception, through our sensory nerves, that our body, as opposed to mind, is tense. The muscular tension partly constitutes or causes the emotion. This is why relaxation techniques often concentrate on easing the muscles, because this will relax the mind. Massage and movement therapies, such as yoga, also aim to treat stress by the removal of muscular tension.

Muscular fatigue is different from muscle tension, and partly constitutes what we mean by feeling fatigued, tired or low in energy. Fatigued muscles feel different because they have a different chemistry and tension and many sensory nerve fibres in the muscles convey this information back to the brain. Fatigued muscles become acidic because of the production of lactic acid, and have a high level of potassium outside the cells because it is expelled during contraction. A fatigued muscle may contract or relax more slowly, or have a lower tension when fully contracted. We can detect all these properties in our muscles because they are full of nerves sensitive to tension, stretch and chemicals. Damaged or inflamed muscles ache because of the stimulation of pain receptors. In vivid contrast to fatigue, the activation of the sympathetic nervous system and adrenaline release causes increased muscle tension or tremor and increased sensitivity and force of contraction. Sensing these changes, we may feel more powerful, vigorous or strong.

However, the symptoms of sympathetic stimulation – increased heart and breathing rate, sweating, stomach cramps and high tension in the neck, jaw and other muscles – may be interpreted either in terms of energy, tension, anxiety or stress depending on what we are thinking and feeling in our brains at that time. Sensations in the body are interpreted in the context of what is going on in the brain. There is no obviously distinct feeling in the mind which accompanies arousal or vigorous mental activity, there is rather an increased intensity of thought or feeling. Although alarm, tension, fear and anxiety do all involve distinct subjective emotional feelings. Sleepiness, drowsiness and tiredness are also accompanied by vague but characteristic feelings, although when we describe ourselves as sleepy we are probably judging our mental capacities, as well as our feelings.

The judgement of ourselves as energetic or tired is thus often a complex assessment, and we probably use different criteria in various circumstances. This involves not only judging our sensations (from body and brain), but our capacities (of body and mind), and even our motivation. And energy is a relative term, so we judge our energy relative to what we expect, or what we have felt in the past. So different people, or the same person in different circumstances, may judge the same state differently.

So, given we can judge ourselves as energetic, tense or whatever, in what conditions do we actually do so? Robert Thayer, professor of psychology at California State University, has analysed the origin of everyday feelings of energy, tension and stress simply by asking people to rate whether they feel energetic or tense in different circumstances. He distinguishes four basic moods that we encounter every day: calm-energy, calm-tiredness, tense-energy and tense-tiredness. Calm-energy is the ideal, good mood where we feel energetic and aroused, but without any tension or anxiety. Calm-tiredness is how we might feel after exercise or before bed, tired but relaxed. Tense-energy is how we might feel when working on an important project, aroused and full of energy but with some anxiety or edge. Some people (type A personalities and adrenaline junkies) find this mood pleasurable, and seek it out in dangerous pursuits, thrilling films or hard business. Tense-tiredness is the classic bad mood, where we are anxious or stressed, but without the energy to deal with it. Young children at the end of the day, before feeding, often end up in this mood, often crying or throwing tantrums. Adults in a similar situation will be susceptible to anger, arguments, pessimistic thoughts and depression.

What determines how energetic we feel? Thayer identified a number of crucial factors. Firstly, there is a daily rhythm of energy. By asking people to rate how energetic they feel on a scale of one to five, at different times of day, and averaging the results over a number of days, Thayer found that there is a basic energy cycle. People generally feel low in energy when they get up in the morning, but their feelings of energy increase continuously reaching a peak in the late morning; energy then generally dips during the mid to late afternoon, peaking again in the early evening, declining to a minimum before going to sleep. Of course, not everybody has the same rhythm, some are morning people and others night owls. But generally this basic rhythm means we are best able to cope with difficulties in the late morning or early evening, and least able in the early morning, late evening and mid to late afternoon. We are most likely to fall into a tense-tired (i.e. bad) mood when a stressful situation coincides with a day's low energy phase. We may be overly optimistic during our energy peaks and overly pessimistic during the troughs. So, Thayer recommends getting to know your own daily energy cycle and assessing your present thoughts, feelings, relationships and decisions in terms of where you think you are in your energy-tiredness dimension.

Another important factor influencing how energetic we feel is exercise. But we need to distinguish between its short and long-term effects. Thayer has found that if people take a brisk walk for as little as ten minutes, they immediately report feeling more energetic, and this energizing effect lasts for at least an hour after the exercise. This is a dramatic effect that anyone can easily self-administer to increase their energy levels. But the immediate mood effect of low-level exercise is rather different from the consequences of intense or long-term exercise. Half an hour of aerobics results in an immediate feeling of fatigue, but often substantially increases feeling of energy an hour or so later. A long-term exercise programme, increasing our fitness level, also causes an enduring improvement in how energetic we feel. Exercise is one of the most effective treatments for depression and anxiety. Many studies have shown that an exercise regime decreases clinical depression, and, in fact, is as effective as a programme of psychotherapy. Similarly, other studies have shown that exercise lessens both acute and chronic anxiety. Taking into account the physical health benefits, exercise would seem to be a panacea, but unfortunately our motivation to exercise is often lacking.

Food seems to have a significant effect on our subjective feelings of energy, although there is little scientific evidence linking food to mood, except in relatively extreme conditions. Semi-starvation has been shown to cause chronic feelings of tiredness in a controlled study on conscientious objectors during the Second World War, and there have been similar findings on famine victims. A low blood sugar level causes tense-tiredness in people, particularly diabetics, who cannot control their blood sugar level properly. Whether this occurs in ordinary people, after – say – missing a meal, has been more difficult to prove, although there is some circumstantial evidence for a mild increase in tense-tiredness. Certainly, most people believe that fasting causes tiredness and/or tension and that food reverses these feelings. This may well be an important motivation for eating or snacking. Thayer has studied the mood effects people report after eating a candy bar, averaged over a large number of such experiments. Immediately after eating the bar, subjective feelings of energy increased as expected, but an hour later the energy dropped to levels below those before eating and the feeling of tension was increased. The immediate energizing property of high-sugar snacks or drinks may be what motivates us to use them when tired. However, we do need to recognize that beyond the immediate positive response, there may lurk a medium-term energy-draining effect of sugar. A heavy meal makes many people feel drowsy and obese people often report feeling tired. The multiple effects of food on mood are obviously complex and difficult to disentangle.

The impact of illness on energy is more clear cut. Healthy people feel more energetic than sick people. Many surveys have shown that the most common complaint doctors hear is fatigue and lack of energy. For example, a study by Dr Buckwald and his colleagues of five hundred medical patients seen in a general health centre near Boston found that thirty-seven per cent reported feeling very tired, often for months before seeking treatment. People who feel energetic generally are healthy, whereas people who feel tired all the time are ill or will soon be ill. Many illnesses lead to decreased feelings of energy. Jane Dixon and her colleagues at Yale assessed the health status and mood of more than three hundred nurses, discovering that their reported energy level had the highest correlation with general health status. Moreover, energy was the best predictor of both physical and psychological health over time. So, feelings of energy may act both as a symptom of present health and as a predictor of future health or illness.

Sleep, or lack of it, obviously has an impact on how energetic we feel. Our need for sleep follows a daily cycle, matching the daily cycle of our feelings of energy. This endogenous cycle becomes obvious if we abruptly change the time at which we sleep, as when we fly through several time zones. This results in jet lag as our body clock continues to generate a twenty-four-hour cycle, of energy followed by tiredness, which does not coincide with the day and night of our new location. Sleep disorders and deprivation can also cause fatigue. Research has suggested that up to one-third of all Americans may be suffering from sleep disorders resulting in significant daytime tiredness.

There may also be a seasonal cycle of energy, although there is, as yet, no direct evidence for this in the general population. However, some researchers believe that five per cent or more of the population suffer from seasonal affective disorder (SAD). This is a moderately debilitating depression, usually occurring during winter. It is characterized by inactivity, anxiety, weight gain, carbohydrate craving, increased sleep and sleepiness and decreased libido. SAD can be treated by light, and this has led to the theory that the disorder is due to light starvation in wintertime and this may in turn affect melatonin secretion within the brain. Melatonin is a brain hormone secreted mainly in the dark, regulating the sleep-waking cycle. However, there are many other theories attempting to explain SAD, and it is still unclear whether SAD is a real disorder or a medical artefact.

Various other factors influence perceived levels of energy, including social interaction and drugs. Many people report using social interaction as a method of mood regulation; that is if they are feeling tense or low in energy they will phone or visit other people to improve their mood and make themselves happier. Several studies have shown that this can be a successful strategy, and furthermore that people with a high level of social interaction generally have a more positive mood. On the other hand, it seems unlikely that people who are depressed, anxious or socially introverted would automatically benefit from increased social interaction. Caffeine, nicotine, cocaine and amphetamines all increase subjective feelings of energy and many people use them, consciously or unconsciously, to regulate their energy level. However, energy levels then decline below normal levels after use, and repeated use requires higher and higher levels to get the same effect.

Finally we should note Thayer's finding that people's judgement of their present energy level affects both what they choose to do in the present, and their assessment of their capacity for the future. We therefore adjust our tasks depending on how much physical or mental energy we think we have. When we get sluggish during the day or tired in the evening we naturally switch to less demanding activities, such as chatting to friends, watching television or listening to music. If we are mentally fatigued but unable to switch from a task requiring a lot of energy, if for example we have to meet a work deadline, then inevitably the sympathetic nervous system will be stimulated, leading to an increased supply of energy, but also an accompanying feeling of tension and anxiety. In such circumstances we may seek out sugar, caffeine or nicotine to boost our energy levels, but as these remedies cause a medium to long-term drop we may be better taking a brisk ten-minute walk. When in an energetic mood, we may project this assessment of our capacities into the future, committing ourselves to tasks that we may have insufficient energy to fulfil. For example, in a good mood we may agree to take on a new commitment or relation-ship, start an exercise programme, stop a bad habit, or just go to a party, but may be overly optimistic about how much mental and emotional energy we will have when these commitments must be fulfilled. By contrast, when we are low in energy or depressed we may shy away from any future commitment requiring physical, mental or emotional energy. In this case, we may be overly pessimistic about our future capacities, potentially leading to a downward spiral in the quantity and quality of our activities. Thayer's suggested solution is to attempt awareness of your own mood cycles and then make a realistic assessment of your future capacities, not solely based on your present mood.

Chapter 11

BRAIN ENERGY

THE MIND AND ITS MESSENGERS

The nature of the mind is humanity's most profound mystery. This is a mystery of gargantuan proportions, stretching back millennia, reaching out from the centre of the brain to the edge of the Universe, and one inducing vertigo and depression in some of the world's greatest philosophers and thinkers. However, this vast vacuum of ignorance is penetrated by several rays of knowledge, which will help us understand how mind energy is regulated.

Although we may not know what the mind is, we know a lot about the brain. It consists of a spaghetti of electrical wires, snaking through a mass of neurochemicals. There are perhaps one hundred thousand million neurons in the human brain, each receiving electrical input from about a thousand neurons, and contacting and talking to perhaps one hundred other neurons. Imagine one hundred thousand million telephone exchanges all talking to each other, blending and merging the different telephone messages they receive, and each sending the result out to hundreds of other exchanges. The input into this multitude of messages comes from the senses detecting the external and internal environment, and the output is then sent to the muscles to direct what we do and say. So the brain is like a massive computer, performing a series of computations on the information from the senses, and then sending a final output to the muscles. But, unlike a computer, the amount of material going in and out is dwarfed by the internal activity. If we stop all sensory input and motor output, the brain is hardly less active. We are still thinking, feeling and processing information when we rest and close our eyes.

The unit from which all the brain's fabulous activities are constructed is a brain cell, the neuron. Neurons are fantastically branched and extended cells, but minute. So it was very difficult to find out whether the neurons in the brain were physically continuous, forming one giant networked cell, or whether the walls (membranes) of neurons were discontinuous, giving separate cells as in the rest of the body. This issue, obsessing scientists at the end of the nineteenth century, was only resolved by the discovery by Camillo Golgi (1843–1926) that individual neurons could be stained black, throughout the entire cell, by the soaking of brain tissue in a silver chromate solution, now known as the Golgi stain. This produced delicately beautiful images of the tree-like structure of individual neurons within the brain. However, Golgi himself believed that these images indicated that the neurons were continuous with each other, forming a vast network akin to the vascular system of the blood. It was only when the Golgi stain was taken up by Santiago Ramón y Cajal (1852–1934) and used in a masterly series of experiments, that the neuron hypothesis of anatomically separate cells was finally established. Although Golgi and Cajal shared the Nobel Prize in 1906, they remained deadly rivals to the end.

If all the one hundred thousand million neurons of the brain are anatomically separate from each other, how could the electrical messages passing through the individual neuron jump from one neuron to the next? The answer is that they don't, but something else does; and this is of central significance to how the brain functions. This discovery was made by Otto Loewi, working in Austria in the 1920s. Loewi was working on the neural transmission from the brain to the heart, via the vagus nerve. He isolated a frog's heart with its vagus nerve intact, and showed that stimulation of the nerve caused the heartbeat to slow. But Loewi wanted to know how the electrical message in the vagus nerve was transmitted to the heart. Was it an electrical or chemical connection, or something else all together? The critical experiment proving that this connection was chemical was when Loewi took the solution that bathed the heart after the stimulation of the vagus nerve, and applied it to a second beating heart, and showed that this chemical solution was itself sufficient to slow the heart. This demonstrated for the first time that stimulated nerves release a chemical at their ends, which mediates the transmission of the message from one cell to the next.

The inspiration for this historic experiment was a recurring dream, described below in Loewi's own words:

'In the night of Easter Sunday, 1921, I awoke, turned on the light, and jotted down a few notes on a tiny slip of paper. Then I fell asleep again. It occurred to me at six o'clock in the morning that during the night I had written down something most important, but I was unable to decipher the scrawl. That Sunday was the most desperate day in my whole scientific life. During the next night, however, I awoke again, at three o'clock, and I remembered what it was. This time I did not take any risk; I got up immediately and went to the laboratory, made the experiment on the frog's heart described above, and at five o'clock the chemical transmission of the nervous impulse was conclusively proved . . . Careful consideration in daytime would undoubtedly have rejected the kind of experiment I performed, because it would have seemed most unlikely that if a nervous impulse released a transmitting agent, it would do so not just in sufficient quantities to influence the effector organ, in my case the heart, but indeed in such an excess that it could partly escape into the fluid which filled the heart, and therefore be detected. Yet the whole nocturnal concept of the experiment was based on this eventuality, and the result proved to be positive, contrary to expectation.'

Thus, electrical nerve impulses pass to the end of neurons, where the impulse's arrival causes the nerve ending to release a chemical (a neurotransmitter), which crosses the narrow gap between two neurons (the synapse), and the chemical then acts on the second neuron to change its ability to, in turn, fire nerve impulses. Each particular neuron will release only one type of neurotransmitter (usually), but will release it to many different neurons. There are two main neurotransmitters in the brain: glutamate and GABA. Glutamate acts on the second neuron to increase its likelihood of firing a nerve impulse (and thus is an excitatory transmitter); whereas GABA acts to decrease the likelihood (and is an inhibitory transmitter).

But a neuron does not receive a single input from a single neural synapse, it receives many thousands. Tens of thousands of synapses from thousands of different neurons cover the branched surface of a single neuron. If released, transmitters acting at each of these synapses either increase or decrease the likelihood of the neuron firing. The neuron listens democratically to these many small voices, each telling it to fire or not to fire, and then based on the overall balance of opinion either fires or does not fire an impulse to other neurons (or if already active fires faster or slower). Thus the neuron sums up the information supplied by other neurons, through the input synapses, and sends a message through its output branches (axons) in the form of nerve impulses. A nerve impulse is a single electrical signal which travels down the axon like a wave. The rate at which a neuron fires impulses (the number of impulses travelling down the axon a second) depends on the sum of the excitatory and inhibitory inputs. These nerve impulses then again stimulate neurotransmitter release at the ends of the axons, where they synapse onto many other neurons. The amount of neurotransmitter released depends on the number of nerve impulses arriving at the nerve endings a second (the activity of the neuron). Moreover, the amount of neurotransmitter released determines how effective it will be at exciting or inhibiting the activity of the next neuron. A single neuron thus integrates information about the electrical activity of many input neurons, and this influences its own electrical activity, which is then sent to many other output neurons. A neuron, or network of neurons, can thus integrate information from many sources, including the senses, memory and emotions, to control its output signal, which may eventually cause a muscle to contract or relax.

Glutamate is the brain's main neurotransmitter, but is paradoxically also a powerful toxin for nerve cells. Low levels of glutamate act as a signal between neurons, but excessive levels of glutamate overexcite and kill them. This 'excitotoxic' action of glutamate appears to be the cause of neuronal death during strokes and neurodegenerative diseases, such as Alzheimer's, Parkinson's, and multiple sclerosis. Glutamate is one of the most common food additives in the form of its salt, monosodium glutamate (MSG). It acts as a flavour enhancer and is ubiquitous in Chinese cooking: soy sauce is a particularly rich source of glutamate. Luckily glutamate in the gut and blood barely penetrates into the brain, because the 'blood-brain' barrier prevents glutamate crossing from the blood into the brain. However, there is a medical condition known as 'Chinese restaurant syndrome' which may result from eating too much glutamate-saturated food, where the glutamate levels in the blood are so high they penetrate the brain, causing neuronal death. However, recent research has indicated that this syndrome maybe a myth. GABA is a chemical closely related to glutamate. It acts as the yin to glutamate's yang in neurotransmission: whilst glutamate stimulates or excites neurons, GABA inhibits or calms them. In fact, drugs with a calming or depressing action on the brain generally act through the GABA system. Barbiturates, the active principle in sleeping pills and benzodiazepines, such as Librium or Valium which reduce anxiety, act, for example, by enhancing the action of GABA at its neuronal receptor. Alcohol, too, may exert part of its magical effects on the brain by stimulating GABA receptors on the surface of brain neurons, generally slowing and calming the nervous system, but also having a disorganizing effect on neural information, which leads to disinhibition.

Although glutamate and GABA are the neurotransmitters mediating virtually all the brain's information traffic, there are many other neurotransmitters and neuromodulators in the brain, which modulate this traffic. Two neuromodulators central to the control of brain energy are noradrenaline and serotonin. These different neurotransmitters appear to act on two different dimensions of brain energy. Noradrenaline controls arousal, attention and excitement within the brain. Thus amphetamines (speed), cocaine and other stimulants work mainly by stimulating the brain's noradrenaline pathways, whereas serotonin controls mood, happiness and euphoria. Thus Ecstasy (MDMA), Prozac and LSD probably work mainly by acting on the brain's serotonin pathways. So, noradrenaline is the brain's own speed, while serotonin is the brain's own Ecstasy.

Most of the brain's neuronal networks act through conveying information rapidly to precise locations, so each neuron may send impulses to between a dozen and a few hundred other neurons. This is essential if information, such as visual information, is to be retained, while being quickly processed. However, the noradrenaline and serotonin systems of the brain act in a radically different way. A few neurons from a tiny area at the base of the brain send axons to a vast number of other neurons throughout the brain, releasing the neuromodulator diffusely, acting slowly but over a much longer period. Thus, these diffuse systems do not carry detailed sensory information, but rather perform regulatory functions, modulating vast assemblies of neurons so that they become more or less excitable, or more or less synchronously active, as well as controlling the flow of information into and out of the higher brain areas. Their function is akin to the volume or bass controls on a radio, which while not affecting the lyric or melody of a song, nevertheless regulate the impact of both.

As we have seen, the noradrenaline system of the brain is central to brain energy, and regulates both arousal and attention. Most noradrenaline neurons arise from a tiny spot (in the brain stem where the spinal cord meets the brain), known as the *locus coeruleus*. *Locus coeruleus* is Latin for 'blue spot', and indeed that is its appearance when the brain is cut at this point, due to the presence of blue pigments. This 'blue spot' is one of the brain's most remarkable structures. In human brains, it contains only about ten thousand neurons, but these few neurons reach out to virtually the whole brain, touching in some estimates one-third of all neurons in the brain – that is a few billion. Thus, each noradrenaline neuron may regulate up to a quarter of a million others, through a vast number of very long axonal branches. Electrical recordings from electrodes implanted in the 'blue spot' of awake rats and monkeys show that it becomes most active (and thus releases most noradrenaline) when the animals are presented with new and unexpected stimuli, when the brain needs to be aroused. The spot is least active when the animal is resting and there is nothing going on in the environment. Thus the *locus coeruleus* is the brain's fire alarm, which alerts the rest of the brain to the fact that something new and unexpected has happened, spraying the brain with noradrenaline to make it more alert and work faster.

Noradrenaline is, of course, also the alarm signal of the body, as well as the brain, when dispensed by the sympathetic nervous system. As we saw in previous chapters, the sympathetic nervous system is activated by emotional centres in the brain during crises, signalling to the rest of the body with noradrenaline and adrenaline to prepare for high-energy use. The noradrenaline system of the brain can thus be regarded as a branch of the sympathetic nervous system which acts to alert the brain, increasing its energy levels and preparing it for action. So there is an integrated system for increasing energy levels in both body and mind.

Serotonin, the brain's own Ecstasy, is controlled from a cluster of neuronal centres known as the *raphe nuclei*. *Raphe* is Greek for ridge or seam and the nine nuclei form a ridge through the centre of the brain stem, close to the blue spot. Neurons in this ridge send axons throughout the brain, where they release serotonin. As with the blue spot and the noradrenaline system, the neurons of the *raphe nuclei* fire most rapidly when we are awake, aroused and active. The neurons are least active, thus releasing least serotonin, when we are asleep: for both the noradrenaline and serotonin systems are intimately involved in regulating our cycles of sleep, waking and dreaming. Both these systems also regulate mood by sending signals to the brain's emotional centres, but serotonin and noradrenaline regulate different aspects of our mood. Noradrenaline promotes a feeling of vitality and power – typical of stimulants – but also anxiety and fear. Serotonin appears to promote a more subtle feeling of well-being and suppresses aggression. We might characterize noradrenaline as the hard man of the brain, and serotonin as the hippie. Drugs which stimulate both systems give a feeling of euphoria and can be used to treat people suffering from depression. Prozac specifically targets the serotonin system and can be very effective in relieving depression.

The link between serotonin and aggression has been investigated in unfortunate laboratory rodents. Male mice or rats on their own in a small cage for four weeks often become extremely aggressive towards other mice, and there is a simultaneous decrease in the serotonin activity of their brains. Only those mice who show a drop in serotonin levels also manifest an increase in aggression. Female mice do not show changes in serotonin or aggression during isolation. Moreover, drugs that block the synthesis or release of serotonin increase aggression, resulting in, for example, increased attacks on mice by rats. Recently new DNA technology has been used to produce transgenic mice that lack one particular type of serotonin receptor. Serotonin, like most neurotransmitters, has several different types of receptor, which sit on the cell surface and are activated by the neurotransmitter, but each receptor sends a different signal inside the cell to change its function in different ways. Mutant mice lacking the serotonin receptor were indistinguishable in normal conditions, but when placed in a stressful situation, such as having a new mouse placed in their cage, they were far more aggressive. The benefits of producing a race of super-aggressive mutant mice are not apparent, but perhaps this research will have some eventual application to human aggression if we can find drugs activating just this serotonin receptor, and thus calming overaggressive individuals.

Two other neurotransmitters are important in regulating the overall activity of the brain. Acetylcholine, the neurotransmitter that activates our muscles to contract, is also present in the brain, and seems important in memory formation. Dopamine, which is chemically very similar to noradrenaline, is involved in reward pathways in the brain. What are reward pathways? They reward the mind for doing what the drive centres and our genes want us to do. In a real sense, they are the goal and meaning of life. One of the most basic principles of psychology is that humans (and animals) are motivated to perform actions that produce positive (good) feelings. This mechanism helps us learn to do things promoting our survival and that of our genes, such as finding food and sex. Over forty years ago, James Olds stuck an electrode in an area of a rat's brain he subsequently called a reward centre. Electrical stimulation of this area appeared to induce happiness, and the rat would enthusiastically learn a variety of tricks to receive this electrical stimulation as a reward. In an ingenious twist to this experiment, Olds put a lever in its cage, so that when it pressed down on the lever the rat could stimulate the reward centre itself. The rat ended up spending all its time pressing the lever, ignoring food and sex. The same centres and pathways appear to exist in humans. Inserting electrodes into the brains of severely depressed patients has shown that stimulation of reward pathways, generally – but not always – produces very positive feelings in humans. The reward pathway consists of a relatively small number of nerve cells that send axons and electrical signals from one part of the brain to another releasing the neurotransmitter dopamine. Drugs such as cocaine, heroin and alcohol stimulate this pathway and cause dopamine release, and this may in part explain why taking these drugs is 'rewarding'. The downside to this reward is that when these drugs are withdrawn, the activity of the brain's reward pathway is dramatically reduced well below normal. So, to a person withdrawing from these drugs, nothing may appear pleasurable or rewarding – except the drug itself. This may well be the basis of our addiction to cocaine, heroine, alcohol and nicotine. The addict is in a similar predicament to the rat in his cage, ignoring the rest of life because he has a short cut to nirvana.

But the reward pathway is not merely relevant to drug addicts, it may be one of the central motivating mechanisms inside all of us. Paul Grasby and his colleagues at Imperial College, London recently found that this pathway was activated in people playing video games. As subjects navigated a tank through enemy bunkers, positron emission tomography (PET) was used to monitor the amount of dopamine released within their brain's reward pathways. The subjects were also motivated with an external reward: £7 ($10) for each game level completed. Grasby found that not only did playing the game cause dopamine release within the subject's brains, but that the amount of dopamine released correlated with the individual's success playing the game. Thus, even quite mundane activities, if associated with some kind of benefit, can stimulate the brain's endogenous reward pathway, perhaps providing the psychological motivation to initiate and maintain these activities. The pathway may be part of the mechanism for drives in the brain, using both a carrot and a stick to motivate us to perform activities that stimulate the pathway. The carrot would be a feeling of pleasure or reward that may accompany stimulation of the pathway; while the stick would be the reduced activity of the pathway, and associated displeasure, when we withdraw from performing the activity. Perhaps, then, we are all like rats in cages trying to stimulate parts of our brain for rewards. But on the more positive side, both rats and humans can be trained and untrained to associate different things with reward. And humans, to some extent, have a choice as to what thing or activity they train (or untrain) themselves to associate with reward. We just need to choose wisely.

BRAIN STIMULANTS

In every culture and every age, humans have sought 'magic' substances to boost the energy levels of mind and body. Ever since history began, quacks, charlatans and sorcerers have been peddling tonics, pep pills and stimulants to power up the brain, so that today we have an impressive arsenal of mind-altering drugs which increase mental performance. Stimulants are drugs with an alerting effect, improving mood and quickening the intellect, and therefore potentially increasing mental performance and relieving depression. Legal stimulants such as nicotine in cigarettes and caffeine in coffee, tea and cola drinks, are used all the time to regulate mind energy at optimum level. Illegal stimulants such as cocaine and amphetamines differ from legal stimulants in that they promote euphoria but at the price of dependence. But stimulants are interesting not only for their potential to boost brain energy, but also for the light they throw on the nature of mind energy.

Cocaine is a drug with a fascinating history. Today, it is one of the most expensive and sought-after drugs in the world, used regularly by about four million people in the USA, costing about forty billion dollars a year. This promotes a huge, illegal international trade, which finances some countries, while destabilizing and devastating others. But the coca leaves, from which cocaine is extracted, have been used for their stimulant properties by the Andean Indians for over a thousand years. The leaves produce essentially the same effects as the crystalline extract, but, as the leaves are chewed, the cocaine inside is only slowly released and absorbed into the blood through the gut. Thus the psychoactive effects of the leaves are more gradual and less intense than the pure powder, normally inhaled or injected.

The Inca civilization of Peru regarded coca as the gift of the Sun god, claiming that:

> 'God's angels have presented man with the coca leaf to satisfy the hungry, provide the weary and fainting with new vigour, and cause the unhappy to forget their miseries.'

Initially the Incas restricted its use to the royal classes and priests, but over time its use spread widely. This process was speeded up by the Spanish conquest, as the Spanish were much impressed by the ability of this leaf to increase the work and endurance of the captive Indians. Spanish chroniclers noted:

'This herb is so nutritious and invigorating that the Indians labour whole days without anything else, and on the want of it they find a decay in their strength.'

Hence the Spanish were keen to encourage the use of coca by the Indians, particularly when working the gold mines at high altitude.

Coca did not enter Europe in substantial quantities until the mid-nineteenth century, and then it was largely due to a Corsican chemist, Angelo Mariani. He popularized coca by developing products which used extracts of coca, including coca lozenges, coca tea and coca wine. The last of these was Vin Mariani ('the world famous tonic for body and brain'), which rapidly became Europe's most popular beverage. Promoted as both wine and medicine, it was a heady mixture recommended by doctors throughout Europe and America for everything from a sore throat to clinical depression. No wonder late nineteenth-century ladies and gentlemen drank Vin Mariani with enthusiasm, as it combined a pleasantly intoxicating wine with an invigorating dose of cocaine, and the whole package came with a strong medical recommendation. What more could a man ask for! Mariani was hailed as one of the great citizens of Europe and awarded a special medal by the pope.

Vin Mariani's success inspired a Georgia pharmacist, John Pemberton, to invent in 1886 Coca-Cola. The original preparation contained an alcoholic wine, and was described as a 'French wine of coca, ideal tonic', recommended as a stimulant and headache remedy. However, this was not successful and the wine was rapidly replaced by an extract of the kola nut, a source of caffeine. This new Coca-Cola was advertised as 'the intellectual beverage and temperance drink'. Soda water was added in 1888, producing the 'Classic' form of the drink, except that of course it still contained cocaine. This was removed from Coca-Cola in the early twentieth century, when its addictive properties were appreciated, and replaced by higher levels of caffeine. The stimulant properties of present day Coca-Cola and other cola drinks are mainly due to this caffeine, as well as to the high levels of sugar.

Cocaine was purified from coca leaves in 1860 and this marked the start of the trouble. Coca and coca extracts had been used for hundreds of years without causing any obvious psychological dependence on the drug or any apparent negative side-effects. But purified cocaine was different, and this difference was only slowly appreciated. One of the most influential advocates of pure cocaine was Sigmund Freud. As a young neurologist in 1884, Freud borrowed the large amount of money required to purchase the pure drug, and tried it on himself and many of his friends and patients. He found that the drug boosted his energy and virility, and banished depression. He wrote to his fiancée Martha on hearing that she had lost her appetite:

'Woe to you, my Princess, when I come I will kiss you quite red and feed you till you are plump. And if you are forward you shall see who is the stronger, a gentle little girl who does not eat enough or a big wild man who has cocaine in his body. In my last severe depression I took cocaine again and a small dose lifted me to the heights in a wonderful fashion. I am just now busy collecting the literature for a song of praise to this magical substance.'

Freud did indeed write a long scientific paper eulogizing the medical and stimulant properties of cocaine, and recommending it for a variety of purposes. This resulted in a much more widespread use of cocaine: it was widely prescribed for the relief of anxiety and depression, and Freud basked in reflected glory.

However, it was gradually discovered that cocaine was psychologically addictive. Freud's close friend Fleischl became uncontrollably addicted, and Freud found him one evening in a critical state, with delirium tremens, imagining white snakes crawling all over his skin. Freud spent the night with his friend – the most frightful of his life. The glory of cocaine was unravelling, reports came in from all over the world that it was addictive, toxic, and useless for all medical purposes, save as a local anaesthetic. Cocaine was denounced as 'the third scourge of mankind', along with alcohol and morphine. And, to Freud's chagrin, the credit for discovering cocaine's local anaesthetic properties went to a friend, to whom he had suggested this possibility. So, Freud missed out on fame and, crestfallen, went into private practice. The father of psychoanalysis later tried to play down this episode, suppressing a paper where he had recommended cocaine's intravenous injection. But his own cocaine use may have inspired some of his early theories of psychoanalysis.

Pure cocaine has been abused throughout the twentieth century, but its widespread illegal use really took off in the 1980s, particularly in America, so that today the international trade in cocaine is among the largest of any commodity in the world. Cocaine is inhaled, injected or smoked, resulting in euphoria, exhilaration, increased energy and suppressed appetite. But excessive use causes extreme restlessness, irritability, anxiety and occasionally paranoid psychosis. How does cocaine exert these mind-altering effects? Essentially by stimulating the noradrenaline system of the brain. Part of the cocaine molecule is of a similar structure to noradrenaline and another neurotransmitter dopamine, so it binds to the proteins mediating the effects of these neurotransmitters in the brain. It appears that cocaine both pushes these neurotransmitters out of the nerve terminals and blocks their uptake by the terminals, so there are greatly increased levels of noradrenaline and dopamine in the synapses. So, the net effect is a stimulation of the brain's noradrenaline system, which as we saw in the last section causes alertness, euphoria and increased energy.

Amphetamine has a similar stimulant effect to cocaine, but the story of its development is rather different. That starts with the search for effective treatments for asthma in the 1920s. Asthma's real cause is still unclear, but the source of the symptoms is a chronic lung inflammation constricting the bronchial tubes, resulting in wheezing and difficulty in breathing. The most effective treatment of asthma in the early 1900s was adrenaline, which causes dilation of the bronchial tubes, and thus relieves the symptoms. Unfortunately adrenaline is not effective when swallowed, and had to be injected into the blood, and could thus only be used as an emergency treatment. Chemists sought to make a derivative of adrenaline that might be taken orally, but success was limited. Then in the early 1920s K. K. Chen, a pharmacologist working for the Lilly Drug Company, began to investigate a plant called *ma huang* (*Ephedra vulgaris*). Chen was fascinated by Chinese herbal remedies, and noticed that *ma huang* was frequently used as a treatment for asthmatic wheezing. He obtained a plant extract and showed that it did indeed cause dilation of the bronchial tubes. He then (with other chemists) set about isolating the active ingredient and named the resulting chemical, ephedrine. Ephedrine was effective in relieving wheezing when taken orally, rapidly becoming the most popular drug treatment for asthma.

Unfortunately ephedrine had to be isolated from *ma huang*, and supplies of this plant rapidly became limited. The solution was to chemically synthesize ephedrine, and in the course of such attempts, a Los Angeles chemist, Gordon Alles, in the mid-1930s, synthesized a closely related chemical, amphetamine. Amphetamine proved an improvement on ephedrine, because it could be prepared in a volatile form, which could be inhaled directly into the lungs. The volatile form of amphetamine was marketed under the brand name, Benzedrine, and quickly became a very popular asthma treatment in the late 1930s and 40s. Benzedrine inhalers became widely available over the counter, and the drug-abusing public rapidly discovered that if the inhaler was opened and the contents ingested, a rapid 'high' could be achieved.

Psychologists at the University of Minnesota inadvertently contributed to the spread of amphetamine abuse by testing and reporting the effects of its ingestion on students. They noted that the drug prevented sleepiness and 'pepped up' those who were weary. News of the drug's energy-enhancing effects rapidly spread through the students by word of mouth, and many students acquired amphetamine from drug stores, using it to prevent sleepiness and fatigue in preparation for examinations, and to speed the brain during the exams.

Amphetamine was used to such an extent by the armed forces involved in World War Two that this could well be described as the first drug-enhanced war. The British routinely dispensed tablets to their soldiers, and although the Americans did not, they obtained them easily from the British army doctors. The Germans supplied their bomber pilots with amphetamines to keep them alert during all-night raids over England. The Japanese provided amphetamines not just to the military but also systematically administered it to civilians involved in wartime industries, to increase their productivity. After the war, amphetamine was advertised in Japan for the 'elimination of drowsiness and repletion of the spirit', and the Japanese were in sore need of such sustenance, by 1948 five per cent of all Japanese between sixteen and twenty-five were dependent on it, and the world's first amphetamine epidemic was under way.

In the late 1960s, hippies and addicts used LSD and amphetamine in combination to achieve a higher high. Amphetamine began to be injected intravenously to give a more rapid rush of euphoria: this was often described as a 'whole-body orgasm'. Amphetamine, like cocaine, reduces fatigue, sleepiness, hunger and depression, inducing euphoria and vitality, but withdrawal after overuse results in the opposite effects, so the user compulsively seeks out larger and larger doses to avoid the depressive crash. Also like cocaine, amphetamine has a similar structure to noradrenaline, and acts on the brain by stimulating the noradrenaline system.

Alcohol is not a classic stimulant, but at low levels it does have a stimulant effect on the brain. Moderate levels, however, depress brain activity, causing the psychological disinhibition of behaviour, which can reduce anxiety and increase sociability and sexual interest. High doses cause motor dysfunction and can cause the blood glucose level to fall dangerously low. This is because alcohol inhibits the liver's glucose production.

Possibly the most commonly used drug to boost energy is nicotine. Within ten seconds of taking the first drag on a cigarette the EEG shows a change to more desynchronized brain waves, indicating a more alert, less relaxed mind. The tobacco plant is native to the Americas, and was probably first used by the Mayas of Central America. It was smoked in tubes by the Caribbean Indians when Columbus arrived in 1492, and was introduced into Europe soon after. Nicotine mimics one of the main neurotransmitters in the brain and body, acetylcholine. It binds and stimulates the receptor for acetylcholine on neurons and muscle. The result is arousal in the brain, and a fight-or-flight response in the body, which causes an immediate kick of energy. Nicotine can also increase concentration, learning and memory. The increase in arousal caused by nicotine is short-lived relative to that of other stimulants, and is inevitably followed by a period of decreased arousal. High doses of nicotine just cause a lessening of arousal. Nicotine's downside is that the brain adapts to it, so that higher and higher levels are required to achieve the same effect, and if it is withdrawn brain stimulation is much lower than normal, and the consequence is addiction. In addition, other components of the cigarette (tar and nitrogen dioxide) cause lung damage and cancer; carbon monoxide poisons the blood making it less able to carry oxygen; and the blood vessels are damaged increasing the danger of heart disease. The overall effect of longterm use is substantially reduced energy.

Another very popular, but much milder stimulant is caffeine, which is found in coffee, tea, cola drinks and chocolate. Coffee was probably first cultivated in Arabia at about the time of Mohammed. According to legend, an Arab goatherd noticed his goats became frisky after eating the berries of wild coffee bushes. He told some monks who then collected the berries and made a brew, which kept them awake during the long hours of prayer. Visiting pilgrims travelling to Mecca then tried this new drink, and word soon spread of its stimulating properties. Yet coffee was not extensively grown in the Middle East until the fifteenth and sixteenth centuries. In sixteenth-century Egypt, it was declared illegal because of its intoxicating effects, and the coffee houses were burned down. Coffee drinking and coffee houses became fashionable in seventeenth-century Europe. This inspired the Dutch to cultivate it in their colonies. But it was the French who eventually succeeded in transporting a coffee tree cutting to the West Indies in 1714: this single tree is the ancestor of every tree in all the plantations of Latin America, now supplying the bulk of the world's coffee. The tea plant comes from South East Asia, and its dried leaves have been used in China probably as far back as the twenty-eighth century BC. The Dutch brought tea to Europe in the seventeenth century, but its popularity never equalled that of coffee, except in England. Tea is still very popular in Asia, and is regularly drunk by half the world's population. Caffeine was discovered in coffee in 1820. Caffeine has multiple biochemical and physiological actions, which include increasing blood pressure and stimulating the brain, heart and lungs. It has a stimulant effect on the brain, causing the brain waves to adopt the characteristic pattern of tense alertness. It increases concentration and can improve the performance of repetitive tasks requiring high concentration. It also suppresses sleep and feelings of sleepiness. Caffeine causes arousal partly by raising adrenaline and cortisol levels, and partly by blocking adenosine receptors in the brain. In the brain, adenosine can act as a neurotransmitter or neuromodulator, where it binds to adenosine receptors, generally causing a slowing of neuronal activity. Caffeine binds to the same receptors and blocks the action of adenosine, thus increasing brain neuronal activity and excitability.

This all sounds great but unfortunately, as with all other stimulants, the regular caffeine user (or abuser) develops caffeine tolerance, and may thus require higher and higher levels to get the same buzz. And if the high-dose coffee user stops drinking coffee there can be withdrawal symptoms, although these are less dramatic than those of other stimulants. Even overnight caffeine deprivation is sufficient to induce significant negative effects, including tiredness, headaches, depression, anger and dejection. The coffee user can relieve all these symptoms merely by downing their first coffee of the day, and this can lead the user to believe that coffee is essential to maintaining their energy levels. However, long-term coffee use can cause stress, tiredness and sleep disruption. Lowering or increasing coffee intake over the weekend may also cause caffeine withdrawal symptoms for the coffee drinker. To avoid such problems it may be best to drink coffee at a low to moderate level every day, but not too late in the day. Caffeine is also present in tea, cola drinks and chocolate in sufficient quantities to cause similar, but usually less strong, effects.

So all common stimulants – cocaine, amphetamine, nicotine and caffeine – give short-term energy boosts, but chronic use causes tolerance and leads to a long-term drain of energy. In general, it is ill advised to try and chronically boost energy levels with a stimulant, because the body adapts by attempting to maintain the same energy level, and thus, when the stimulant is withdrawn, energy levels fall below normal.

All these stimulants are commonly and repeatedly used, which raises the interesting question of why? Why do we continuously try to boost our energy levels, even at the risk of damaging our bodies? Why isn't the natural unstimulated energy level sufficient to meet our needs? After all, our energy producing machinery has evolved by natural selection to meet all our energy needs. Why do we need more? Is modern life more demanding than the conditions under which we evolved? This seems unlikely: certainly people in the developed world use less energy than those in the developing world. So why? The answer may simply be that we have a drive for arousal. We like being stimulated. We are seeking our optimum level. And arousal stimulates the reward centres of the brain, making us feel good. Probably it is as simple as that: energy makes us feel good.

ENERGY IN THE BRAIN

The human brain uses a lot of energy. In fact it is one of the most energy-hungry organs in the body, and this is the cause of its dramatic vulnerability. If its energy supply is cut for more than ten minutes, as during a stroke or heart attack, the brain is irreversibly damaged. No other organ is so sensitive to changes in its energy supply. The human brain makes up only two per cent of the weight of the body, but consumes about twenty per cent (one-fifth) of the total energy in the body at rest. That means that per gram of tissue, the brain consumes energy at ten times the rate of the rest of the body. And because the brain is fussy and will not use fat as a fuel, it may (in some conditions) consume most of the glucose in the body. The body is in constant danger of being depleted by a greedy brain, but cannot afford to let the brain go hungry as that would rapidly lead to death.

Where does all this energy used by the brain go? Most ends up used for information processing at the synapses between neurons. Ion channels, gates in the nerve cell membrane, are constantly being opened and shut, letting ions in and out of the neurons; and these ion movements and the electrical changes they induce cause the changes in neuronal excitability underlying the brain's information processing. But the ions that enter or leave the neuron through the ion channels have to be pumped out or in again if the neuron is to continue its work, and this constant pumping of ions requires energy directly or indirectly derived from ATP. If the ion channels and electrical activity of the brain are completely blocked by using a general anaesthetic, then the energy use of the brain falls by one-half. Thus, although information processing seems a rather nebulous activity, it requires large quantities of energy, just as it does in a silicon chip.

So, if the brain uses so much energy for mind activity, can we see changes in this energy use from moment to moment as we think and feel? Indeed, using powerful new technologies, we can look into the human brain and see changes in the energy usage pattern as the mind thinks. These technologies have been used to reveal the mind's intimate secrets, such as what goes on in the brain during the solving of a mathematical equation or the hallucinations of a schizophrenic. The first of these methods has the somewhat intimidating name of 'Positron emission tomography', but the more reassuring acronym of PET. But the intimidating title is well deserved, as I now know to my cost. I volunteered for a PET scan of my own brain to find out what it was like. First, a needle was inserted into an artery in my arm (itself a rather hazardous procedure), and this was connected to a long length of tube originating from a cyclotron, located on the floor above. The cyclotron was continuously producing strongly radioactive oxygen (oxygen thirteen) of a very short half-life, which was then fed down the tube into my artery, from there rapidly spreading throughout my body. Before turning on the radioactivity, I lay down and inserted my head into a ring of gamma detectors, which surrounded my head like a massive halo. The assembled doctors and researchers then retreated behind a lead wall, and I was left alone in near silence to contemplate the cyclotron's steady hum, as the radioactivity flooded into my blood stream. Once inside my brain, the radioactive oxygen decayed sending out positrons. A positron is a piece of antimatter, the stuff of science-fiction: when the antimatter collided with the matter of my brain, they annihilated each other producing an explosion of high-energy gamma rays. These emitted out of my head and were caught by the ring of gamma detectors. By tracing back the trajectory of gamma rays emitted simultaneously in different directions, a computer could extrapolate where the collision had occurred and thus roughly where the radio-active oxygen was at various times after being introduced into my blood stream. Activation of part of my brain by some mental task caused increased energy use by that part of the brain, and thus an increased requirement for oxygen and glucose from the surrounding blood. The local energy usage in the brain actually stimulates supply by dilating local blood vessels, thus increasing blood supply and there-fore fuel supply to purely this area of the brain. The radioactive oxygen in my blood penetrated very slowly into the inactive areas of my brain, but rapidly into active areas, because of the increased blood supply. By comparing the pattern of penetration of radioactive oxygen in my brain during different mental tasks, the researchers, with the help of powerful computers, could work out which areas became active during which task. Unfortunately, the task has to be repeated many times to separate the signal from the noise, so my mind was numb by the end of the experiment.

PET scans can be used not just to follow oxygen in the brain, but any substance to which a positron-emitting molecule can be attached. Thus, for example, a positron-emitting form of glucose has been used to monitor changes in energy metabolism in different parts of the brain during mental tasks. Many studies have shown that a given mental activity, such as doing mental arithmetic, increases energy use in a number of small and specific areas of the brain, while decreasing it in others. Thus, the overall energy use of the brain does not change much when we use it for something specific, although the local energy use may increase dramatically. For example, the brain's total oxygen consumption only increases by ten per cent when we go from rest to solving a difficult mathematical equation, and only falls by roughly twenty per cent when we fall asleep. This finding, that the brain's global energy use changes relatively little during mental activity, did seem at first paradoxical given that the brain consumes so much energy and that its main function is mental activity. But the PET scans resolve the paradox by showing that any particular mental activity uses a relatively small area of the brain; and changing mental activities involves increasing the activity of one area while decreasing the activity of others. Thus the total change in activity may be small. Not all brain areas can be fully active simultaneously: we cannot solve a mathematical equation while talking to our broker on the phone at the same time. Life might be more productive if we could, but we can't. Attention acts like a search light inside the mind, switching our mental focus from one task to the next, but we are prevented from attending to more than one or two mental tasks at once. If all areas of the brain were to be fully active at the same time, then the brain's energy use would go up dramatically. And indeed this does sometimes occur in pathological conditions such as epileptic seizures, when the brain's oxygen consumption may increase by four or five hundred per cent: however, the only result is total mental confusion.

One consequence of this surprising finding that mental activity does not dramatically increase the brain's overall energy use, is that if you spend an hour or a day thinking hard it does not have much impact on your total energy use or need for food. A static office worker, even an Einstein, uses far less energy than a coal miner (whose total energy use in a day is triple that of an office worker). Thus if prolonged mental activity is tiring, it is not because it depletes the body, or even the brain, of energy. On the other hand, even the weariness of a coal miner or a runner is rarely due to energy depletion of the whole body, but rather it may be due to energy depletion (or other changes) inside the particular muscles involved. Similarly, the fatigue of a mental worker may occur in the particular brain areas involved. Thus, in some cases, fatigue may be circumvented by changing to an entirely different type of mental task, and using parts of the brain not yet fatigued. Unfortunately, as yet, little is known about the causes and consequences of mental fatigue.

Relatively undaunted by my experience of positron emission tomography, I volunteered for the other main method of imaging brain activity, 'functional magnetic resonance imaging' (fMRI). Fortunately, this was in contrast a relatively painless experience, although it involved putting my head into a black hole at the centre of a machine, which was basically a massive magnet, producing a huge magnetic field across my brain. The magnetic field caused some of the spinning protons in my brain to align with it. A burst of radio waves was then pulsed through my head, causing protons to ripple in the magnetic field. The movement of the protons caused in turn the emission of radio waves from my brain, which were then detected by a radio detector. A powerful computer then constructed an incredibly detailed image of the interior of my brain. That gives a static picture of the brain: the dynamic part comes from the useful fact that the molecule – haemoglobin – that carries oxygen in the blood, giving blood its red colour, interacts with the magnetic field when carrying oxygen, but not when it is not. This means that the MRI image is foggy in brain areas where there is copious oxygen, but is clear where there is little. By comparing two different images when the brain is doing two mental tasks, we can get an idea of where in the brain energy is being used; and hence where electrical activity and information processing is occurring specific to those tasks. It is a very clever idea, but I found it hard to keep my mind focused and my head completely still inside a black hole full of excruciating noise.

Functional MRI has been used recently to test the effect of attention on perception. Nilli Lavie and colleagues in London tested his theory that there is a roughly constant and limited capacity in the brain for processing information, so that if we concentrate on a single demanding task then we automatically ignore other stimuli, whereas if the task is undemanding then we also pay attention to other distracting stimuli. Lavie gave subjects either an easy or difficult task to perform with words on a computer screen, which also had a pattern of moving dots at the screen's edge. Previous research had shown these moving dots activated a part of the brain which analysed moving objects, and this activity could be detected by fMRI. Sure enough, when the subjects were performing the easy task, the movement detection centre of the brain was activated, even though the subjects had been told that they might suffer from unpleasant after-effects if they paid these dots any attention. But when the subjects performed the difficult task, the motion centre of the brain was not activated by the dots, and consequently they did not perceive the distracting stimuli. The point of this research is that we can have focused or less focused attention, but the brain's total capacity to process information is limited and roughly constant. Why there should be such a limit still remains a mystery.

The large energy requirements of the brain contribute to its extreme sensitivity to an energy supply failure. After just five to ten seconds without oxygen we lose consciousness; after twenty seconds we lose muscle control; after four minutes the neurons are seriously damaged; and after ten minutes we may die. Other organs, such as muscles, can survive for hours without oxygen or any fuel. This sensitivity of the brain is partly due to its high energy requirements and low energy storage capacity; and partly to the rather bizarre property that the brain's main neurotransmitter – glutamate – is also a powerful poison for neurons.

Glutamate is released intermittently at most of the trillions of synapses throughout the brain, acting to transmit information across the synapse from one neuron to the next. However, glutamate released out of the neuron is immediately pumped back into the cell to terminate the signal and provide for further glutamate release. This pumping back of glutamate requires energy, which is derived from the sodium electricity of the cell membrane. When the energy runs out, as it rapidly does when – say – the blood supply to the brain is blocked in a stroke, glutamate floods out of the neuron and into the synapse. Once in the synapse, glutamate stimulates all its normal receptors on the next neuron, but also stimulates a special receptor which is an important cause of the subsequent damage. This receptor is not normally stimulated by glutamate alone, because it has a dual key mechanism. It only opens if glutamate is present and if the neuron on which it is located is electrically excited. This dual key mechanism functions as a kind of memory for the neuron. The receptor is only activated when the neuron simultaneously receives many excitatory messages: the receptor's activation sends a signal into the neuron, which may well change its function. This is essential to the brain's process of learning and memory formation, but this receptor proves to be the Achilles' heel of the brain because continuous activation causes neuronal death. And this is why our neurons are killed during strokes or neurodegenerative disease.

A decline in the brain's capacity to produce energy may contribute to many of the debilitating, neurodegenerative diseases that seem to increasingly afflict the developed world. These include Parkinson's, Alzheimer's, Huntington's, multiple sclerosis and motor neuron disease. An important clue to the nature of Parkinson's disease was found in 1982, when neurologists at Stanford were startled by the sudden appearance of large numbers of drug addicts who appeared frozen into immobility. These 'frozen addicts' had acquired Parkinson's symptoms overnight, whereas the progress of this debilitating disease is usually a slow degeneration of the aged brain. Careful neurological detective work found that the addicts had ingested a toxic impurity, MPTP, in their designer drugs. This toxin had penetrated to the core of their brains, killing a small number of neurons controlling body movement, rapidly resulting in the symptoms of Parkinson's: tremors, muscle rigidity and a loss of spontaneous motion. MPTP had killed the neurons by blocking the electron transport chain inside the cell's mitochondria, so starving them of energy. Might this be a clue to how the disease was normally caused? Doctors then examined the brains of deceased Parkinson's patients, finding that neurons in the same area had a similar mitochondrial blockage, probably resulting from attack by free radicals, nitric oxide or other poisons. We still do not know the ultimate cause of Parkinson's and other neurodegenerative diseases, but a decline in mitochondrial energy production appears to be a significant part of the puzzle.

The brain's capacity to produce and use energy declines with age. The reason why is unclear. It may be due to mutations of the mitochondrial DNA, which increase dramatically with age; or to the steadily accumulating damage by free radicals, to which neurons may be particularly susceptible because they are unable to divide and renew themselves; or it may simply reflect a decline in the brain's energy requirement with age. Animal experimentation has shown that the amount of mitochondria within a certain area of the brain can change dramatically if its use increases or decreases. Thus, for example, when one eye of a cat was permanently covered, the parts of the brain analysing visual information from that eye contained few mitochondria, and could produce relatively little energy, presumably because very little energy was required. These experiments were, however, on young animals rather than old humans, so we cannot be sure whether decreased use of an adult human brain area would lead to less energy production. But it does seem likely since this happens in other body organs. For example, decreased muscle use by humans results in a diminished mitochondrial content, and thus a decreased muscle capacity. If this occurs in the brain, it may be possible to stop or even reverse the decline in energy production with age by exercising the brain. Much evidence supports the idea that the decline in mental functions with age can be slowed by vigorous mental activity, and is accelerated by a boring and undemanding mental life. And this may be true at all ages. Recent research by German psychologists has shown that even going on holiday for ten days can significantly decrease your IQ. People, tested before and after their holiday, were found to temporarily lose up to 20 IQ points, presumably because of the intentional lack of mental stimulation during the holiday. The slogan has to be: 'Use it or lose it'.

Chapter 12

SEX AND SLEEP

SEXUAL ENERGY

*S*he had been working late in the White House that night. The lonesome *sound of her high-heels echoed and re-echoed in the dark corridor ahead of her. She might have been afraid if the day's exhilarating excitement had not still been pulsing through her veins – like liquid electricity. She was aching for sex. As she passed the Presidential suite, a door opened and a slice of light irradiated her nubile form. A shadow in the doorway beckoned her in and pressed a finger to her lips. The lights went out, and a man and a woman ignited in the darkness, fueled by raging hormones. When the fire finally burnt out, the man sneaked out, and, as he closed the door, whispered: 'Thank you, Mrs President.'*

Sexual energy is one expression of an individual's general state of energy. So, for example, physical fitness is associated with high sexual energy; whereas tiredness, fatigue, and ill health reduce sex drive. Mania is often characterized by promiscuity, while depression can result in a low sex drive – or even impotence. Extroverts have more sex, with more partners, in more ways, than introverts. And, as we have seen, general arousal, caused by fear, excitement or almost any arousing stimulus (such as political power) can overflow into increased sexual arousal. So sexual energy is strongly associated with general energy levels.

Sexual energy can be divided into sex drive (the desire to have sex) and sexual potency (the ability to perform). Interestingly, these two are strongly connected, so that a high sex drive is often associated with high potency. But they can also become disconnected, so that for example you can have a high sex drive with low potency.

The concept of sexual energy and its central role in an individual's energy economy, goes back at least to the ancient Chinese Taoists. They used an extensive array of herbal aphrodisiacs, and an intricate *ars erotica*, to channel and modulate the flow of sexual energy throughout the body, in the belief that this would not only increase sexual pleasure, but also increase general vitality and life span. This association may also underpin the ancient Roman prescription for rejuvenation of old men: a night spent sleeping between two virgins. In Indian Tantric Yoga, ritualized sex was used to release female energy (Kundalini) from the base of the spine, causing its union with male energy in the head, and resulting in spiritual enlightenment. Freud believed sexual energy (or libido) to be one of the most powerful forces in the psyche. His disciple Reich took sexual energy even further, turning orgone energy, as he called it, into a universal life-force, which was released during orgasm, and could be visualized as a pulsating blue light.

The anatomy of the *Human Sexual Response* was dissected by Masters and Johnson's pioneering book of the same name, published in the permissive 1960s. According to their detailed analysis, sex can be divided into four states: (1) excitement, leading to penile erection in the male, and erection of the nipples and clitoris, breast enlargement and vaginal lubrication in the female; (2) plateau, when heart rate, blood pressure, respiration rate and muscle tension all increase; (3) orgasm, accompanied by ejaculation in the male, and rhythmic contraction of the vagina in the female; and (4) resolution, when the changes of the first three phases are reversed, followed by a refractory period (in men) of variable length, during which no further orgasm or ejaculation is possible. The amount of time spent in these various phases varies with the individual. Many females, unlike most men, are multi-orgasmic, capable of experiencing more than one orgasm with no refractory period, if intense sexual arousal is maintained. Ageing, in general, causes a decrease in intensity of all these responses, and decreased penile firmness and vaginal lubrication can make sex difficult, but the penis, clitoris and vagina remain sensitive to stimulation well into old age.

Men of all ages have been concerned with the enhancement and loss of their sexual potency, as this has been for many synonymous with being a 'man'. Sexual potency is controlled by the male sex hormones, particularly testosterone. Castration cuts off the testosterone supply, usually causing a loss of sexual energy or libido, but this can be restored by testosterone replacement therapy. Low testosterone levels are similarly associated with a low sex drive and reduced capacity for erection and ejaculation. So testosterone acts both on the brain, promoting sexual drive, and the body, enhancing sexual performance. Sex drive peaks in late adolescence simultaneous with a peak in testosterone levels (a phase of 'raging hormones'); these levels gradually decline after the age of fifty-five paralleling a decline in sexual performance. Testosterone replacement therapy is widely used to treat impotency, but is also sometimes recommended to reverse the general loss of energy through ageing. However, testosterone is certainly not all there is to male sexual energy. Castrated, but sexually experienced, men can in some cases still be sexually motivated and potent for many years, so testosterone is not an absolute necessity for either sex drive or behaviour.

How often a man ejaculates, whether in intercourse, masturbation or wet dreams, is closely related to his rate of sperm production, varying from man to man, dependent on the size of his testes, and age. After puberty to the age of thirty the average man produces around three hundred million sperm a day and needs to ejaculate between three and four times a week. By fifty, these rates have dropped to one hundred and seventy-five million sperm a day and ejaculation twice a week; and by seventy-five, it has dropped to twenty million a day and ejaculation to less than once a month.

In animals, the female sex hormone oestrogen, which oscillates with the menstrual cycle, is associated with sex drive and behaviour. But there is little evidence for this in women. Oestrogen does, however, control vaginal lubrication and elasticity, so at menopause, when oestrogen production stops, sex can become painful. These changes can easily be reversed by oestrogen replacement therapy. Surprisingly, removal of the adrenal glands, which secrete low levels of the male sex hormones (such as testosterone), decreases the sex drive in both female monkeys and women. And in both species, treatment with testosterone can restore it. Thus, 'male' sex hormones may play a greater role than female hormones in women's sexual arousal. However, in the brains of both men and women testosterone, the male sex hormone, is converted into oestrogen, the female sex hormone, and it is in this form it acts on the brain to increase sex drive.

Sex starts in the brain. Arousing stimuli from the body, imagination or outside world are synthesized in the mind's dark recesses into SEX, and the body responds with a surge of testosterone. Testosterone production is boosted not only by sex, but also by the mind's anticipation of sex. The testosterone produced has a whole variety of effects on the body and mind, including the stimulation of beard growth in men. This has the surprising consequence that beard growth is related to sexual activity – so perhaps bearded men really are sexy after all. This discovery was made by an unnamed man in the 1960s, who noticed that the amount of beard clippings collected in his electric razor each day increased when he was more sexually active. But the mere anticipation of sexual activity was also sufficient to stimulate beard growth. The man published his results in *Nature*, but had to do so anonymously, presumably because publication of his name would have alerted his wife to his activities. However, some wives can use his results today to monitor the sexual activity of their husbands; by keeping track of how much their partner's facial hair grows between regular shavings; for example by feeling the roughness of his chin before he shaves in the morning; or by examining the darkness of his five o'clock shadow.

Contrary to expectations, recent research suggests that women have the same hormonal response to sexual stimuli and pornography as men. Astrid Jütte and colleagues at the Ludwig Boltzmann Institute in Vienna asked ten men and ten women to watch a fifteen-minute pornographic film. The level of testosterone in the blood of both men and women doubled after viewing the film. Other studies have shown that the more testosterone a woman produces over her monthly cycle, the more sexually active she tends to be, but little is known about the effect of short-term testosterone surges on female sex drive or sexual motivation.

Testosterone acts on the brain to increase sexual energy mainly through the sex centres of the hypothalamus. The hypothalamus, at the brain's base, contains two distinct areas (*nuclei*), one of which is specialized in regulating sex in men, and the other in women. Electrical activity in these nuclei increases during sex in animals; and electrical stimulation causes male-typical sexual activity when the male nucleus is stimulated; and female-typical activity when the female nucleus is stimulated. Castration causes a decrease in the male nucleus' electrical activity, which can be recovered by injecting tiny quantities of testosterone into this centre, resulting in the restoration of male sexual activity. The female sex hormones, oestrogen and progesterone, act on the female nucleus to promote female sexual activity – at least in animals. Other parts of the hypothalamus are involved in controlling ejaculation and the release of oxytocin, which may mediate the intensely pleasurable feelings during orgasm. Thus, the hypothalamus is the brain's sex organ. But many other parts of the brain are also involved in sexual arousal and response.

The brain causes the erection of the penis, through the parasympathetic nervous system. But erection is not caused by a contraction of skeletal muscle, although there is a thin muscle in the penis, which is involved in ejaculation. Erection is rather caused by the engorgement of the penis with blood, a process akin to blowing up a balloon. The parasympathetic nerves act on blood vessels in the penis to open them up and allow the blood to flow in. The messenger released by the nerves to open the blood vessels is not a neurotransmitter. It is, in fact, a gas – nitric oxide. So nitric oxide gives men an erection. That is how erection drugs, such as amyl nitrate (poppers), a favourite of gay men, work. Amyl nitrate releases nitric oxide in the penis, causing blood vessels to open and blood to engorge the penis, initiating and sustaining an erection. Nitric oxide also mediates part of the female sexual response, by increasing blood flow to the vagina, clitoris, labia and breasts, resulting in enlargement of these tissues and vaginal lubrication.

Viagra, the male potency pill, works in a somewhat different way, inhibiting the enzymes that break down cyclic GMP. Cyclic GMP is a messenger molecule inside the muscle wall of the blood vessels, which tells the muscle to relax, so that the blood vessel gets wider and opens up, thus allowing more blood to flow through. Nitric oxide causes blood vessels to open by stimulating the production of cyclic GMP. Viagra has the same effect by blocking the breakdown of cyclic GMP, so that if there is any production of cyclic GMP, it rapidly builds up to a very high level, and this level will be sustained. Thus, in the presence of Viagra, any sexual stimulus causing the production of nitric oxide and cyclic GMP will lead to a hard erection, which is sustained for a long period, because Viagra blocks the breakdown of cyclic GMP. So Viagra thus makes the penis more sensitive to any nitric oxide around. Viagra may also help women's sexual potency as well, as it increases blood flow to the vagina, which, in turn, can increase sexual response by for example increasing lubrication.

Viagra can, however, be fatal if nitric oxide-producing drugs are present at the same time. This is because the nitric oxide stimulates cyclic GMP production, while Viagra blocks its breakdown, so the cyclic GMP level goes sky-high. This may have positive results for the penis, which gets a rock-hard erection, but unfortunately the same interaction can occur in blood vessels throughout the body. So all the body's blood vessels relax and open at the same time, causing the blood pressure to fall disastrously, and precipitating cardiac arrest in people with heart disease.

Nitric oxide is not just important in causing penile erection and engorgement of the vagina and clitoris. It can mediate the relaxing effects of the parasympathetic nervous system throughout the body: controlling, for example, blood flow in many organs; the emptying of the bladder; the opening of the anus; uterine contractions during birth; the wave-like movements of the gut; and the opening of airways in the lungs. Nitric oxide is also a messenger in the brain, important in memory formation, and the control of sexual behaviour. It is also vital to the body's defences, controlling blood clotting, and is used to kill invading organisms. This is an impressive list of credentials for a gas that was, until 1987, famous only as a car pollutant, causing photo-chemical smog. Nitric oxide is now known as one of the most important molecules in the body.

Nitric oxide was found by Joseph Priestley in the 1770s just before his discovery of oxygen, but as it is a highly reactive gas and at high concentrations is toxic, it was presumed for over two hundred years that the human body did not contain any. So it came as quite a shock to the scientific community when, in 1987, Salvador Moncada in London and Louis Ignarro at UCLA showed that nitric oxide was actually produced by cells in the body, and was controlling the rate of blood flow in blood vessels. At around the same time, John Hibbs of the University of Utah found that a type of white blood cell (macrophages) produced large amounts of nitric oxide to kill invading pathogens, such as bacteria, fungi, parasites and cancer cells. Within the next few years, researchers seemed to find nitric oxide everywhere, and it was shown to be involved in almost everything in the body and brain. Solomon Snyder and David Bredt of the Johns Hopkins University showed in 1992 that nitric oxide mediated penile erection. More recently, I and others have found that nitric oxide is an important regulator of energy production in cells, because it acts directly on the mitochondria to control the flow of electrons down the electron transport chain.

A fundamental discovery, such as the role of nitric oxide in biology, causes a wave of interest in the scientific community. The bigger and more surprising the discovery, the larger and more turbulent the wave. A successful scientific career is all about surfing these waves. It's best to get in early when the wave is small, but you have to choose your wave carefully because it's only worth riding if it is going to get bigger; but you don't want anything too big, otherwise it's going to roll right over you. Getting onto the wave means taking the new-wave idea, finding or technique, and applying it to something else (something you know and can research) and generating important new ideas and findings, which many other scientists want to use. If you successfully get on to a wave of discovery, then your research starts to gain momentum; because you produce lots of scientific papers, you get invited to talk at scientific conferences; bright young scientists want to work in your laboratory or collaborate with you; and most importantly you get generous grants so that you can put more people and equipment in your laboratory to generate yet more research. Things are looking good, but if your wave (or idea) really starts to grow, then it attracts more and more laboratories into the field to compete with you. The wave of discovery starts to move faster and faster, as these competing laboratories are producing and using results in the same area of research, generating data and ideas at a hectic pace, which may be difficult to keep up with. This is why your laboratory has to grow too, at least as fast as the rest, to keep just ahead of the wave. The adrenaline really starts flowing, and you have to work flat-out to stay ahead of the pack. If your laboratory falls behind in generating new ideas and results, then you will also fall behind in terms of grants, people and interest in your work. In such conditions, laboratories become aggressively competitive, because they need to have the edge on their competitors to survive and succeed. In science, there is no consolation prize for being second – the only prize is for being first. Eventually the wave of interest will peter out, as everything there is to be discovered in that area using that set of ideas, knowledge or technique has been found. But if you have successfully surfed the wave you will have achieved a large laboratory and a powerful reputation. The ultimate goal is, of course, to create your own wave with an entirely new idea, discovery or technique that creates such a splash that everybody wants to jump into the resultant monster wave. With that you can collect the Nobel Prize.

The intimate relationship between sex and energy is exemplified by the impact of physical fitness on sexual energy. Researchers put a group of sedentary men on a vigorous exercise programme, and after nine months more than three-quarters of the exercisers reported making love more frequently. Another study found that middle-aged swimmers are more sexually active, enjoying lovemaking more than their non-exercising peers. Three forty-five-minute workouts a week was sufficient to increase sexual desire. This study concluded that: 'The sex lives of women and men over forty who exercise are similar to those of people in their late twenties and early thirties.' One survey found that eighty per cent of runners claimed running improved their sex lives, and another survey found that two-thirds of cyclists claimed that their sport made them better lovers. A survey of eight thousand American women by the sex therapist Linda de Villers found that among women who exercised regularly, a quarter reported that sexual desire increased after exercise; forty per cent that they were more easily aroused; one-third said they had sex more often; and a quarter that they climaxed faster. There appears little doubt that exercise can increase sexual energy, but the mechanism of this effect remains controversial. Exercise increases testosterone levels that boost sex drive, but this increase generally lasts less than an hour, which might not be sufficient to explain the effect. Mood-elevating endorphins are released in the brain after twenty minutes of intense exercise, and can last for up to three hours after exercise. This post-exercise high might contribute to the alleviation of depression and the increase of sexual desire, at least temporarily. Physical fitness can also improve self-image and desirability, leading to increased self and sexual confidence.

Sex is like eating. We eat because we are hungry and we have sex because we are hungry for sex. After we have eaten, we are satiated, and avoid eating for a certain time. Similarly after sex, our sexual hunger is satiated. Our hormones and mind determine the level of our sex drive, but sexual arousal is usually triggered by external stimuli, such as the sight, smell, or image of someone we find sexy, just as hunger can be by the sight, smell or thought of food. The experience of sex itself has obvious similarities to eating: it is a sensory experience also, although one that involves the whole skin surface and orifices, not just the mouth. But unlike eating, we can abstain from sex without apparent harm.

Different cultures have radically different quantities and qualities of sex. The Mangaia of Polynesia become sexually active in early adolescence and enjoy sex frequently throughout adulthood. It is not unusual for couples to engage in intercourse three or four times a night, five or six times a week, for years. In stark contrast, the Dani of New Guinea show little interest in sex. Intercourse does not occur before marriage, and may not occur during the first two years. After the birth of a child, there is no sex for four to six years. Why and how do the Dani starve themselves of sex in this way? They do not report feeling any stress, tension or any sense of deprivation. Apparently they are just not interested in sex. The contrast between the Mangaia, the Dani and ourselves suggests that the culture we are brought up in is extremely important in determining our level of sex drive.

Although we are normally satiated after sex, this can be overridden if the partner is changed, at least for men (and male animals). One study found that in male rats sexual exhaustion and cessation of mating required an average of seven ejaculations if the male was left with one female throughout. But if the female was changed every fifteen minutes, an average of thirteen ejaculations was required to produce exhaustion. This effect of variety is even more marked in sheep. When a ram was presented with the same ewe again and again, the ram was slower and slower to initiate mating, and apparently exhausted or lost interest after five matings. But if different ewes were presented each time, then the ram immediately mated again and again – until it was the experimenter who was exhausted. Similar experiments have not been done on humans, but anecdotal evidence suggests that the same effect occurs in men, and that sexual activity is increased if a variety of partners is available.

The effect of variety on sexual activity is known as the Coolidge Effect. The name is derived from an story told about an American President. One apocryphal day, President Coolidge and his wife were visiting a chicken farm. The two went separate ways: the President with the farmer, and Mrs Coolidge with the farmer's wife. As Mrs Coolidge walked past a particular assertive-looking rooster, she wondered aloud how many times a day roosters copulated. 'Dozens of times!' she was told. 'Please tell the President that,' she said. So the farmer's wife did so. Coolidge listened quietly and asked, 'Same hen every time?' 'Oh no, Mr President; different hen every time.' Coolidge nodded and said, 'Tell Mrs Coolidge that.'

Men, in general, do have more sexual partners than women, but it is not clear whether this has to do more with our genes or our culture (or the genetics of our culture, or the culture of our genes). It certainly makes evolutionary sense for men to seek more sexual partners than women, since the more partners he has the more possible babies and the further he has spread his genes, while if he sticks to a single partner he can have a maximum of one baby every nine months. Whereas women cannot produce more babies or genes by having different sexual partners. Of course, this does not require a conscious calculation by men or women, rather the genes would determine the level of sexual energy; what is sexually arousing; and how much Coolidge Effect to mix in. This difference in sexual energy and motivation in men and women continues to be one of the major causes of social disharmony and angst in our modern world.

SLEEP AND SLEEPINESS

Feeling tired? Well, wake up – it's time to talk about sleep. It might seem at first that there is little connection between sleep and energy, but they are in fact rather intimately related. There are basic biological rhythms, in cycles of a year, a month, a day and possibly every ninety minutes, which may determine how tired or alert we feel. The daily cycle of tiredness/alertness is the most obvious and hardest to ignore, as anyone who has tried to get up very early or who has experienced jet lag can testify. When we wake up, we are generally still sleepy (depending on how much sleep we have had) but slowly become more alert. During the day our alertness oscillates, generally peaking in the late morning and early evening. There is then a steady decline in alertness and a rise in sleepiness, until we are overcome by sleep. During sleep the decline in alertness continues, although again there are substantial oscillations in the depths of sleep. Alertness then increases and sleepiness diminishes before we wake. Of course these cycles of alertness can be interrupted by external stimuli, such as an emergency or exciting situation, but the daily cycle is an important biological determinant for our energy level.

The father of modern sleep research was Nathaniel Kleitman. Born a Jew in 1895 in Russia, he left for Palestine at seventeen having experienced both persecution and pogroms. He studied medicine in Beirut, but with the outbreak of the First World War he took the first boat available, which happened to be going to America. Kleitman ended up in Chicago, and eventually established the first sleep laboratory there. He was then the world's only full-time sleep researcher, and there was at that time little general interest in sleep which was viewed as a passive process with no relevance to the waking state. However, Kleitman proceeded to make some startling discoveries that changed our whole conception of sleep. In particular, he discovered that there are cycles of activity during sleep, periods of deep sleep interspersed by those of light accompanied by Rapid Eye Movement (REM), and most dreams occurred during these periods of – as he called it – REM sleep. Thus sleep is not the passive process it had been thought.

So, what causes our daily cycle, and can we do anything about it? It is still not clear what exactly causes sleep and waking, but again noradrenaline, serotonin and the hypothalamus are involved. The hypothalamus contains a biological clock, which cycles roughly every twenty-four hours. In fact, the cycle time varies between twenty-three and twenty-seven hours (on average twenty-five hours) in different individuals, if isolated from the day-night cycle and from clock time. Normally the endogenous biological clock is kept in tune with the day/night cycle by the light stimulation of our eyes, sending neural signals to the hypothalamic clock to keep it in time. However, when we fly through several time zones, the clock abruptly finds it is radically out of phase with the day/night cycle, and this can throw the cycle of alertness and sleepiness into confusion.

That Monday-morning feeling may well be a result of letting ourselves shift to a more natural 25-hour biological rhythm during the weekend. If we follow our internal clock during the weekend and go to bed an hour later each night, by Monday morning, our body may not become alert until two hours later than normal.

Most people experience a dip after lunch, and sleep research has shown that we go to sleep much more easily in the early afternoon. Thus the habit of having a siesta after lunch in some countries follows a natural arousal rhythm.

Next to the clock in the hypothalamus is a sleep centre. Electrical stimulation of this centre in rats causes sleep, and its destruction causes insomnia. The clock may control the sleep/wake cycle partly by sending neural messages to the neighbouring sleep centre, but the clock may also indirectly control the noradrenaline and serotonin centres in the brain stem. These centres control general brain levels of arousal and alertness, by regulating the excitability and rhythmic activity of neurons in the rest of the brain, and by regulating how much sensory information actually reaches the conscious areas of the brain. And the noradrenaline and serotonin centres become less and less active as we gradually fall asleep, while stimulation of these areas causes waking and alertness. Stimulants, such as amphetamine or cocaine that mimic or enhance the activity of noradrenaline, generally cause alertness, suppressing sleep and sleepiness. Similarly, psychological stimulation caused by exciting or frightening situations, activates the brain's alarm system, keeping us alert and awake. An exciting or stressful event will cause arousal, often preventing us falling or staying asleep, and thus causing sleep disturbances. The hypothalamus and the noradrenaline system also regulate the sympathetic nervous system and adrenaline in the body, and there is some evidence that adrenaline is associated with waking and alertness. When adrenaline levels rise we wake up;

when they fall, we tend to fall asleep. However, the neural and bio-chemical basis of sleep is still not well understood.

Many physiological processes follow a daily cycle, including body temperature, which falls by one degree centigrade when we sleep. You may have noticed that if you stay up very late at night, your body feels surprisingly cold: this fall in temperature may be involved in both initiating and maintaining sleep. During the day the rise in body temperature is associated with both alertness and attention. The release of many hormones also follows a daily cycle, for example growth hormone is released immediately after we fall asleep, while cortisol, which prepares the body to expend energy, is released before we wake up.

Different people have varying patterns of sleep and alertness during the day, and some of these differences may be related to personality. For example, introverts and extroverts tend to have a different daily cycle. Extroverts often have a higher temperature, performing better in the evening; while introverts often peak both in performance and temperature in the morning. Some people tend to sleep longer or shorter than the norm. One study found that short sleepers tended to have an extrovert personality, and long sleepers are introverted. Personality differences are partly determined by genetics, and may reflect differences in the brain's emotional and arousal centres, which then impact on sleep and alertness. However, the cause and effect may well be the other way around, as your sleep pattern may affect your waking activity, levels of arousal and behaviour. Other studies have suggested equally conclusively that there is no consistent connection between number of hours slept and personality.

How much sleep do we actually need? Researchers have studied the performance of volunteers who slowly reduced their number of hours sleep per night. No volunteer was capable of reducing their sleep to less than four and a half hours a night for an extended period. Reduction to five hours a night did not produce significant personality changes or reduce performance at a number of tasks, but did cause persistent feelings of fatigue. However, sleep deprivation does in general cause more subtle changes in performance, particularly in speech, thinking, decision-making and memory. There are well-documented cases of particular people only sleeping one or two hours a night, without any apparent detrimental effects, but these are extremely rare. Most of us require seven or eight hours of continuous sleep a night to perform optimally. But not all are getting that amount, for a variety of reasons, and this is, obviously, one of the most common causes of fatigue.

Separate from the daily cycle there may also be a basic cycle of rest and activity every ninety to a hundred and twenty minutes. This type of cycle has been found in many activities, such as the ability to detect a stimulus; or attend to some task; or fantasize; or to fall asleep. Even in our sleep, we follow a ninety-minute cycle, oscillating between deep and relatively light sleep with dreams. And there is furthermore some evidence that the relative dominance of the left and right sides of the brain oscillates every ninety to a hundred minutes, so that we may swing back and forth between fantasy/intuitive thought and verbal/intellectual thought over this cycle.

Surprisingly the functions of sleep and dreaming remain a total mystery, although many ideas have been suggested. Plato and Galen suggested that vapours arising from food in the stomach condensed in the brain, causing a blockage of pores in the brain, resulting in the brain's isolation from the body and senses, and hence sleep. This theory may have been inspired by the habit of upper-class Greeks and Romans to gorge on large meals and then sleep. Thus the Greeks thought that sleep had no function, rather that it was a passive process enforced by the body on the brain. Similar passive theories of sleep have been proposed more recently, in particular the popular theory that sleep is caused by the fatigue of body or brain. It may seem self-evident that the function of sleep is to rest and repair the body and brain. However, there is no obvious reason why the body or brain needs rest, except because we tire, and we get tired not because we run out of body energy (as there is just as much body energy at the day's end as at the beginning), but rather because the brain wants to put us to sleep. It would appear that the fundamental function of sleep is not to cure tiredness, but rather tiredness may function to put us to sleep. For there is no evidence that either the body or brain repairs itself more rapidly during sleep than when we are awake. On the other hand, non-dreaming sleep is certainly a resting, low-energy state for both body and brain, and indeed the lowest energy state that we normally enter before death. The temperature and energy consumption of the body are lowered. Muscle tension is reduced, and movement is minimal. Heart rate, breathing and kidney function slow down. The brain also enters a rest mode of low energy consumption and low neuronal activity. However, about twenty-five per cent of the time we are asleep we spend in a radically different state of existence – REM sleep – which is, basically, dream sleep. Ninety to ninety-five per cent of people awakened in this state report vivid dreams. In REM sleep the brain's energy consumption increases to levels greater than the peak when awake and the neurons become very active. The body, however, is paralysed (except for the eyes and respiratory muscles), in order to prevent us from acting out our dreams. But the sympathetic nervous system and brain arousal system get activated, presumably by the excitement of our dreams, and cause rapid and irregular heart and breathing rates. Thus, REM and non-REM sleep are radically different states of existence, with very different energy levels.

If sleep does not function as a cure of tiredness, and does not repair or detoxify body or brain, then what is its function? Actually nobody knows. Recent theories from neuroscientists have proposed that both sleep and dreaming are active processes essential to reprogram the brain's neural networks, in particular to rework memory, but there is not much supporting evidence for such attractive theories. Perhaps sleep simply functions to save energy. Energy expenditure is at a minimum during sleep, but a sleeping animal can continue to grow, develop and repair itself. An animal needs to divide its time and energy between feeding, reproduction and growth. Hunting and eating food provides energy, but it also uses it, and exposes the animal to predators. Sex requires relatively little time. Thus once an animal has satisfied its food and reproductive requirements, it is safest and most energy-efficient to rest or sleep. And it makes sense to co-ordinate the sleep-wake cycle with the night-day cycle, since many animals are unable to hunt or feed nocturnally. However, it seems unlikely that energy conservation is sleep's only function, since resting does not use appreciably more energy than sleeping, and sleeping is such a universal phenomenon amongst animals.

Freud suggested that dreams acted as a safety valve to drain off our excess mental energy, generated by unfulfilled needs or wishes. Thus, for example, an unfulfilled drive for sex could be partially dissipated in a (disguised or undisguised sexual) dream, thus preventing an excessive accumulation of excitement, anxiety or conflict. Updating this theory, Gerald Vogel, a psychiatrist from Georgia, has suggested that the greater neural activity during REM sleep dissipates some factor responsible for neural excitability, arousal or motivation, and that this can in some conditions cause decreased excitability in a waking state. Effectively, Vogel is saying that dreaming can use up so much mental energy that there is less available when awake. He suggested this because he discovered that he could completely deprive people of REM sleep (by waking them up as soon as REM started) for three weeks without any serious ill-effects; depriving animals of REM sleep actually increased their arousal level. Clinically depressed humans were significantly improved by REM deprivation, and Vogel proposed that this worked because REM sleep dissipated their mental energy and motivation. Cogently pointing out that the most effective anti-depressant drugs also suppressed REM sleep, he suggested that the reason these drugs lifted depression was because they eliminated REM sleep, and thus prevented the dissipation of neural excitability. One of the most common symptoms of depression is a disturbed sleep pattern, including less deep sleep and more vigorous REM sleep, so perhaps REM sleep drains off mental energy. It is certainly a very active brain state. Thus, according to both Freud and Vogel, dreaming drains mental energy, but Freud emphasized that if mental energy is excessive drainage is a good thing, while Vogel emphasized that if mental energy is low this drainage can be bad.

A range of different sleep disorders have now been characterized, and may be a common cause of day-time tiredness. A significant proportion of the world's population may be suffering from chronic sleep deprivation. Large-scale surveys have found that about fourteen per cent of the population feel they have some difficulty with sleep, and the proportion is greater in older people. In America, the National Commission on Sleep Disorders Research compiled an exhaustive review, concluding:

'One thing is absolutely certain in America: The quality and quantity of sleep obtained are substantially less than the quality and quantity needed ... A convincing body of scientific evidence and witness testimony indicates that many Americans are severely sleep deprived and, therefore, dangerously sleepy during the day.'

Astonishingly, the commission suggested that as many as one-third of all adult Americans may be suffering from one form or another of sleep disorder. They stated that most people need at least seven hours of untroubled sleep a night to avoid symptoms of sleep deprivation, and many require more than eight hours.

Chapter 13

MOOD, MADNESS AND CREATIVE ENERGY

What makes some people energetic and others chronically fatigued? Why are we sometimes full of creative energy, and at others depressed and anxious? Is creativity akin to madness? Are energetic people born or made? Can a society increase the energy of its members? What is an energetic life? These are the difficult questions this chapter will tackle.

MOOD AND HEALTH

Another realm lies deep below everyday life, the dark world of depression, where everything is infinitely alone and silent, closed in on itself. There is no broader vision, no prospects and no hope. No view of anything wider than the collapsing self, spiralling into the pain of a meaningless existence. Al Alvarez, the poet and critic, described it thus in his book *The Savage God* (1972):

'After all this, I have to admit that I am a failed suicide . . . I built up to the act carefully and for a long time, with a kind of blank pertinacity . . . Each sporadic burst of work, each minor success and disappointment, each moment of calm and relaxation, seemed merely a temporary halt on my steady descent through layer after layer of depression, like an elevator stopping for a moment on the way down to the basement . . . My life felt so cluttered and obstructed that I could hardly breathe. I inhabited a closed, concentrated world, airless and without exits. I doubt if any of this was noticeable socially: I was simply more tense, more nervous than usual, and I drank more. But underneath I was going a bit mad.'

Depression and mania are at opposite ends of the mind-energy spectrum. Depression is characterized by depressed mood, lack of interest and pleasure in life; disturbed thinking, appetite and sleep; feelings of worthlessness; thoughts of suicide; fatigue and loss of energy. It is distinguished from ordinary sadness, in that these symptoms occur for most of the day, and last longer than three months. Depression is remarkably common, and appears to be on the rise. At any time roughly two per cent of the population is clinically depressed, and these rates are similar throughout the world, but twice as many women suffer from depression as men. It is estimated that five to twelve per cent of men, and ten to twenty per cent of women in America will suffer from at least one major depressive episode at some time in their life. About ten per cent of these individuals will experience manic phases in addition to their depressive phases – that is one to one and a half per cent of Americans will experience manic-depressive illness or bipolar disorder. In America, in 1992, the estimated costs of depression came to forty-three billion dollars, mostly from reduced productivity. But putting the expense to one side, depression is sheer hell to live with. Up to fifteen per cent of those afflicted commit suicide each year.

Depression appears to be caused by the reduced activity of the brain's two energizing systems: the noradrenaline and serotonin systems. This venerable hypothesis is based on a number of different findings, which make it attractive but not conclusive. Serotonin levels have been found to be decreased in the brains of suicides suffering from depression. Drugs that deplete serotonin and noradrenaline in the brain cause depression in humans. The three classes of drugs that have been used to successfully treat depression each enhance the serotonin or noradrenaline systems in different ways. However, the causes of depression are likely to be much more complex than this. More recent evidence suggests that depression is related to a disorder in the stress response of the hypothalamus-pituitary-adrenal axis, and in particular the release of corticotropin-releasing hormone (CRH) by the hypothalamus.

The central command centre for energy control in body and mind is the hypothalamus. But it controls the arousal centres of the body and mind largely through a single, master hormone or neurotransmitter: CRH. CRH is the neurotransmitter released by the neurons of the hypothalamus to stimulate the brain's arousal centres, and the sympathetic nervous system. It is the emission of CRH from the hypothalamus that is the signal that eventually causes the release of the stress hormone, cortisol, from the adrenal glands. And again, it is CRH from the hypothalamus which stimulates the release of endorphins, which in turn regulate mood and pain.

There is growing, but still tentative, evidence linking energy, mood and inflammatory disorders with malfunctions of the hypothalamus' stress response. Atypical depression lacks the anxiety-related symptoms of major depression, but has the symptoms of lethargy, fatigue, increased sleep and increased eating. This type of depression is associated with a blunted stress response and impaired CRH function. A person with chronic fatigue syndrome or ME classically has symptoms of lethargy and fatigue lasting longer than six months, but also usually has depression, feverishness, aches in their joints and muscles, allergic symptoms and higher levels of antibodies to viruses (such as the Epstein-Barr virus). It has been suggested that a deficiency of CRH or a hypothalamus malfunction could cause the lethargy of chronic fatigue syndrome, because CRH controls both body and mind energy through its stimulation of the sympathetic nervous system and the brain's arousal centres. Similarly a dysfunction of the hypothalamus or pituitary could explain the apparently overactive immune system in patients with chronic fatigue syndrome. This possibility is supported by the finding that injection of CRH into patients with chronic fatigue causes a delayed and blunted response. This same defective response is seen in patients with an injured hypothalamus, suggesting, but not proving, that chronic fatigue sufferers may perhaps have some defect in the hypothalamic control of the stress response.

In contrast to atypical depression, major depression, which is the most common form, is characterized by some symptoms that could be described as a state of hyper-arousal, including chronic anxiety and insomnia. One of the most reproducible and widely recognized biological changes in patients with major depression is the high levels of cortisol found in the blood, due to high levels of CRH release by the hypothalamus. CRH levels are increased in the brains of depressed patients and are reduced by treatment with antidepressants or electro-convulsive therapy (ECT). Moreover, delivering CRH to the brains of laboratory animals causes them to develop the characteristic behaviour patterns of patients with major depression: these include insomnia, decreased appetite, decreased libido and increased anxiety. However, rats can't speak to tell us whether they are feeling the blues, and it's not strictly ethical to inject a potentially depressive hormone into a human's brain. So we can't be sure that CRH causes depression in humans. However, the tentative hypothesis is that major depression can be caused by the overactivity of the stress-responsive, CRH-releasing neurons of the hypothalamus. This could cause the anxiety, insomnia and increased cortisol levels characteristic of depression.

But if depression is caused by overactivity of stress-responsive cells in the hypothalamus, what causes this overactivity in the first place? Charles Nemeroff of Emory University has proposed that childhood stress, twinned with a genetic disposition to depression, may cause overactivity of the stress-responsive neurons of the hypothalamus. This overactivity may persist into adulthood, causing high levels of CRH, which in turn induce the behavioural characteristics of depression. Thus, the hypothesis is that childhood stress, abuse or neglect induces permanent changes in the brain's stress response, which then triggers depression in adulthood. And the hypothesis has been tested in rats, by repeatedly separating young rats from their mothers, in order to make them stressed. When these rats grew up, they were found to have high levels of CRH in their brains, and an increased stress response, thus supporting the hypothesis. However, rats are not humans, and how the CRH story fits in with the serotonin and nor-adrenaline theory of depression is not known. All we have are some pieces of a giant jigsaw, some of which fit together and others do not.

The stress response system of the hypothalamus is controlled by the brain's emotional centres, which directly stimulate the hypothalamus in alarming, fearful or stressful situations. And on the whole most of the system's actions are designed to cope with this stress. However, there is one rather surprising exception. Cortisol suppresses the immune system. The immune system defends the body against harmful intruders, such as bacteria, and thus prevents infection. It is hard to see what advantage there might be in suppressing the immune system during stress. But this is in fact what happens. Chronic stress causes cortisol to be released into the blood, and this suppresses the activity of virtually all cells involved in the immune system, leading to increased vulnerability to infection and illness. Stressed people have been shown to be more susceptible to colds and flu. Viruses, such as the Epstein-Barr virus and Herpes, which are normally suppressed by the immune system, remaining latent in the body, become active during stressful periods, such as exams or marital problems. Chronic stress promotes a whole range of diseases, such as hypertension, heart disease, stomach and gut ulcers, and asthma.

If cortisol's suppression of the immune system is so potentially damaging to the body, why does it happen? The answer seems to be that an unrestrained immune system itself is even more potentially damaging to the body. The immune system, once activated, is armed with some extremely powerful weapons, which are lethal not only to the pathogens they are aimed at, but also to the body's own cells caught in the cross fire. This is shown clearly in inflammatory diseases, such as arthritis, ulcers and asthma, where the overactive immune system causes inflammation, and when the inflammation is not suppressed, causes tissue damage. Corticosteroids, such as cortisol, are medically prescribed to suppress persistent inflammation, in part because of the potential for chronic inflammation to cause damage to the body. An out-of-control immune system can rapidly kill the patient, as occurs in septic shock and toxic shock syndrome.

The mind or brain can talk to the immune system, and thus affect illness, through the stimulation of the hypothalamus and the stress response: but the immune system in illness can also talk back to the brain, affecting our energy level. When immune cells (in particular, white blood cells called macrophages) are activated by infection they release hormones, whose name, interleukins, signifies 'between the white blood cells'. And these act on the hypothalamus to cause what is called 'illness behaviour', including lethargy, excess sleepiness, cautious avoidance, irritability, loss of appetite and loss of interest in external affairs. This is part of the reason why we lack energy when we are ill. Presumably, this behaviour actually benefits an ill human or animal, causing them to retire from activity and sleep until they are better. But for chronically ill patients, the loss of energy can itself be one of illness' most frustrating aspects.

The multiple interactions between mood and illness, or between the mind and the immune system have spawned a whole new science called 'Psycho-immunology'. The interaction goes both ways: illness can affect mood and mood can affect illness. In one study on the effect of mood on the immune system, researchers at the State University of New York collected saliva from medical students over an eight-week period, to measure their immune system activity. By comparing this immune response with mood on a daily basis the researchers found that the immune response was lower on days of strong negative mood, and also that the inverse was true: it was higher on days of strong positive mood. Because the immune response determines how resistant we are to infection and disease, it seems likely those students in a negative mood were more vulnerable to illness. A number of studies have in fact shown that negative mood can cause an increased susceptibility to infection and illness. Interactions between mood, energy and illness have proved one of science's most fascinating and challenging areas, as this straddles the normally impenetrable barriers between body, brain and mind. The science of psycho-immunology is still young, and many of its findings are still tentative, but for the sake of the many, many sufferers of mood or energy related illnesses, we can only hope that the science matures rapidly.

CREATIVE ENERGY AND MANIA

Where does the capacity to be creative come from? Why do great thoughts, great art and great actions appear when they do, as if from nowhere? What divides the creative from the lazy, mundane or merely proficient? We all need some creativity in our life and work, something that takes us out of the ordinary. But what can we do when creative energies desert us? The Greeks thought that inspiration was a gift of the gods, literally breathed into the lucky mortal: the very roots of the word, inspiration, link it to breathing. Creativity has often been described as a divine madness. Recent research has suggested that great artists, musicians, novelists and even politicians may indeed suffer from a certain kind of madness. This throws a fascinating light on the link between creativity and energy within the brain.

Genius and insanity have often been linked in the popular imagination in the form of the 'mad genius'. Edgar Allan Poe wrote:

> 'Men have called me mad, but the question is not yet settled, whether madness is or is not the loftiest intelligence – whether much that is glorious – whether all that is profound – does not spring from disease of thought – from moods of mind exalted at the expense of the general intellect.'

Men, and Poe, might think it so, but can we find a solid link between creativity and madness? Contrary to expectation, there is no connection between artists and general mental illness, but there is rather a strong, specific link between artists and the mood disorders manic depression and major depression; and there is also an increased risk of suicide. Major depression is the main clinical form. Everyone has phases of depression, but major depression is distinguished from ordinary blues by its lasting at least two to four weeks and being of sufficient depth to significantly interfere with a person's everyday functioning. Depression is a common disorder: roughly five per cent of people suffer from major depression during their lifetime. A mild episode of mania (hypomania) has essentially opposite symptoms to depression: elevated mood, confidence and self-esteem, increased energy and productivity, less sleep, faster thinking and speech. But in full-blown mania these symptoms are exaggerated, resulting in excessive irritability; paranoia; overconfidence; excitability; impulsive behaviour; and – in some cases – violent agitation; delusional thoughts and hallucinations. Manic depression is a distinct mood disorder involving alternating phases of depression and mania. Approximately one per cent of the population suffers from manic depression, while a further three may suffer from a milder form, known as cyclothymia.

Several different studies have examined the occurrence of these mood disorders in artists in comparison to the general population, and all these investigations have shown dramatically increased rates of major depression, manic depression, and suicide amongst artists. The first rigorous study was in the 1970s, by Nancy Andreasen of the University of Iowa. She interviewed thirty American authors and a matched control group. She found that eighty per cent of the writers had experienced at least one episode of major depression, mania or hypomania; forty-three per cent reported a history of mania or hypomania. In the 1980s Kay Jamison, a professor of psychiatry at Johns Hopkins University, studied forty-seven of the most distinguished British writers, playwrights, poets, painters and sculptors. She found that thirty-eight per cent had already been treated for mood disorders. The poets were particularly badly hit, half requiring medication or hospitalization. Subsequent studies on European writers and artists, American blues musicians and British poets, have all confirmed that artists suffer eight to ten times the rate of depression, ten to twenty times the rate of manic depression and mild manic depression relative to the normally expected rate. One of the most extensive studies was by Arnold Ludwig of the University of Kentucky, published in 1992. He surveyed the biographies of one thousand and five famous twentieth-century artists, writers and other professionals, and found that artists and writers experienced two to three times the rate of psychosis, suicide attempts, mood disorders and substance abuse of comparably successful people in business, science and public life. The poets were particularly likely to suffer from mania and psychosis, and were eighteen times more likely to commit suicide.

None of this looks very attractive if you are thinking of making a career of the creative life; perhaps your mother was right after all and you should stick with accountancy. But does an artistic life cause mood disorders such as depression, or, on the contrary, does a mood disorder aid creativity? This is not an easy question to answer. But at least in the case of manic depression we have some clues. Studies of identical twins have shown that if one twin has a manic-depressive illness, the other twin typically has a sixty to a hundred per cent probability of also having the disease. Manic depression is largely a genetic disorder inherited from our parents, and although there is a non-genetic component, this suggests that its occurrence is not normally caused by the sufferer being creative or otherwise. Many writers and artists have a family history of mood disorders. If we take, for example, Alfred Tennyson, we discover that not only does he appear to have suffered from both depression and hypomania, but also turns out to have had a family history of depressive illness; his father and four siblings similarly suffered from depression or manic depression, while yet another brother was confined to an insane asylum for almost sixty years with severe melancholia, finally dying from manic exhaustion. Thus, if there is a link between manic depression and creativity, it appears that manic depression must somehow promote a creative life. This strange possibility is supported by a study by Ruth Richards and her colleagues at Harvard University, who attempted to assess the creativity of manic depressive patients. She presented patients with a set of creative tasks, which were then rated for original thinking, and found that those suffering from mild or serious manic depression showed a higher level of creative and original thinking than a control group with no history of psychiatric disorders.

How could it be that a mood disorder promotes creativity? It seems unlikely that depression itself could aid creativity as major depression is characterized by apathy, lethargy, hopelessness, sleep disturbances, slowed physical movements, impaired concentration and loss of pleasure in typically enjoyable events. On the other hand, during periods of mania and hypomania the symptoms are in many ways the opposite of those of depression. Mood and self-esteem are elevated. The 'sufferers' sleep less and have abundant energy, and their productivity increases. Their speed and originality of thinking increases. Patients with modest hypomania appear clever and charming. They manifest abundant self-confidence, boundless energy and are able to achieve massive amounts of work cheerfully, effortlessly, and often with high quality results. It has been suggested that some of history's most productive individuals were at times hypomanic, such as Churchill, Lincoln, Roosevelt and Franklin. Mild mania can be very creative and productive. But manics frequently become paranoid and irritable. Their thoughts move too quickly and fluidly from one topic to another, and their speech is often rapid, excitable and intrusive. They often hold tremendous conviction in the correctness and importance of their own views and ideas. This grandiosity can contribute to poor judgement and impulsive behaviour, including wild extravagance, sexual promiscuity and spending sprees. Some of these symptoms may well contribute to the creative process. But Kay Jamison has suggested that the creative process may also benefit from the ability to experience a profound depth and variety of emotions:

> 'In a sense, depression is a view of the world through a dark glass, and mania is that seen through a kaleidoscope – often brilliant but fractured.'

The stark contrast and often traumatic changes of the cycle between these states may help to break up the fixed view of the world that most hold, creating new viewpoints full of ambiguities important to the arts.

The molecular basis of manic depression is unknown, although an effective treatment, in the form of lithium, does exist. But the symptoms of hypomania are similar to those induced by stimulants such as cocaine and amphetamine, suggesting that the underlying process is a stimulation of the brain's noradrenaline system.

Many of us in our personal or professional lives have occasionally had euphoric states, where our mind shifts up a gear and a new realm of existence is suddenly visible. Your mind is spinning so fast that you rise up, above the confusion of everyday life, and suddenly everything is laid out below you in crystal clarity. But such moments are all too brief, and we fall back into chaos again, hungry for those brief moments of clarity. It seems as if there are two parallel realms of existence, one on the ground in our ordinary, self-absorbed lives, and another high above in an upper atmosphere of omnipotence and omniscience. The ancient Greeks believed that there were two levels of air; the normal, everyday air breathed by mortals; and the higher Olympian air which could only be breathed by the gods or those touched by the divine – too rarefied for any non-divine lungs. This theory not only neatly explained why altitude sickness happened but also that the 'divine' force of inspiration changed the views and ambitions of oracles and seers – showing them a realm of the mind and spirit rather than the physical. The searing power and light of such elevated states may be too overwhelming for most of us mortals to sustain for more than few minutes in a lifetime. But to others, such as the seer, the aesthete or the drug addict, this is the only life that counts, and they may abandon everything in their ordinary life to maintain themselves in that higher state. If such individuals do not fall as Icarus did or burn their wings as the moth is burnt by the flame, they may bring back as a gift to us ground-dwellers pieces of that other world in the form of great thoughts or great art. Nietzsche believed that all that was of value in human life was due to those rare moments of Dionysian ecstasy experienced by the exceptional individual: the 'superman'.

Studies of the exceptionally creative have indicated surprisingly that they tend to come from somewhat stressful backgrounds. A psychologist, Victor Goetzels, found that three-quarters of his selection of the world's great creative talents came from families marred by poverty, divorce, abuse, alcoholism, bankruptcy, or the loss of one or more parents. Most of the families offered plenty of stimulation, but little support. Why such a background should foster genius is unclear, but as we saw in the last section, stress in childhood can lead to an increased adult stress response, which may cause increased arousal. What is also clear is that creative geniuses often work extremely hard and are terrifyingly productive. Picasso had created 20,000 works of art, Edison had 1,093 patents, and Freud 330 publications. Dean Keith Simonton, another psychologist, has found that the most successful creators in western culture are also paradoxically those with the most failures. What makes them different is that they are so much more productive, refusing to be put off by their mistakes.

So why is it that some people are more creative, productive or energetic than others? Why is it that some people are able to achieve so much more in their work, creative and emotional lives than others? Why is it that some people are apparently unable to produce or do anything in their lives? Clearly part of the answer is skill: some people have the opportunity to acquire skills and some people have innate ability. You cannot be a productive footballer, musician, novelist, politician or scientist without either acquiring or being born with the right skills. But the skills are not enough, we also need the drive or energy to acquire those skills in the first place and to use them time and again. As we have seen there are the basic drives, such as those for food and sex, and the acquired drives, such as for money, status, and the approval both of our peers and of society. These drives set up a tension, which may be experienced as an energizing force or as anxiety, depending on the level of stimulation and the individual's ability to satisfy the drive. Without these drives and their accompanying tensions and pleasures, we would have no motivation to do anything. But different people react to tension differently. Some people actively seek out stress to gain the pleasure derived from fulfilling the goal of a drive; for example they may seek out sexual tension, and then the relief of that tension in sexual activity. Whereas others avoid all tension because it causes unbearable anxiety. Most of us experience some anxiety when meeting new people in either uncontrollable or unpredictable circumstances, but many people experience unbearable levels in these circumstances, and actively avoid such events. Part of the reason someone may experience this tension as an anxiety, rather than as an energizing force, is that they lack the skills (innate or acquired) to fulfil this drive. For example, if someone undergoing sexual tension does not know how to engage successfully in sexual activity, then their inability to relieve or control the tension will cause anxiety. Or someone in a social situation without successful social skills is likely to become anxious or leave. However, irrespective of the possession of skills, it seems that some people prefer or need a high level of tension, while some prefer or need a low level. Psychologists and doctors originally characterized the type A personality as a driven, ambitious person, seeking out risk, and eventually suffering from stress-related disorders due to an adrenaline overload. These personalities are generally the most energetic and high-achieving, whereas those who avoid tension or have innately low levels of tension generally do not achieve much. Of course, what is perceived as high-achieving or energetic depends on your or society's perspective. You might think that having sex with a lot of people was a big achievement, but society might think otherwise.

Are energetic people born or made? Steadily accumulating evidence suggests that our genetic make-up is a major determinant of both personality and energy. Jerome Kagan has shown that the so-called inhibited temperament, related to shyness, anxiety and introversion, is present from birth, and is probably determined by brain physiology. Marvin Zuckerman has investigated the opposite temperament type in adults, the sensation seekers, characterized by their search for thrills and new experience, lack of inhibitions, and a low boredom threshold. This temperament appears to be inherited, and linked strongly to the occurrence of low levels of an enzyme (monoamine oxidase) that breaks down noradrenaline and other neurotransmitters in the brain. The mood disorders of anxiety and depression, related to high or low mental energy, and high and low activities of the brain's arousal system, also appear to be inherited. Identical twins are about five times more likely to suffer a similar degree of major depression or generalized anxiety than fraternal twins. Thus there is a major genetic component to both depression and anxiety, but non-genetic factors also play a role.

What are these non-genetic factors? Whether tension is experienced as either energy or anxiety is partly a learned response from our past experience. If tense situations have led to failure and anxiety in the past, then we learn to associate the situation or tension with anxiety. Whereas, if our attempts at social, sexual, or intellectual advances are supported, not rebuffed, by other people, then the tension will be discharged as pleasure, and we will associate the tension with energy rather than anxiety. This is classical operant conditioning, and the basis of educational theory. The relevance of this to energy is that energetic people do more things partly because they have had positive reinforcement from doing those things in the past, and so associate them with pleasure rather than anxiety. Whereas, low-energy people don't do much partly because negative reinforcement has caused them to associate doing things with anxiety rather than pleasure.

It is clear therefore that the people around us and society in general can have a long-term effect on our energy level, depending on what drives are constructed within us in the first place, and whether these are nurtured and reinforced. Our friendships, marriages, jobs and other activities sap our energy when they fail to provide positive reinforcement. Some people give energy and some take it away: you should stick around people who give you positive reinforcement because they give you energy, whereas you should avoid those who provide negative reinforcement because they take it away. A society or culture as a whole can provide energy to its members either by enabling all drives (for food, sex, excitement and status) to be realized, or by instilling drives that are positively reinforced. Thus a capitalist society that instils a drive for money in its citizens, needs to supply the means to realize that drive to all its citizens, otherwise the drive will lead primarily to widespread frustration and anxiety.

Whether as a whole, any society or culture can be described as energetic or lacking in energy is doubtful. Some southern and equatorial countries have been characterized by outsiders as lethargic, *mañana* cultures, interested in the pleasures of the present, but uninterested in work and achievement. While northern cultures have generally been described (by northerners, of course) as driven and energetic, due either to the cold climate or the Protestant work ethic. It seems obvious that differences in achievement between north and south, and between countries generally, are mainly a consequence of economics, technology, education and history. But economic historians have also pointed out the important role a country's culture can play in providing goals, motivation, rewards, assistance and encouragement to its citizens. While other cultures may actually suppress their own energy by failing to reward or actively discouraging enterprise, creativity and expression.

Chapter 14

HOW TO GET
MORE ENERGY

Sometimes it seems the whole world is shouting, telling us how to get more energy. You can hardly pick up a magazine nowadays without an eight-page supplement falling out, offering you instructions on re-energizing your life: 'the new vital you in ten easy stages'. There is a flood of self-help books, all with inspirational titles: *Your Vitality Factor*, *Fatigue* or *Tired All The Time*. Step into any health shop and the aisles are piled high with a hundred different products in handy two-litre tubs promising liquid vitality, a boosted sex drive, and ever longer life. A personal trainer at your local gym or health farm can give a free consultation session on your body energy problems, just as your bank manager used to talk to you about your cash flow. Perhaps you should try aromatherapy, massage, T'ai Chi, yoga, meditation, aerobics, bioenergetics or calisthenics? Have you tried the latest herbs or pep pills? Have you got your Feng-Shui right? Or maybe it's your breathing. How is your *prana* flowing? You can even go to an oxygen bar where you can breathe pure oxygen while sipping a Martini.

Much of this striving after energy is misdirected and wasted, but the goal itself is important. There is abundant evidence that how energetic we feel is a major component of how happy, healthy, productive and creative we are. It may be more important for our overall well-being to track influences that boost or drain our feelings of energy, than to follow our calorie intake or bank accounts. Energy is a central aspect of our lives. When we have no energy our personal world shrinks to a small number of essential tasks, people and places; there is no energy for anything but the essential minimum. When we have abundant energy, the whole world opens up and expands as we take on challenging tasks, meet new people, and visit exotic places. So it is hardly surprising we appear to expend so much energy in seeking energy. It is surprising rather, that we pay so little attention to our energy level and the multiple factors that drain it.

So how do we get more energy? Well, the first decision is whether we need a short or long-term energy supply. Then, we should consider whether we are looking for body or mind energy. Finally, we can choose whether it is best to boost our energy supply or plug our leaks. Let's start with the relatively simple problem of boosting short-term body energy.

In the short-term, we all know how to self-regulate our energy level. If we experience a lack during the day, most people will eat a meal, snack or sweet; drink coffee, tea or another caffeinated drink; have a cigarette; or do something to boost their adrenaline level, such as talk to someone, take a shower, take drugs or put themselves in an unusual or challenging situation. We use these short-term measures throughout the day to regulate our energy at an optimum level. Most work reasonably well, in part through boosting our energy production. But, these only work in the short-term. If used repeatedly, day in and day out – as most of us do use them – they lead to a long-term energy drain. This is because the body adapts to having more energy pushed into it, either by decreasing energy levels or its own production of energy. For example, when we snack to boost our blood sugar level, the body adapts by releasing hormones (mainly insulin) to counteract that change and reduce the sugar level again. And if we challenge our bodies continually with sugar highs, long-term changes ensue that can be counter-productive in energy terms and can lead to serious damage, such as diabetes. Again, the body rapidly adapts to repeated shots of caffeine or nicotine by maintaining a lower energy level in their absence, thus inducing dependence on higher and higher doses to attain a normal level of energy. A long-term dependence on adrenaline highs leads to multiple changes in the body, resulting in all the energy-depleting effects of long-term stress. Thus the message is clear that while all these means of boosting energy do work and can in the short-term be very useful, if used repeatedly as an everyday means of maintaining energy, the long-term result will be exhaustion.

The most common causes of energy depletion are physical or mental ill health, stress, poor nutrition, lack of sleep or overwork. These factors continuously drain energy and need to be plugged if energy is to accumulate. Unfortunately, fatigue is a common symptom of a wide range of diseases and conditions, so it is impossible to diagnose a particular problem solely using this symptom. However, your doctor or various self-help books may be able to help. The most common physical-illness related causes of fatigue are: a previous or on-going infection; diseases of the heart, blood, lung, kidney, muscles, bowels or liver; cancer, arthritis or inflammatory diseases; a hormonal problem such as thyroid disease or diabetes; or a nutritional deficiency, particularly of iron or B vitamins. Mild anaemia or iron deficiency is often found in women of child-bearing age. Overwork, stress, depression and a lack of sleep are the most widespread causes of fatigue.

Chronic fatigue can also have a variety of causes. John Morrison, a Denver doctor, reported in 1980 that of one hundred and seventy-six patients with chronic fatigue about forty per cent had only physical problems, a further forty per cent only psychological problems, and ten per cent had both. The physical problems included recent viral infections, heart, lung, thyroid and liver disease, arthritis and nutritional deficiency. Other more recent surveys have come to similar conclusions, pointing to a large range of physical and psychological problems that vary for different people. Drs Wessely and Powell, from London's Institute of Psychiatry, found that seventy per cent of their sample of chronically fatigued patients had symptoms of depression or anxiety. Another survey found that forty per cent of chronically fatigued patients could actually be diagnosed as psychiatric cases. All this research shows is that, unsurprisingly, a range of different physical and mental problems can cause fatigue. But if you are fatigued without any other obvious symptoms then it is unlikely you are suffering from a serious disease – but rather from a lack of energy.

Paradoxically, the only way to boost body energy in the long-term is to use more energy, rather than try to push more energy in. The body adapts to a long-term increase in energy consumption by making long-term increases in energy production. So if we exercise regularly in the short-term it makes us tired, but in the long-term our body adapts, increasing our lung capacity, heart capacity, blood vessels, muscle capacity, mitochondria, and decreasing the production of stress hormones. This increased energy capacity means we are less tired or stressed by the normal energy-requiring tasks of the day. Long-term exercise makes us more energetic, both because our capacity is higher for performing energy-requiring tasks, and because the fit body feels different from the unfit body. A higher energy capacity makes us more optimistic about the future and we are more able to contemplate or deal with new situations, people or places. In addition, exercise also makes us much healthier, both physically and mentally, by combating cardiovascular disease, obesity, depression and anxiety. A controlled physical exercise programme is among the most effective treatments for chronic fatigue, not to mention depression and anxiety. As physical and mental illness are major energy drains this also contributes to exercise's energy-raising effects.

However, maintaining a long-term exercise regime requires considerable mental energy and motivation. And therein lies the problem. How do we get mental energy when we don't have any? How do we 'get motivated' when we haven't got the motivation to get motivated? How do we reach for the stars when we've dug ourselves into a pit? There are no simple solutions to the lack of mental energy or motivation. However, the short-term solutions to boost mental energy are similar to those for body energy discussed above, including eating, snacking, drinking, smoking and raising adrenaline levels by putting ourselves in exciting, stimulating or frightening situations. Other energy boosts are short, brisk walks or cold showers. Smiling and laughing have also been shown to be mood-improving. So it is relatively easy to relieve a short-term energy dip but not so easy in the longer term.

How do we obtain a long-term supply of mental energy? In general, we need motivation. To get motivation, we need goals. If these goals are to be effective, they should be both attainable and consistent with our natures. Setting the goals of running a marathon, writing a book or being an opera star are no good, if we don't enjoy running, writing or singing. The external goals we set need to harmonize, not conflict, with our internal drives, genes and motivators.

One set of mental motivators (pride, ambition and avarice) leads us on with the promise of carrots, while another set (anxiety, worry and guilt) is the stick driving us on from behind. The first set of motivators are like the three witches in *Macbeth*, enticing us to dark or heroic deeds with visions of a grander future. Whereas the three driving spirits resemble harpies, providing a constant source of mental energy, flooding the body with adrenaline and brain with noradrenaline when we have not achieved our own or other people's ambitions. They wake us up night after night, heart pounding, to worry about a book half written, an ambition half thwarted, a dream half crushed. Where else but from anxiety, worry and guilt would we get the mental energy to finish those tasks, and thus to sustain our pride, achieve our ambition, or fulfil our avarice?

Of course the effects of anxiety, worry and guilt are not all good, and different people have different thresholds beyond which they find anxiety unbearable. The Buddha stated that desire, and the consequent comparison of what we have or are with what we want, was the root of all human suffering. However, we might reply that it is the source of everything else as well, including human motivation, production and creation; and a life without desire, and the consequent pain and anxiety, could well be seen as a pale, colourless shadow of a life. The Buddha disagreed. He said if we saw and accepted things as they are and as we are, then barriers to enjoying things would cease to exist. Many prefer to enjoy the present, forgetting past and future: but their need for energy is consequently much less because they have no motivation to 'do' anything.

Excessive anxiety, worry and guilt greedily consume mental energy. They do this by occupying all our mental space, causing mental fatigue. If we worry continuously about something, and are unable or unwilling to do something about it, then our minds will be obsessed with one topic to the exclusion of all others. Both our bodies and brains are then continuously activated by adrenaline and noradrenaline, inevitably leading to stress and exhaustion. As we grow beyond childhood, our minds fill up more and more with the themes of pride, ambition, avarice, anxiety, worry and guilt. Over their constant babbling, it becomes barely possible to think anything new or perceive the world afresh. These old themes are the mind's weeds, and if not rooted out then any mental progress will be strangled by their banality. We should approach our minds like gardeners, examining their contents dispassionately once in a while, weeding out useless worries, thoughts or themes, and leaving the space and energy for those we do want. Only then will the mental energy that we need match that we have available.

The matching of the energy available with that we need to spend demands constant reassessment. The energy we have available is continuously changing with the time of day, season, our health, age and the unpredictable 'vitality factor' – somehow we have to match supply with consumption. Mental energy consumption divides between work and home projects, friends and family, ambitions, worries and anxieties. Occasionally we need to expand or contract our commitments to get our expenditure more in line with supply. If our energy expenditure is greater than supply, the result is constant exhaustion. If it is the other way around we will be bored or frustrated.

Energy can come from other people. They can be both sources and sinks of energy. Some people seem to radiate enthusiasm, dynamism and vitality, so that their energy seems contagious. Some people communicate and interact in such a positive, warm, sympathetic and interested way that you come away feeling both valued and confident. These people give off energy. Others can suck energy out by being negative, critical, cynical, aggressive, abusive or by simply ignoring you. An unhappy relationship or a hostile work environment can do enormous psychological damage by the slow diminishing of confidence, motivation and optimism. Our interactions with people should be carefully selected, so that energy is not sucked from us, but such that we will have sufficient energy when we choose to share it with others. Often the most effective cure for low energy, depression and a lack of motivation is to talk or do something with others, particularly those we find sympathetic, positive and optimistic.

Optimism, confidence and an avoidance of negative thoughts have been repeatedly shown to be the key attitudes necessary for energy, success and happiness. And this then generates positive feedback because these positive emotions promote increasing optimism and confidence. While, in stark contrast, the opposite attitudes of pessimism, lack of confidence and negative thoughts induce a vicious circle of low energy, failure and depression. Can we intervene to break this vicious circle? Psychological research and the application of cognitive therapy very much suggest we can. The way we talk to ourselves and how we interact can be altered. Negative thoughts such as 'I am useless' or 'I can't do it' or 'I'm a failure' are a cause, not consequence, of unhappiness and low energy. And since we produce them ourselves, they can be changed, and replaced by more positive thoughts, such as 'I am great' or 'I can do it' or 'I am a success'. The choice is ours: we can choose to concentrate on our strengths and successes, rather than dwell on our weaknesses or failures. Or at least that's cognitive therapy's plausible theory which has proved successful in treating anxiety and depression.

We can also alter the quality of our interactions with people, projects and the world, maximizing energy gain and minimizing loss. We need to learn to assess our surroundings and ourselves in terms of energy sources and drains. The writer Carlos Castaneda created a modern American myth in the Mexican/Indian sorcerer, Don Juan. Don Juan's goal was to increase his own energy level, and to that end he evaluated all his interactions with the world, people and himself in terms of the increase or decrease of his energy levels, and balanced whether any energy expenditure was worthwhile. We should do the same. We are used to assessing every transaction in terms of money and value. Some assess calorie intake and expenditure equally minutely. We need to take just as much care with our body and mind energy, because in the long-term this is absolutely vital to our health, success and happiness.

I hope I have proved to you in this book just how central the idea of energy is to understanding the life and death of our molecules, cells and bodies. Energy, matter and information entwine to form life, and their inevitable unravelling causes death. If we want to slow down our own unravelling, we need to pay more attention to energy, the creator and destroyer of all things.

'All Bibles or sacred codes have been the causes of the following Errors:

1. That Man has two real existing principles: Viz: a Body & a Soul.
2. That Energy, call'd Evil, is alone from the Body; & that Reason, call'd Good, is alone from the Soul.
3. That God will torment Man in Eternity for following his Energies.

But the following contraries to these are True:

1. Man has no Body distinct from his Soul; for that call'd Body is a portion of Soul discern'd by the five Senses, the chief inlets of Soul in this age.
2. Energy is the only life, and is from the Body; and Reason is the bound or outward circumference of Energy.
3. Energy is Eternal Delight.'

William Blake: *The Marriage of Heaven and Hell* (1790)

SOURCES AND FURTHER READING

Chapter 1. ORIGINS

Ackerknecht, E H *A Short History of Medicine* (Johns Hopkins University Press, Baltimore, 1982)

Bastien, J W 'Qollahuaya-Andean Body Concepts: a Topographical-Hydraulic Model of Physiology' *American Anthropologist* 87, 595–610, 1985

Florkin, M *A History of Biochemistry* (Elsevier, Amsterdam, 1972)

Gregory, R L *Mind in Science* (Penguin, London, 1981)

Lloyd, G E R *Early Greek Science: Thales to Aristotle* (W W Norton, New York, 1970)

Lloyd, G E R *Greek Science after Aristotle* (W W Norton, New York, 1973)

Mitchell, E *Your Body's Energy* (Mitchell Beazley, London, 1998)

Onians, R B *The Origins of European Thought* (Cambridge University Press, Cambridge, 1951)

Padel, R *In and Out of the Mind: Greek Images of the Tragic Self* (Princeton University Press, Princeton, 1992)

Page, M *Understanding the Power of Ch'i: An Introduction to Chinese Mysticism and Philosophy* (Thorsons, London, 1998)

Phillips, E D *Greek Medicine* (Thames & Hudson, London, 1973)

Porter, R *The Greatest Benefit to Mankind: A Medical History of Humanity from Antiquity to the Present* (HarperCollins, London, 1997)

Russell, B *A History of Western Philosophy* (George Allen & Unwin Ltd, Woking, 1946)

Chapter 2. THE STORY OF LIVING ENERGY

Ackerknecht, E H *A Short History of Medicine* (Johns Hopkins University Press, Baltimore, 1982)

Caneva, K L *Robert Mayer and the Conservation of Energy* (Princeton University Press, Princeton, 1993)

Cobb, C and Goldwhite, H *Creations of Fire* (Plenum Press, New York, 1995)

Harman, P M *Energy, Force and Matter* (Cambridge University Press, 1982)

Donovan, A *Antoine Lavoisier: Science, Administration and Revolution* (Cambridge University Press, Cambridge, 1983)

Florkin, M *A History of Biochemistry* (Elsevier, Amsterdam, 1972)

Gregory, R L *Mind in Science* (Penguin Books, London, 1982)

Keilin, D *The History of Cell Respiration and Cytochrome* (Cambridge University Press, Cambridge, 1966)

Kuhn, T S *The Essential Tension* (The University of Chicago Press, Chicago, 1977)

Leicester, H M *The Historical Background of Chemistry* (John Wiley & Sons, 1956)

Lloyd, G E R *Early Greek Science: Thales to Aristotle* (W W Norton, New York, 1970)

Greek Science after Aristotle (W W Norton, New York, 1973)

Needham, D M *Machina Carnis: The Biochemistry of Muscular Contraction and its Historical Development* (Cambridge University Press, Cambridge, 1971)

Nussbaum, Martha C *Aristotle's De Motu Animalium* (Princeton University Press, New Jersey, 1978)

Padel, R *In and Out of the Mind: Greek Images of the Tragic Self* (Princeton University Press, Princeton, 1992)

Phillips, E D *Greek Medicine* (Thames & Hudson, London, 1973)

Porter, R *The Greatest Benefit to Mankind: A Medical History of Humanity from Antiquity to the Present* (HarperCollins, London, 1997)

Rabinbach, A *The Human Motor: Energy, Fatigue and the Origins of Modernity* (University of California Press, Berkeley, 1990)

Russell, B *A History of Western Philosophy* (George Allen & Unwin Ltd, Woking, 1946)

Chapter 3. ENERGY ITSELF

Atkins, P W *Atoms, Electrons and Change* (Scientific American Library, W H Freeman and Co, New York, 1991)

Atkins, P W *The Second Law: Energy, Chaos and Form* (Scientific American Library, W H Freeman and Co, New York, 1994)

Bridgman, P W *The Nature of Thermodynamics* (Harper & Row, New York, 1961)

Edsall, J T & Guttfreund, H *Biothermodynamics* (Wiley, New York, 1983)

Fen, J B *Engines, Energy and Entropy* (W H Freeman and Co, New York, 1982)

Feynman, R *Six Easy Pieces: Essentials of Physics Explained by its Most Brilliant Teacher* (Addison-Wesley, New York, 1995)

Goldstein, M & Goldstein, I F *The Refrigerator and the Universe* (Harvard University Press, 1993)

Harman, P M *Energy, Force, and Matter* (Cambridge University Press, Cambridge 1982)

Harold, F M *The Vital Force: A Study of Bioenergetics* (W H Freeman and Co, New York, 1986)

Schrödinger, E *What is Life?* (Cambridge University Press, Cambridge, 1967)

Wrigglesworth, J *Energy and Life* (Taylor & Francis, London, 1997)

Chapter 4. THE MACHINERY OF LIFE

Alberts, B et al *The Molecular Biology of the Cell* (Garland Publishing Inc, New York, 1994)

Goodsell, D S *The Machinery of Life* (Copernicus Books, New York, 1993)

         Our Molecular Nature: the Body's Motors. Machines and Messages (Copernicus Books, New York, 1996)

Rensberger, B *Life Itself: Exploring The Realm of the Living Cell* (Oxford University Press, Oxford, 1996)

Rose, S *The Chemistry of Life* 3rd edition, (Penguin Books, London, 1991)

Chapter 5. THE BODY ELECTRIC

Brown, G C & Cooper, C E *Bioenergetics: A Practical Approach* (IRL Press, Oxford, 1995)

Harold, F M *The Vital Force: A Study of Bioenergetics* (W H Freeman and Co, New York, 1986)

Keilin, D *The History of Cell Respiration and Cytochrome* (Cambridge University Press, Cambridge, 1966)

Nicholls, D G and Ferguson, S J *Bioenergetics 2* (Academic Press, London, 1992)

Piccolino, M 'Luigi Galvani and Animal Electricity: Two Centuries after the Foundation of Electrophysiology' *Trends in Neurosciences* 20, 443–448, 1997

Skulachev, V P *Membrane Bioenergetics* (Springer-Verlag, Berlin, 1988)

Wrigglesworth, J *Energy and Life* (Taylor & Francis, London, 1997)

Chapter 6. MITOCHONDRIA: THE MONSTERS WITHIN

Barinaga, M 'Death by a Dozen Cuts' (*Science* 280, 32–34, 1998)

Brown, G C 'The Leaks and Slips of Bioenergetic Membranes' (*FASEB Journal* 6, 2961–2965, 1992)

Clark, W R *Sex and the Origins of Death* (Oxford University Press, Oxford, 1996)

Lehninger, A L *The Mitochondrion* (W A Benjamin Inc, New York, 1964)

Mignotte, B & Vayssiere, J-L 'Mitochondria and Apoptosis' *European Journal of Biochemistry* 252, 1–15, 1998

Miller, R J 'Mitochondria – the Kraken Wakes!' *Trends in Neuroscience* 21, 95–97, 1998

Nicholls, D G and Ferguson, S J *Bioenergetics 2* (Academic Press, London, 1992)

Wallace, D 'Mitochondrial *DNA* in Aging and Disease' *Scientific American* August 1997, 22–29, 1997

Chapter 7. THE PACE OF LIFE AND DEATH

Austad, S N *Why we Age* (John Wiley & Sons, New York, 1997)

Blaxter, K *Energy Metabolism in Animals and Man* (Cambridge University Press, 1989)

Cahill, L, Prins, B, Weber, M and McGaugh, J L 'Beta-adrenergic activation and memory for emotional events' (*Nature* 371, 702–4, 1994)

Calder III, W A *Size, Function, and Life History* (Harvard University Press, Cambridge, Massachusetts, 1984)

Clark, W R *Sex and the Origins of Death* (Oxford University Press, Oxford, 1996)

Reiss, M J *The Allometry of Growth and Reproduction* (Cambridge University Press, Cambridge, 1989)

Rolfe, D F S & Brown, G C 'Cellular Energy Utilisation and the Molecular Origin of Standard Metabolic Rate in Mammals' *Physiological Reviews* 77, 731–758, 1997

Schmidt-Nielsen, K *Scaling: Why is Animal Size So Important?* (Cambridge University Press, Cambridge, 1984)

Chapter 8. GETTING FAT AND STAYING THIN

Halaas, J L et al 'Weight-reducing effects of the Plasma protein encoded by the obese gene' (*Science* 269, 543–546, 1995)

Kiberstis, P A and Marx, J (eds) 'Regulation of Body Weight' *Science* 280, 1363–1390, 1998

Kopelman, P G and Stock, M J (eds) *Clinical Obesity* (Blackwell Science, Oxford, 1998)

Levine, J A, Eberhardt, N L and Jensen, M D 'Role of non-exercise activity thermogenesis in resistance to fat gain in humans' *Science* 283, 212–214 and 184–185, 1999

White, D A & Baxter, M *Hormones and Metabolic Control* (Edward Arnold, London, 1994)

Zhang, Y et al 'Positional Cloning of the Mouse Obese Gene and its Human Homologue' *Nature* 372, 425–432, 1994

Chapter 9. EXERCISE, FATIGUE AND STRESS

Alberts, B et al *Molecular Biology of the Cell* 3rd edition (Garland Publishing, New York, 1994)

Bagshaw, C R *Muscle Contraction* 2nd edition (Chapman & Hall, London, 1993)

Brooks, G A and Fahey, T D *Exercise Physiology: Human Bioenergetics and its Applications* (Wiley, New York, 1984)

Brown, G C 'Control of Mitochondrial Respiration and ATP Synthesis in Mammalian Cells' (*Biochemical Journal* 284, 1–13, 1992)

Fell, D *Understanding the Control of Metabolism* (Portland Press, London, 1997)

Hargreaves, M *Exercise Metabolism, Human Kinetics* (Champaign, Illinois, 1995)

Kleiner, S M *High-performance Nutrition: The Total Eating Plan to Maximise your Workout* (John Wiley & Sons, New York, 1996)

Lovallo, W R *Stress and Health, Biological and Psychological Interactions* (Sage Publications, London, 1997)

Martin, P *The Sickening Mind* (HarperCollins, London, 1997)

McArdle, W D, Katch, F I & Katch, V L *Exercise Physiology: Energy, Nutrition and Human Performance* (Lea and Febiger, London, 1991)

Needham, D M *Machina Carnis: the Biochemistry of Muscular Contraction and its Historical Development* (Cambridge University Press, Cambridge, 1971)

Newsholme, E, Leach, T & Duester, G *Keep on Running: the Science of Training and Performance* (John Wiley & Sons, Chichester, 1994)

Powers, S K & Howley, E T *Exercise physiology: Theory and Application to Fitness and Performance* (W C Brown, Dubuque, Iowa, 1990)

Rhoades, R & Pflanzer, R *Human Physiology* (Saunders College Publishing, Philadelphia, 1989)

Simmons, R M (ed) *Muscle Contraction* (Cambridge University Press, Cambridge, 1992)

Whipp, B J & Ward, S A 'Will Women Soon Outrun Men?' *Nature* 355, 25, 1992

White, D A & Baxter, M *Hormones and Metabolic Control* (Edward Arnold, London, 1994)

Wirhed, R *Athletic Ability and the Anatomy of Motion* (Wolfe Medical, London, 1994)

Chapter 10. MIND ENERGY

Buckwald, D, Sullivan, J L & Komaroff, A L 'Frequency of "Chronic Active Epstein-Barr Virus Infection" in a General Medical Practice' (*Journal of the American Medical Association* 257, 2303–7, 1987)

Cannon, W B *Bodily Changes in Pain, Hunger, Fear and Rage* (Appleton, New York, 1929)

Darwin, C *The Expression of the Emotions in Man and Animals* 3rd edition (ed) Paul Ekman (HarperCollins, London, 1998)

Dixon, J K, Dixon, J P & Hickey, M 'Energy as a Central Factor in the Self-assessment of Health' *Advances in Nursing Science* 15, 1–12, 1993

Dutton, D G and Aron, A P 'Some Evidence for Heightened Sexual Attraction in Conditions of High Anxiety' *Journal of Personality and Social Psychology* 30, 510–517, 1974

Franken, R E *Human Motivation* (Brookes/Cole, Pacific Grove, 1998)

Freud, S & Breuer, J *Studies on Hysteria* (Penguin Books, London, 1974)

Izard, C E *Facial Expressions and the Regulation of Emotions* Journal of Personality and Social Psychology 58, 487–498, 1990

James, W *Principles of Psychology*, vol.II, p.449 (Holt, New York, 1890)

Jones, E *The Life and Works of Sigmund Freud* (Penguin Books, London, 1993)

Kagan, J *Galen's Prophecy* (Free Association Books, London, 1994)

LeDoux, J *The Emotional Brain* (Weidenfeld & Nicolson, London, 1998)

Mook, D G *Motivation: the Organisation of Action* (W W Norton, New York, 1996)

Morgan, W P (ed) *Physical Activity and Mental Health* (Taylor & Francis, Washington, 1997)

Rabinbach, A *The Human Motor: Energy, Fatigue, and the Origins of Modernity* (University of California Press, Berkeley, 1990)

Thayer, R E *The Origin of Everyday Moods: Managing Energy, Tension, and Stress* (Oxford University Press, Oxford, 1996)

Watson, D & Tellegen, A 'Towards a Consensual Structure of Mood' *Psychological Bulletin* 98, 219–235, 1985

Webster, R *Why Freud was Wrong: Sin, Science and Psychoanalysis* (HarperCollins, London, 1995)

Weiner, B *Human Motivation: Metaphors, Theories and Research* (Sage Publications, London, 1992)

Chapter 11. BRAIN ENERGY

Bear, M F, Connors, B W & Paradiso, M A *Neuroscience: Exploring the Brain* (Williams & Wilkins, Baltimore, 1996)

Cooper, J R, Bloom, F E & Roth, R H *The Biochemical Basis of*

Neuropharmacology 6th edition (Oxford University Press,Oxford, 1991)

Greenfield, S *The Human Brain: a Guided Tour* (Weidenfeld & Nicolson, London, 1997)

                The Human Mind Explained (Cassell, London, 1996)

Olds, J & Milner, P 'Positive Reinforcement Produced by Electrical Stimulation of Septal Area and Other Regions of the Brain' *Comp. Physiol. Psychol.* 47, 419–427, 1954

Posner, M I & Raichle, M E *Images of Mind* (Scientific American Library, New York, 1994)

Rees, G, Frith, C D & Lavie, N, 'Modulating Irrelevant Motion Perception by Varying Attentional Load in an Unrelated Task' *Science* 278, 1616–1619, 1997

Snyder, S H *Drugs and the Brain* (Scientific American Library, New York, 1996)

Strange, P G *Brain Biochemistry and Brain Disorders* (Oxford University Press, Oxford, 1992)

White, F J 'Nicotine Addiction and the Lure of Reward' *Nature Medicine* 4, 659–660, 1998

Chapter 12. SEX AND SLEEP

Anch, A M et al *Sleep: A Scientific Perspective* (Prentice-Hall, Englewood Cliffs, NJ, 1988)

Anonymous 'Effects of Sexual Activity on Beard Growth in Man' *Nature* 226, 669–670, 1970

Barker, R *Sperm Wars* (Fourth Estate, London, 1996)

Bellis, M & Barker, R *Human Sperm Competition: Copulation, Masturbation and Infidelity* (Chapman & Hall, 1995)

Borbely, A *Secrets of Sleep* (Basic, New York, 1986)

Burnett, A L, Lowenstein, D J, Bredt, D S, Chang, T S K & Snyder, S H 'Nitric Oxide: a Physiologic Mediator of Penile Erection' *Science* 257, 401–404, 1992

Davidson, J M, Camargo, C A & Smith, E R 'Effects of Androgen on Sexual Behavior in Hypogonadal Men.' *Journal of Clinical Endocrinology and Metabolism* 48, 955–958, 1979

Franken, R E *Human Motivation* (Brookes/Cole, Pacific Grove, 1998)

Hobson, J A *Sleep* (Scientific American Library, New York, 1989)

Horne, J *Why We Sleep* (Oxford University Press, New York, 1988)

Lavie, P *The Enchanted World of Sleep* (Yale University Press, New Haven, 1996)

LeVay, S *The Sexual Brain* (MIT Press, Cambridge, 1993)

Masters, W H and Johnson, V E *Human Sexual Response* (Little, Brown, Boston, 1966)

Moir, A & Jessel, D *Brainsex: the Real Difference Between Men and Women* (Arrow Books, London, 1998)

Mook, D G *Motivation: The Organization of Action* (W W Norton, New York, 1996)

Morgenthaler, J & Joy, D *Better Sex through Chemistry* (Smart Publications, Petaluma, 1994)

'Wake up America: A National Sleep Alert' Vol. 1 of *Report of the National Commission on Sleep Disorders Research, Department of Health and Human Services*, Washington DC, 1993

Winson, J 'The Meaning of Dreams.' *Scientific American* November 1990, 58–67, 1990

Chapter 13. MOOD, MADNESS AND CREATIVE ENERGY

Barondes, S H *Molecules and Mental Illness* (Scientific American Library, New York, 1993)

Goodwin, F K & Jamison, K R *Manic-Depressive Illness* (Oxford University Press, Oxford, 1990)

Jamison, K R *Touched with Fire: Manic-Depressive Illness and the Artistic Temperament* (Free Press/Macmillan, 1993)

Jamison, K R 'Manic-Depressive Illness and Creativity' *Scientific American* February 1995, 44–49, 1995

Kagan, J *Galen's Prophecy* (Free Association Books, London, 1994)

Kendler, K S, Heath, A, Martin, N G and Eaves, L J 'Symptoms of Anxiety and Depression in a Volunteer Population.' *Archives of General Psychiatry* 43, 213–221, 1986

Martin, P *The Sickening Mind* (HarperCollins, London, 1997)

LeDoux, J *The Emotional Brain* (Weidenfeld & Nicolson, London, 1998)

Lovallo, W R *Stress and Health: Biological and Psychological Interactions* (Sage Publications, London, 1997)

Nemeroff, C B 'The Neurobiology of Depression' *Scientific American*, June 1998, 28–35, 1998

Slater, E and Shields, J 'Genetic Aspects of Anxiety.' *British Journal of Psychiatry* 3, 62–71, 1969

Snyder, S H *Drugs and the Brain* (Scientific American Library, New York, 1996)

Sternberg, E M & Gold, P W 'The Mind-Body Interaction in Disease.' Special Issue Vol. 7, pp. 8–15, *Scientific American*, New York, 1997

Stone, A A et al 'Evidence that Secretory IgA Antibody is Associated with Negative Mood.' *Journal of Personality and Social Psychology* 52, 988–93, 1987

Wender, P H, Ketty S S, Rosenthal D, Schulsinger F, Ortmann J, Lunde I 'Psychiatric disorders in the biological and adoptive families of adopted individuals with affective disorders' *Archives of General Psychiatry* 43, 923–929, 1986

Zuckerman, M *Behavioural Expressions and Biosocial Bases of Sensation Seeking* (Cambridge University Press, Cambridge, 1994)

Chapter 14. HOW TO GET MORE ENERGY

Fenn, C *The Energy Advantage: Fuelling Your Body and Mind For Success* (Thorsons, London, 1997)

Morrison, J D 'Fatigue as a Present Complaint in Family Practice' *Journal of Family Practitioners* 10, 795–801, 1980

Shape, M, Hawton, K, Seagroatt, B and Pasvol, G 'Follow up of patients presenting with fatigue to an infectious-diseases clinic' *British Medical Journal 305*, 147–152, 1992

Stewart, A *Tired All the Time: The Common Causes of Fatigue and How to Achieve Optimum Health* (Vermilion, London, 1993)

Thayer, R E *The Origins of Everyday Moods: Managing Energy, Tension, and Stress* (Oxford University Press, Oxford, 1996)

Wessely, S & Powell, R 'Fatigue Syndromes: A Comparison of Chronic Post-Viral Fatigue with Neuromuscular and Affective Disorder' *Journal of Neurology, Neurosurgery, Psychiatry*, 52, 940–948, 1989

Williams, X *Fatigue: The Secrets of Getting Your Energy Back* (CEDAR, London, 1996)

Wood, G C, Bentall, R P, Gopfert, N, & Edwards, R H T 'The Comparative Psychiatric Assessment of Patients with Chronic Fatigue Syndrome and Muscular Disease' *Psychological Medicine* 21, 619–628, 1991

GLOSSARY

ADP: Adenosine diphosphate, which when another phosphate is added becomes ATP.

ADRENALINE: Hormone released by the adrenal glands in threat situations, causing the mobilization of body energy.

AMINO ACIDS: Small molecules that can be strung together like beads to make proteins.

AMPHETAMINE: Stimulant drug ('speed') causing increased vigour and reduced tiredness.

ANS: Autonomic nervous system.

APOPTOSIS: An active form of cell death, where the cell destroys itself without damaging the rest of the body.

AROUSAL: Increased sensitivity and vigour of mental capacities.

ATP: Adenosine triphosphate, molecule carrying phosphate electricity within cells.

AUTONOMIC NERVOUS SYSTEM: A system of nerves running from the base of the brain to the rest of the body, having two branches: the sympathetic and parasympathetic nervous system.

AXON: Long, thin extension of neuron, along which a nerve impulse can travel.

BASAL METABOLIC RATE: Rate of energy use by the whole body while resting in a comfortable environment, several hours after the last meal.

BIOCHEMISTRY: Biology at the molecular and cellular level.

BIOENERGETICS: The science of body energy.

BODY MASS INDEX: Weight in kilos divided by the square of the height in metres.

CARBOHYDRATE: Complex molecules made from sugars.

CHARGE: Property of matter enabling it to respond to electrical force.

COMBUSTION: Process of burning.

CORTISOL: Stress hormone released by the adrenal glands causing mobilization of energy and suppressing the immune system.

CREATINE: A small molecule capable of carrying phosphate electricity as phospho-creatine.

CRH: Corticotropin-releasing hormone. Produced by hypothalamus during stress, activating RAS and sympathetic nervous system, also regulating release of cortisol and endorphins.

CYTOCHROME: Coloured protein containing iron, functioning to carry electrons and thus electricity in the cell.

CYTOCHROME OXIDASE: Part of the mitochondrial electron transport chain that passes electrons to oxygen.

DIABETES: Disease characterized by abnormally high blood glucose level.

EEG: Electroencephalogram, measures electrical activity in the brain.

ELECTRICAL IMPULSE: Electrical signal passing down neuron's axon, or other cell membrane.

ELECTRON: Smallest particle of matter, having a negative charge.

ELECTRON TRANSPORT CHAIN: A series of proteins within the mitochondria that act as a wire carrying electrons from food to oxygen.

ENDORPHINS: Brain hormones regulating mood and pain.

ENERGY: The capacity to do work.

ENTROPY: A measure of how randomly distributed the matter and energy are.

ENZYME: A protein machine, that can convert one molecule into another.

FAT: A complex molecule made mainly from carbon and hydrogen, acting as a fuel store, located either in brown fat or white fat tissue.

FATTY ACID: Small molecule carried by the blood, acting as fuel for the body, stored as fat. One molecule of fat is made from three molecules of fatty acid and one of glycerol.

FERMENT: Alchemical concept of catalyst, later meaning enzyme.

FIGHT-OR-FLIGHT RESPONSE: Body and mind's response to an alarming situation, caused by activation of sympathetic nervous system and adrenaline release.

FREE RADICAL: Molecule having an unpaired electron, capable of snatching electrons from other molecules.

FORCE: Cause of acceleration or deceleration.

FOUR ELEMENTS: Greek and later theory that everything consisted of only four indestructible elements: fire, water, earth and air.

GLUCOSE: A sugar which is an important energy fuel for the body and brain.

GLYCOGEN: A storage form of glucose, found mostly in liver and muscle.

GLYCOLYSIS: The process by which glucose or glycogen is converted to lactic acid in cells.

HAEMOGLOBIN: Protein carrying oxygen in the blood.

HORMONE: Molecule carried in the blood stream that functions to carry a signal from one tissue to others.

HPA: Hypothalamus-pituitary-adrenal axis. System of nerves and hormones controlling the stress-response.

HUMOURS: Body fluids, according to Greek theory acting like elements of the body.

HYPOGLYCAEMIA: Low blood sugar level.

HYPOMANIA: Mild mania.

HYPOTHALAMUS: Part of the brain controlling psychological drives.

IMMUNE SYSTEM: Body system for recognizing and killing invading pathogens.

INSULIN: Hormone, released into the blood by the pancreas when the blood sugar level is high, stimulating growth and the storage of glucose.

ION: Atom or small molecule that is electrically charged.

LACTIC ACID: End product of glycolysis, causing burning sensation in unfit runners.

LEAN MASS: Mass of non-fat tissue.

LEPTIN: Hormone produced by fat tissue acting on brain to decrease fat content of body.

LIBIDO: Sexual energy.

LIMBIC SYSTEM: Part of the brain dealing with emotions.

MEMBRANE: Thin wall bounding the cell or compartments within the cell.

METABOLIC PATHWAY: Series of enzymes by which molecules are consecutively transformed within cells.

METABOLIC RATE: Rate at which energy is used by an animal or human.

METABOLISM: The chemical transformations occurring within cells.

MITOCHONDRIA: Particles within our cells, that burn food converting the energy into cellular electricity.

MOLECULAR BIOLOGY: Biology studied at the molecular level.

MOLECULE: A stable arrangement of atoms.

MRI: Magnetic resonance imaging, a non-invasive method of visualizing the insides of the brain and body.

NECROSIS: A passive, chaotic form of cell death, which may damage surrounding cells.

NEGENTROPY: A measure of how ordered something is.

NERVE IMPULSE: Electrical signal travelling down axon of neuron.

NEURODEGENERATIVE DISEASE: Disease, such as Alzheimer's, that causes slowly progressing degeneration of brain functions.

NEURON: Brain cell capable of sending electrical impulses.

NEUROTRANSMITTER: Chemical released by neuron at synapse acting on muscle or other neurons to transmit signal.

NEUTRON: Particle of matter having no charge.

NORADRENALINE: Neurotransmitter released by RAS within the brain, and sympathetic nervous system in the body in alarm situation, causing the mobilization of body and mind energy, and the release of adrenaline.

OBESITY: Body mass index greater than thirty, or weight more than twenty per cent greater than the ideal.

PARASYMPATHETIC NERVOUS SYSTEM: A system of nerves counteracting the effects of the sympathetic nervous system, terminating the fight-or-flight response.

PET: Positron emission tomography, a method of visualizing changes within the brain or body.

PHLOGISTON: A source of heat and flame released by burning, according to phlogiston theory.

PHOSPHATE: A small molecule consisting of one phosphorus and a few oxygen and hydrogen atoms, having a negative charge when dissolved in water.

PHOSPHO-CREATINE: A small molecule carrying phosphate electricity within neurons and muscle cells.

PITUITARY: Part of the brain releasing a number of hormones into the body.

PNEUMA: Greek concept of energy as air, spirit or breath, both inside and outside the body.

PROTEIN: One of the three main types of complex molecule in the body, made from a string of amino acids.

PROTEINS: Complex molecules, made from protein, that perform all the essential tasks in the body.

PROTON: Particle of matter having a positive charge.

PROTON LEAK: Leak of protons across the mitochondrial membrane.

RAS: See reticular activating system.

RECEPTOR: A protein located on the cell membrane, which binds a hormone or neurotransmitter, and produces an appropriate signal within the cell.

REM: Rapid eye movement.

REM SLEEP: Distinct stage of sleep with dreams.

RESPIRATION: Originally meaning the gas exchange (oxygen for carbon dioxide) in the lungs; now refers to the oxygen consumption by mitochondria within our cells.

RETICULAR ACTIVATING SYSTEM: A system of neurons running from the base of the brain to the rest of the brain to cause arousal.

SECOND LAW OF THERMODYNAMICS: Entropy always increases.

SEROTONIN: Neurotransmitter acting within the brain to regulate mood and aggression.

SODIUM: A chemical element, that when combined with chloride forms salt (sodium chloride), but when dissolved in water exists as a positively charged sodium ion.

SODIUM PUMP: Transporter located in the cell membrane that pumps sodium ions out of the cell.

STRESS: Sustained or chronic fight-or-flight response.

SYMPATHETIC NERVOUS SYSTEM: A system of nerves running from the base of the brain to the rest of the body, releasing noradrenaline to cause the fight-or-flight response.

SYNAPSE: Thin gap between neuron and muscle or another neuron, across which a neurotransmitter carries a signal.

TENSION: State of vigilance and preparation for action.

THERMODYNAMICS: Science of energy transformations.

TRANSPORTER: A protein machine that can transport particular molecules across a membrane.

VITAL FORCE: A hypothetical force, only present in living things, that powered living processes.

VITALISM: The belief that living processes could not be explained by non-living forces, but rather involved a vital force.

INDEX